365 Days of BLACK HISTORY

2007 ENGAGEMENT CALENDAR

Catalog No. V276
Published by Pomegranate Communications, Inc.
Box 808022, Petaluma CA 94975

THE SCHOMBURG CENTER FOR RESEARCH IN BLACK CULTURE

THE NEW YORK PUBLIC LIBRARY

Available in Canada from Canadian Manda Group
165 Dufferin Street, Toronto, Ontario M6K 3H6

Available in the UK and mainland Europe from Pomegranate Europe Ltd.
Unit 1, Heathcote Business Centre, Hurlbutt Road, Warwick, Warwickshire CV34 6TD, UK

Available in Australia from Hardie Grant Books, 12 Claremont Street, South Yarra, Victoria 3141

Available in New Zealand from Southern Publishers Group, P.O. Box 8360, Symonds Street, Auckland

Available in the Far East from Julian Ashton, Ashton International Marketing Services
P.O. Box 298, Sevenoaks, Kent TN13 1WU, UK

Africa, Latin America, and the Middle East: info@pomegranate.com; 707-782-9000

Pomegranate also publishes the 2007 calendars *African American Art, A Journey into 365 Days of Black History* (wall), *Basquiat, Jacob Lawrence, Romare Bearden, Shan Kelly Cecilio, William H. Johnson,* and *Ancient Egypt* (wall and engagement), as well as many other calendars in several formats. Our products and publications include books, posters, postcards and books of postcards, notecards and boxed notecard sets, magnets, mousepads, Knowledge Cards®, birthday books, journals, address books, jigsaw puzzles, designer gift wrap, stationery sets, and bookmarks. For more information or to place an order, please contact Pomegranate Communications, Inc.: 800-227-1428; www.pomegranate.com.

Front cover: Eldzier Cortor (American, b. 1916)
Dance Composition, 1976
Acrylic on canvas, 48 x 30 in.
© Eldzier Cortor

Designed by Lora Santiago

Dates in color indicate federal holidays.
All astronomical data supplied in this calendar are expressed in Greenwich Mean Time (GMT).
Moon phases and American, Canadian, and UK holidays are noted.

 NEW MOON   FIRST QUARTER   FULL MOON   LAST QUARTER

Dates of Islamic holidays are based on predictions of lunar visibility in North America.

2007

JANUARY

s	m	t	w	t	f	s
	1	2	3	4	5	6
7	8	9	10	11	12	13
14	15	16	17	18	19	20
21	22	23	24	25	26	27
28	29	30	31			

FEBRUARY

s	m	t	w	t	f	s
				1	2	3
4	5	6	7	8	9	10
11	12	13	14	15	16	17
18	19	20	21	22	23	24
25	26	27	28			

MARCH

s	m	t	w	t	f	s
				1	2	3
4	5	6	7	8	9	10
11	12	13	14	15	16	17
18	19	20	21	22	23	24
25	26	27	28	29	30	31

APRIL

s	m	t	w	t	f	s
1	2	3	4	5	6	7
8	9	10	11	12	13	14
15	16	17	18	19	20	21
22	23	24	25	26	27	28
29	30					

MAY

s	m	t	w	t	f	s
		1	2	3	4	5
6	7	8	9	10	11	12
13	14	15	16	17	18	19
20	21	22	23	24	25	26
27	28	29	30	31		

JUNE

s	m	t	w	t	f	s
					1	2
3	4	5	6	7	8	9
10	11	12	13	14	15	16
17	18	19	20	21	22	23
24	25	26	27	28	29	30

JULY

s	m	t	w	t	f	s
1	2	3	4	5	6	7
8	9	10	11	12	13	14
15	16	17	18	19	20	21
22	23	24	25	26	27	28
29	30	31				

AUGUST

s	m	t	w	t	f	s
			1	2	3	4
5	6	7	8	9	10	11
12	13	14	15	16	17	18
19	20	21	22	23	24	25
26	27	28	29	30	31	

SEPTEMBER

s	m	t	w	t	f	s
						1
2	3	4	5	6	7	8
9	10	11	12	13	14	15
16	17	18	19	20	21	22
23	24	25	26	27	28	29
30						

OCTOBER

s	m	t	w	t	f	s
	1	2	3	4	5	6
7	8	9	10	11	12	13
14	15	16	17	18	19	20
21	22	23	24	25	26	27
28	29	30	31			

NOVEMBER

s	m	t	w	t	f	s
				1	2	3
4	5	6	7	8	9	10
11	12	13	14	15	16	17
18	19	20	21	22	23	24
25	26	27	28	29	30	

DECEMBER

s	m	t	w	t	f	s
						1
2	3	4	5	6	7	8
9	10	11	12	13	14	15
16	17	18	19	20	21	22
23	24	25	26	27	28	29
30	31					

IOKTS Productions ("I Only Know the Story") is dedicated to the research of documented history for the purpose of exhibiting the contributions of black people from all cultures, races, and geographic locations. Through this work we strive to promote awareness, knowledge, and understanding among all people while furthering pride, dignity, and inspiration in those who identify directly with this heritage.

For more information, e-mail us at ioktspro@verizon.net or contact:

Mr. G. Theodore Catherine
IOKTS Productions
P.O. Box 11275
Takoma Park, MD 20913
(301) 270-1920

Dr. Susan Smith McKinney Steward
American, 1848–1919

In an era when women doctors were a rarity in America, Susan Smith McKinney Steward distinguished herself as the first African American medical school graduate in New York State.

After graduating as class valedictorian from New York Medical College for Women, Steward completed her postgraduate studies at Long Island College Hospital in 1860. The only woman and the only black person enrolled at the college, Steward countered racism, sexism, and loneliness with a razorsharp mind, a fierce dedication to her patients' needs, and a passion and talent for music.

Steward married the Reverend William G. McKinney, pastor of St. Stephen's Church in Jamaica, New York, and devoted more than twenty-five years of service to the church. After her husband's death in 1894, Steward remarried and became resident physician at Wilberforce University, in Washington, DC. In 1911, Steward spoke on "Colored Women in America" at the Universal Races Congress in London, the world's first interracial conference. Her 1914 paper "Women in Medicine" was a comprehensive survey of pioneering female physicians in the United States.

s	m	t	w	t	f	s
	1	2	3	4	5	6
7	8	9	10	11	12	13
14	15	16	17	18	19	20
21	22	23	24	25	26	27
28	29	30	31			

JANUARY

NEW YEAR'S DAY
monday
1 1

Kwanzaa ends: Imani (Faith). *To believe with all our hearts in our people, our parents, our teachers, our leaders, and the righteousness and victory of our struggle.*
1804: Haiti declares its independence.
1937: Lou Stovall, artist and master printmaker, is born in Athens, GA.

BANK HOLIDAY (SCOTLAND)
tuesday
2 2

1898: Sadie Tanner Mossell Alexander, first African American to earn a PhD in economics, is born in Philadelphia.
1915: John Hope Franklin, historian, educator, and author of *From Slavery to Freedom: A History of Negro Americans,* is born.

Visits: Red, Lee & Margaret Jones

1621: William Tucker is the first known African child to be born in America.
1956: Colored Methodist Church, established in 1870, officially changes its name to Christian Methodist Episcopal Church.
wednesday
○ **3** 3

PHC-Jeff
Burlington- Rosie
Brunch @ June's
Condo w/ Earline

1787: Prince Hall, founder of the first black Masonic lodge, and others petition the Massachusetts legislature for funds to return to Africa, the first recorded effort by blacks to do so.
1920: Andrew "Rube" Foster organizes the first black baseball league, the Negro National League
thursday
4 4

Garage = Rosie & T
Faxed papers to Jayne- from PHC

1911: Kappa Alpha Psi Fraternity is chartered as a national organization.
friday
5 5

1993: Jazz trumpeter John Birks "Dizzy" Gillespie dies.
1996: Recycling Black Dollars, an organization of black businesses, campaigns for "Change Bank Day" to benefit black-owned financial institutions.
saturday
6 6

1903: Folklorist and novelist Zora Neale Hurston is born.
1997: Former South African president Pieter W. Botha is prosecuted for refusing to appear before the nation's truth commission.
sunday
7 7

Joe Louis
American, 1914–1981

Satchel Paige
American, 1906–1982

It may seem a rare thing to catch two cultural legends together at the same moment in time. But in reality, legends are often found in other legends' presence, due to mutual admiration or the pleasures and obligations of celebrity. Known to fans as the Brown Bomber, Joe Louis—the prizefighter who opened up boxing to blacks—made a point of paying his respects to other athletes, military men, and entertainers. During his prime, his presence was in high demand; consequently he has been seen in many photographs with some of the twentieth century's most famous people.

Satchel Paige was surely a legend in his own time. This Negro Leagues and major-league pitcher kept batters guessing what ball he was about to throw while taunting them with threats of striking them out. On most occasions, he made good on his threats.

Paige pitched year-round in the Negro Leagues for twenty years; in 1948, he became the oldest rookie in the major leagues when he joined the Cleveland Indians.

TM/© 2006 Estate of Joe Louis by CMG Worldwide, www.CMGWorldwide.com
TM/© 2006 Satchel Paige by CMG Worldwide, www.SatchelPaige.com

s	m	t	w	t	f	s
	1	2	3	4	5	6
7	8	9	10	11	12	13
14	15	16	17	18	19	20
21	22	23	24	25	26	27
28	29	30	31			

monday 8
1922: Col. Charles Young, first African American to achieve that rank in the US Army, dies in Lagos, Nigeria.

tuesday 9
1866: Fisk University is founded in Nashville.
1906: Renowned poet and writer Paul Laurence Dunbar dies.
1914: Phi Beta Sigma fraternity is founded at Howard University.

wednesday 10
1864: George Washington Carver, scientist and inventor, is born.
1925: Drummer Max Roach, influential in the development of modern jazz, is born.

thursday 11
1940: Benjamin O. Davis Sr. becomes the US Army's first black general.

friday 12
1890: Mordecai W. Johnson, first black president of Howard University (for thirty-four years), is born. He will receive the NAACP's Spingarn Medal in 1929.
1996: Pioneering sports journalist Sam Skinner dies in Burlingame, CA.

saturday 13
1913: Delta Sigma Theta Sorority, Inc., is founded at Howard University.

sunday 14
1916: Author John Oliver Killens is born in Macon, GA.
1940: Julian Bond, civil rights leader and Georgia state senator, is born.

Dr. Schroeder Cherry
American, b. 1954

Schroeder Cherry is an artist, museum administrator, and puppeteer. Formerly deputy director for education and public programs at the Maryland Historical Society, he was recently named deputy director for museum services at the Institute of Museum and Library Services in Washington, DC.

Cherry earned a BFA (summa cum laude) in puppetry from the University of Michigan; a master's in museum education from George Washington University; and a doctorate in the same subject from Columbia. He has worked at seven museums around the country, including the Baltimore Museum of Art, the J. Paul Getty Museum in Los Angeles, and the Studio Museum in Harlem, and has served as vice president of the African American Museums Association.

A puppeteer since childhood, Cherry gives free public performances on such subjects as the Underground Railroad, using rod puppets, wooden cutouts, and hand puppets to tell his stories.

Black Folk Arts, 1988
Acrylic/collage on canvas,
44 x 34 in.
© Schroeder Cherry
Photograph by
Manu Sassoonian

s	m	t	w	t	f	s
	1	2	3	4	5	6
7	8	9	10	11	12	13
14	15	16	17	18	19	20
21	22	23	24	25	26	27
28	29	30	31			

JANUARY

---

monday
15 15

MARTIN LUTHER KING JR. DAY
1908: Alpha Kappa Alpha Sorority is founded at Howard University by Ethel Hedgeman Lyle.

---

tuesday
16 16

1920: Zeta Phi Beta sorority is founded at Howard University.
1974: Noted singer-composer Leon Bukasa of Zaire dies.

Felecia Tripp Folsom B.D

---

wednesday
17 17

1882: Lewis H. Latimer is granted a patent for the process of manufacturing carbons.
1942: Muhammad Ali, heavyweight boxing champion, is born in Louisville, KY.

Darnell & Karen dies

---

thursday
18 18

1858: Daniel Hale Williams, first physician to perform open-heart surgery and founder of Provident Hospital in Chicago, is born.

---

friday
19 19

MUHARRAM (BEGINS AT SUNSET)
1887: Clementine Hunter, noted African American painter, is born in Natchitoches, LA.
1918: John H. Johnson, editor and publisher of *Ebony* and *Jet* magazines, is born in Arkansas City, AR.

---

saturday
20 20

1893: Bessie Coleman, first female African American aviator, is born in Atlanta, TX.
1974: Stevie Wonder plays a gig at Rainbow Theatre, London, after recovering from a car accident five months earlier that almost killed him.

Bruce's BD.

---

sunday
21 21

1993: Congressman Mike Espy of Mississippi is confirmed as secretary of agriculture.

Red's BD

W. E. B. Du Bois
American, 1868–1963

"It is a peculiar sensation, this double-consciousness, this sense of always looking at one's self through the eyes of others.... One feels this twoness—an American, a Negro; two souls, two thoughts, two unreconciled strivings; two warring ideals in one dark body." W. E. B. Du Bois' words underscore his insight into America's race problem.

Born in Great Barrington, Massachusetts, Du Bois was one of history's most respected spokespersons for the rights of African Americans. Educated at Fisk and Harvard, he was the first African American to earn a doctorate (from Harvard, in 1895). A cofounder of the antiaccommodationist Niagara Movement, he was a key organizer of the NAACP. He battled for true citizenship for blacks and wrote history books, sociological studies, and newspaper editorials about African American life.

Du Bois' public expression of his views brought him often to the center of controversy. Toward the end of his life he grew so discouraged with his struggles in the United States that he moved to Ghana in 1961, becoming a citizen in the year of his death.

s	m	t	w	t	f	s
	1	2	3	4	5	6
7	8	9	10	11	12	13
14	15	16	17	18	19	20
21	22	23	24	25	26	27
28	29	30	31			

JANUARY

monday 22 — 1906: Pioneering aviator Willa Brown-Chappell is born in Glasgow, KY. 1935: Singer Sam Cooke, best known for "You Send Me" and "Twisting the Night Away," is born in Chicago. *Brittany's B.D.*

tuesday 23 — 1941: Richard Wright is awarded the NAACP's Spingarn Medal. 1964: The Twenty-fourth Amendment is ratified, abolishing the poll tax.

wednesday 24 — 1985: Tom Bradley, four-term mayor of Los Angeles, receives the NAACP's Spingarn Medal for public service.

thursday 25 — 1890: National Afro-American League, a pioneering black protest organization, is founded in Chicago. 1966: Constance Baker Motley becomes the first African American woman to be appointed to a federal judgeship.

friday 26 — 1928: Singer, dancer, and actor Eartha Mae Kitt is born in Columbia, SC. 1944: Angela Yvonne Davis, political activist and educator, is born in Birmingham, AL.

saturday 27 — 1972: Gospel music legend Mahalia Jackson dies in Evergreen Park, IL.

sunday 28 — 1944: Matthew Henson receives a joint medal from Congress as codiscoverer of the North Pole.

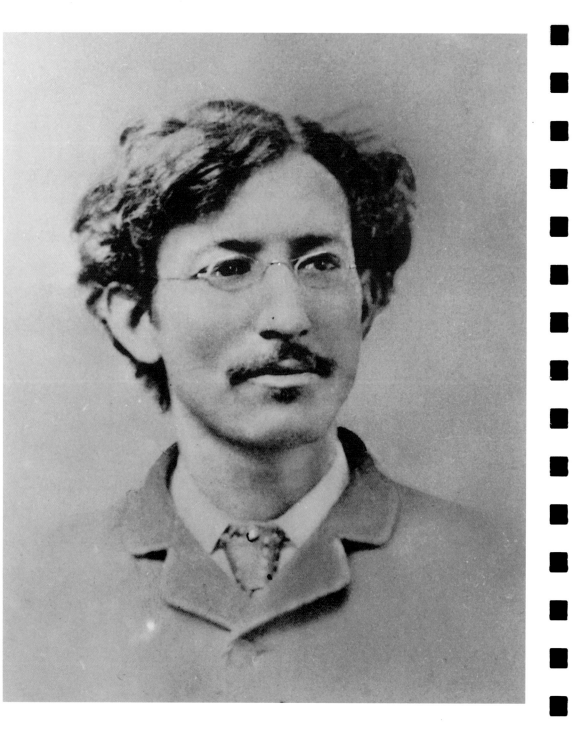

T. Thomas Fortune
American, 1856–1928

This radical civil rights activist fought his battles against discrimination from a strategically valuable position: he owned and edited three newspapers over the course of his life. The fiery journalist made an incalculable contribution to the cause of racial equality through his widely read newspapers.

Timothy Thomas Fortune was born a slave in Marianna, Florida. His father's involvement in politics during Reconstruction infuriated whites. In fear for his life, Emanuel Fortune fled with his family to Jacksonville, leaving behind his farm and all his savings and creating a thirst for justice in his young son.

Fortune's career in journalism and publishing began with an apprenticeship in a printing shop. He learned about "inside" politics and its injustices to blacks as a page in Florida's state senate. After a year's studies at Howard University, he married Carrie Smiley; the young couple moved to New York City and Fortune went into journalism. In 1881 he became editor of the New York Globe; in 1883 he founded the New York Age; and in 1890 he created the Afro-American League, a precursor of the NAACP.

s	m	t	w	t	f	s
				1	2	3
4	5	6	7	8	9	10
11	12	13	14	15	16	17
18	19	20	21	22	23	24
25	26	27	28			

FEBRUARY

---

monday
1872: Francis L. Cardoza is elected South Carolina state treasurer.
1926: Violette Neatley Anderson becomes the first African American woman admitted to practice before the US Supreme Court.
29 29

tuesday
1844: Richard Theodore Greener becomes the first African American to graduate from Harvard University.
30 30

wednesday
1919: Jackie Robinson, first African American to play in major league baseball, is born in Cairo, GA.
2006: Coretta Scott King dies in Mexico.
31 31

thursday
1865: John S. Rock becomes the first black attorney to practice before the US Supreme Court.
1902: Prolific poet Langston Hughes is born in Joplin, MO.
1 32

friday
1915: Biologist Ernest E. Just receives the Spingarn Medal for his pioneering research in fertilization and cell division.
○ **2** 33

saturday
1947: Percival Prattis, of Our World in New York City, becomes the first black news correspondent admitted to the House and Senate press galleries in Washington, DC.
1948: Portraitist and illustrator Laura Wheeler Waring dies.
3 34

sunday
1913: Rosa Parks, initiator of the Montgomery, AL, bus boycott, is born.
1969: The popular Liberation Movement of Angola begins armed struggle against Portugal.
4 35

J. Rosamond Johnson
American, 1873–1954

A consummate entertainer, an ingenious writer of popular music, and a classically trained composer, John Rosamond Johnson learned the rudiments of piano playing from his mother. He studied at the New England Conservatory of Music and took private lessons in technique and composition from some of America's most eminent teachers. But Johnson's interest gravitated toward musical comedy, and he began touring on the vaudeville circuit. An early full-scale musical of his, *Toloso*, failed to make it into production but made his name among others in the business. With his brother Weldon, Rosamond formed a partnership with Bob Cole. They wrote and performed more than two hundred songs, a number of which—while they're largely forgotten today—were wildly successful in their time. "Under the Bamboo Tree" sold more than 400,000 copies.

After Cole & Johnson Bros. broke up, Rosamond Johnson continued to enjoy a successful career, working with the greats of the emerging Broadway revue, directing Oscar Hammerstein's London Opera House, producing *The Book of American Negro Spirituals*, and acting. Johnson can stand as the portrait of the Broadway all-rounder.

Photograph by Apeda Studio, Inc., 1930s

s	m	t	w	t	f	s
				1	2	3
4	5	6	7	8	9	10
11	12	13	14	15	16	17
18	19	20	21	22	23	24
25	26	27	28			

FEBRUARY

---

monday

5 36

1934: Hank Aaron, major league baseball home run king, is born in Mobile, AL.
1994: White supremacist Byron de la Beckwith is convicted of the murder of Medgar Evers, more than thirty years after Evers was ambushed and shot in the back.

---

tuesday

6 37

1993: Arthur Ashe, tennis player, humanitarian, and activist, dies.

---

wednesday

7 38

1926: Negro History Week, originated by Carter G. Woodson, is observed for the first time.

---

thursday

8 39

Independence Day (Grenada)
1944: Harry S. McAlphin of Atlanta's *Daily World* becomes the first black journalist accredited to attend White House press conferences.

---

friday

9 40

1780: Capt. Paul Cuffe and six other black residents of Massachusetts petition the state legislature for the right to vote.
1944: Alice Walker, Pulitzer Prize–winning author, is born in Eatonton, GA.

---

saturday

☽ **10** 41

1869: Nat Love, former slave from Tennessee, goes west to make his fortune. He will become known as Deadwood Dick, one of the most famous cowboys, black or white, in history.
1927: Leontyne Price, internationally acclaimed opera singer, is born in Laurel, MS.

---

sunday

11 42

1990: Nelson Mandela is released from a South African prison after twenty-seven years as a political prisoner.

The Reverend Richard Allen
American, 1760–1831

Richard Allen and his three siblings were born into slavery in Philadelphia. When the family was sold to a Delaware plantation owner, Allen began his fellowship work. He taught himself to read and write; he joined the Methodist Society and was soon leading meetings. Impressed, his owner allowed Allen and his brother to purchase their freedom. In pursuit of that goal, Allen held various jobs, continued his ministry, and converted his owner.

Now free, Allen returned to Philadelphia to establish himself as a minister. He preached in three eastern states, and it is thought that he attended the first organizing conference of American Methodism. During this time Allen met Absalom Jones. The two men were of like mind, wishing to establish a place of worship for newly freed blacks.

In 1787, while kneeling in prayer at St. George's Methodist Episcopal Church, Allen, Jones, and other black worshippers were ejected from the church by St. George officials. In response, Allen and Jones organized the Independent Free African Society, which denounced slavery and spearheaded the establishment of an "African Church."

Lithograph by P. S. Duvall, Philadelphia, n.d.

s	m	t	w	t	f	s
				1	2	3
4	5	6	7	8	9	10
11	12	13	14	15	16	17
18	19	20	21	22	23	24
25	26	27	28			

FEBRUARY

LINCOLN'S BIRTHDAY

monday

1896: Isaac Burns Murphy, one of the greatest jockeys of all time, dies.

12 43

1907: Wendell P. Dabney establishes *The Union*, a Cincinnati paper whose motto is "For no people can become great without being united, for in union, there is strength."
1970: Joseph L. Searles becomes the first black member of the New York Stock Exchange.

tuesday

13 44

VALENTINE'S DAY

wednesday

1817: Frederick Douglass, "the Great Emancipator," is born.
1867: Morehouse College is founded in Augusta, GA; it later moves to Atlanta.

14 45

1961: US activists and African nationalists disrupt UN sessions to protest the slaying of Congo premier Patrice Lumumba.

thursday

15 46

1826: *The Liberia Herald*, first newspaper printed in Africa, is published by C. L. Force of Boston.
1923: Bessie Smith makes her first recording, "Down-Hearted Blues," which sells 800,000 copies for Columbia Records.

friday

16 47

1938: Mary Frances Berry, first woman to serve as chancellor of a major research university (University of Colorado), is born in Nashville.
1982: Pianist Thelonious Monk, founding father of modern jazz, dies from a massive stroke.

saturday

● **17** 48

National Independence Day (Gambia)
1688: Quakers at Germantown, PA, adopt the first formal antislavery resolution in American history.

sunday

18 49

Nora Holt
American, 1885–1974

"Music is one of the greatest refiners of the Race," music critic, composer, and performer Nora Douglas Holt asserted. Born in Kansas City, Kansas, she studied piano and was influenced by her teacher, who took her to concerts. In 1916, she took a bachelor's degree from Western University, and in 1918, she attended the Chicago Musical College, becoming the first black person to earn a master's in music.

While studying for her graduate degree, Holt became interested in music criticism, a skill she learned from her advisor, Felix Borowsky. She landed her first job as a music critic with the *Chicago Defender*. In a male-dominated field, she worked hard to uphold and further the matter of women's equality. Her philosophy was "to offer expert musical judgments; to teach and awaken musical interest in [her] public; to advance young artists and the music of African-Americans; and to provide Black and White communities with quality appraisals."

Nora Holt was instrumental in the formation of the National Association of Negro Musicians.

s	m	t	w	t	f	s
				1	2	3
4	5	6	7	8	9	10
11	12	13	14	15	16	17
18	19	20	21	22	23	24
25	26	27	28			

FEBRUARY

PRESIDENTS' DAY
monday
19 50

1919: W. E. B. Du Bois organizes the second Pan-African Congress in Paris.

---

tuesday
20 51

1927: Sidney Poitier, first African American to win an Academy Award in a starring role, is born in Miami.
1929: Wallace Thurman's play *Harlem* begins a successful run on Broadway.

ASH WEDNESDAY
wednesday
21 52

1965: El-Hajj Malik El-Shabazz (Malcolm X), American black nationalist, is assassinated.

WASHINGTON'S BIRTHDAY
thursday
22 53

1841: Grafton Tyler Brown, one of California's first African American painters, is born.
1962: Wilt Chamberlain sets an NBA record with thirty-four attempted free throws.

Republic Day (Guyana)
friday
23 54

1972: Political activist Angela Davis is released from jail.

---

saturday
☽ **24** 55

1966: Military leaders oust Kwame Nkrumah, president of Ghana, while he is in Peking on a peace mission to stop the Vietnam War.

---

sunday
25 56

1978: Daniel "Chappie" James, first African American four-star general, dies in Colorado Springs.
1991: Adrienne Mitchell becomes the first black woman to die in combat. She is killed in her military barracks in Saudi Arabia during the Persian Gulf War.

Eldzier Cortor
American, b. 1916

Eldzier Cortor is one of the masters of African American art, associated with the likes of Romare Bearden, William H. Johnson, Jacob Lawrence, and Horace Pippin. Fittingly, though, his art has transcended race to become world renowned.

Cortor was born in Virginia and raised in Chicago. Growing up, he was intrigued by comic strips; he copied them and dreamed of creating his own strip.

After attending Englewood High School with the future artists Charles Sebree and Charles White, Cortor took evening classes at the Art Institute of Chicago and worked with the Works Progress Administration.

With the help of a Guggenheim Fellowship, Cortor studied in Jamaica, Cuba, and Haiti; he also taught at the Centre d'Art in Port Au Prince. One of the first artists to make black women a major theme, he has also produced many images involving Haitian culture—which he counts as a strong influence on his artistic sensibility—and the Gullah culture of coastal South Carolina.

Dance Composition, 1976
Acrylic on canvas, 48 x 30 in.
© Eldzier Cortor

s	m	t	w	t	f	s
				1	2	3
4	5	6	7	8	9	10
11	12	13	14	15	16	17
18	19	20	21	22	23	24
25	26	27	28	29	30	31

MARCH

---

monday

1926: Theodore "Tiger" Flowers (aka "the Georgia Deacon") defeats Harry Greb in New York City, becoming the first black middleweight champion of the world.
1928: Singer Antoine "Fats" Domino is born in New Orleans.

26 57

---

tuesday

Independence Day (Dominican Republic)
1872: Charlotte Ray graduates from Howard University's law school, becoming the first female African American lawyer.
1902: Marian Anderson, opera singer and civil rights advocate, is born in Philadelphia.

27 58

---

wednesday

1948: Sgt. Cornelius F. Adjetey becomes the first martyr for national independence of Ghana.

28 59

---

thursday

1871: James Milton Turner is named minister to Liberia, the first black diplomat accredited to an African country.
1914: Ralph Waldo Ellison, author of the award-winning *Invisible Man*, is born in Oklahoma City.

1 60

---

friday

1955: Claudette Colvin refuses to give up her seat on a bus in Montgomery, AL, nine months before Rosa Parks' arrest for the same action sparks the Montgomery bus boycott.

2 61

---

saturday

PURIM (BEGINS AT SUNSET)

Martyr's Day (Republic of Malawi)
National Day (Morocco)
1821: Thomas L. Jennings is the first African American to be granted a US patent, for his technique to "dry-scour" clothes.

○ **3** 62

---

sunday

1932: Zensi Miriam Makeba, "Empress of African Song," is born.

4 63

Jan Ernst Matzeliger
American, b. Dutch West Indies,
1852–1889

Jan Matzeliger was born in Paramaribo, Dutch West Indies, the son of a black woman and a Dutch engineer. As a boy, he apprenticed in his father's machine shop, where his aptitude for machinery and invention began to grow.

Although he spoke little English, Matzeliger came to the United States as a sailor, landing in the Philadelphia area. After hearing that Lynn, Massachusetts, was a center of the shoemaking trade, he moved there to go into business.

Shoemaking was then a slow, tedious process in which the sole was hand stitched to the upper part; a craftsman could produce only about fifty pairs of shoes in a day. Matzeliger sought a faster manufacturing process. Experimenting at his workbench, he developed first a crude wooden machine and then an iron model. After spending ten years perfecting it, he sent his diagrams to Washington, DC, and on March 20, 1883, he received a patent for the "shoe lasting machine." Using his invention, shoemakers increased their production to two hundred pairs of shoes per man per day.

s	m	t	w	t	f	s
				1	2	3
4	5	6	7	8	9	10
11	12	13	14	15	16	17
18	19	20	21	22	23	24
25	26	27	28	29	30	31

MARCH

---

monday

5 64

1770: Crispus Attucks is killed in the Boston Massacre, marking the start of the American Revolution.

---

tuesday

6 65

Independence Day (Ghana)
1857: US Supreme Court rules against citizenship for African Americans in the Dred Scott decision.

---

wednesday

7 66

1539: Estevanico (or Esteban) de Dorantes, native of Azamoor, Morocco, sets out to explore what is now the southwestern United States.

---

thursday

8 67

INTERNATIONAL WOMEN'S DAY
1876: After three years of controversy, the US Senate refuses to seat P. B. S. Pinchback, elected as Louisiana senator in 1873.
1977: Henry L. Marsh III is elected first black mayor of Richmond, VA.

---

friday

9 68

1914: The "New" Southern University campus opens in Scotlandville, LA, with nine teachers and forty-seven students.
1919: Nora Douglas Holt and other black Chicago musicians form the Chicago Musical Association.

---

saturday

10 69

1845: Women's rights activist Hallie Quinn Brown is born in Pittsburgh.
1963: Actor Jasmine Guy, known as Whitley in the TV series *A Different World*, is born in Boston.

---

sunday

11 70

DAYLIGHT SAVING TIME BEGINS
1948: Dr. Reginald Weir of New York City wins his first match in the USLTA Tennis Championship Tournament.

Arthur Schomburg
American, b. Puerto Rico, 1874–1938

The young Arturo Alfonso Schomburg dedicated himself to the liberation of Puerto Rico from Spain. After moving to New York City in 1891, he worked in a law office and a banking firm and taught Spanish. Collecting books, images, and manuscripts addressing black history became his passion.

Schomburg combed bookstores, libraries, and rummage sales in the United States, Europe, and Latin America, amassing a huge collection of materials. In the early 1930s the New York Public Library acquired Schomburg's collection, using a grant from the Carnegie Foundation, and Schomburg became curator of the Division of Negro Literature, History and Prints of the New York Public Library. After his death, the collection was renamed the Schomburg Collection of Negro Literature and History. Today it is the Schomburg Center for Research in Black Culture.

The Schomburg Center is the world's most comprehensive research facility for the study of black history and culture. It began with five thousand volumes, three thousand manuscripts, and two thousand drawings. Today it contains over ten million items that document the black experience worldwide.

Photograph by James Latimer Allen

s	m	t	w	t	f	s
				1	2	3
4	5	6	7	8	9	10
11	12	13	14	15	16	17
18	19	20	21	22	23	24
25	26	27	28	29	30	31

MARCH

---

monday
1791: Benjamin Banneker and Pierre Charles L'Enfant are commissioned to plan and develop Washington, DC.

☾ **12** 71

---

tuesday
1773: Jean-Baptiste Pointe du Sable founds the city of Chicago.
1943: Frank Dixon becomes the first great black miler in track, winning the Columbian Mile in New York City in a record time of 4 minutes, 9.6 seconds.

13 72

---

wednesday
1933: Composer, musician, and producer Quincy Delight Jones is born in Chicago.

14 73

---

thursday
1947: John Lee becomes the first African American commissioned officer in the US Navy.
1968: *Life* magazine calls Jimi Hendrix "the most spectacular guitarist in the world."

15 74

---

friday
1827: John Russwurm, first African American college graduate, begins publication of *Freedom's Journal* with Samuel Cornish.
1995: Mississippi ratifies the Thirteenth Amendment, which abolishes slavery, 130 years after the other states had approved it.

16 75

ST. PATRICK'S DAY **saturday**
1865: Aaron Anderson wins the navy's Medal of Honor for his heroic actions aboard USS *Wyandank* during the Civil War.
1867: Educator Ida Rebecca Cummings is born in Baltimore.

17 76

MOTHERING SUNDAY (UK) **sunday**
1901: Renowned painter William H. Johnson is born in Florence, SC.
1992: Singer Donna Summer gets a star on Hollywood's Walk of Fame.

18 77

Deborah Willis
American, b. 1948

Deborah Willis is an archivist, author, and photographer of the historical treasures of black people around the world. In her many books and exhibitions, she has elucidated important historical events, from slavery to contemporary issues.

Willis grew up in "a very visual" Philadelphia family. She became an accomplished photographer, documenting and publishing her experience of growing up black. In addition to many exhibitions, her projects include *The Black Female Body: A Photographic History* (with Carla Williams); *A Small Nation of People: W.E.B. DuBois and the Photographs from the Paris Exposition; Reflections in Black: A History of Black Photographers, 1840 to the Present; Visual Journal: Photography in Harlem and DC in the Thirties and Forties; Picturing Us: African American Identity in Photography;* and *VANDERZEE: The Portraits of James VanDerZee.*

Formerly curator/archivist of photography at the Schomburg Center for Research in Black Culture and curator of exhibitions at the Smithsonian Institution, Willis teaches photography and imaging at NYU's Tisch School of the Arts. Her many awards and honors include a MacArthur Fellowship and an International Center of Photography Infinity Award for writing on photography.

Photograph by David Ogburn, courtesy Oggi's Kitchen

s	m	t	w	t	f	s
				1	2	3
4	5	6	7	8	9	10
11	12	13	14	15	16	17
18	19	20	21	22	23	24
25	26	27	28	29	30	31

MARCH

monday
1930: Jazz saxophonist Ornette Coleman is born in Fort Worth.
1939: Langston Hughes founds the New Negro Theater in Los Angeles. Its first performance is his play *Don't You Want to Be Free?*
19 78

tuesday
1883: Jan Matzeliger receives a patent for the shoe-lasting machine, which launches the mass production of shoes.
20 79

wednesday
VERNAL EQUINOX 12:07 AM (GMT)
1965: Martin Luther King Jr. leads thousands of marchers from Selma to Montgomery, AL, to dramatize denial of voting rights to African Americans.
21 80

thursday
1492: Alonzo Pietro, explorer, sets sail with Christopher Columbus.
22 81

friday
1985: Patricia Roberts Harris, Cabinet member and ambassador, dies.
23 82

saturday
1907: Nurse and aviator Janet Harmon Bragg is born in Griffin, GA.
24 83

sunday
SUMMER TIME BEGINS (UK)
1931: Ida B. Wells-Barnett, journalist, antilynching activist, and founding member of the NAACP, dies in Chicago.
1939: Toni Cade Bambara, noted fiction writer of such works as *Gorilla and My Love*, is born in New York City.
25 84

EQUAL-RIGHTS NOW

ALL POWER TO THE PEOPLE

MALCOLM X

BLACK PANTHER PARTY

BLACK POWER

THE KING IS DEAD, LONG LIVE THE KING!

Black Power

I HAVE A DREAM

ALL POWER TO THE PEOPLE

PRACTICE BROTHERHOOD

SNCC

POOR PEOPLES CAMPAIGN FOR POOR POWER

"I have a dream . . ."

Rev. Dr. Martin Luther King, Jr.

MAKE LOVE NOT WAR

MARCH ON WASHINGTON FOR JOBS & FREEDOM AUGUST 28, 1963

IF YOU ARE NOT PART OF THE SOLUTION You are part OF the PROBLEM
—cleaver

WE SHALL OVERCOME

BLACK is Beautiful

Protest Buttons

For more than a century, buttons have been worn to express support for a cause, a person, or a point of view. Some become collector's items—evocative relics of important historical matters.

The civil rights movement gave rise to an array of buttons that express key phrases of the struggle, such as "We Shall Overcome," "I Have A Dream," and "The King is Dead." The Black Panther movement inspired buttons like "Power to the People" and "Black Power." "Black is Beautiful" expressed pride among African Americans, while the Poor People's Campaign spoke out against the lack of jobs and freedom. A button worn by many Americans during the 1960s was "Peace/Make Love, Not War"—a sentiment that has lost none of its power and urgency.

monday
26 85

1886: Hugh N. Mulzac, the first black to captain an American merchant marine ship (SS *Booker T. Washington*, 1942), is born in the West Indies.

tuesday
27 86

1872: Musician Cleveland Luca, member of the famous Luca Family Quartet and composer of the Liberian national anthem, dies.
1924: Jazz singer Sarah Vaughan, "the Divine One," is born in Newark, NJ.

wednesday
28 87

1870: Jonathan S. Wright becomes the first African American state supreme court justice in South Carolina.

thursday
29 88

1918: Singer and actor Pearl Bailey is born in Newport News, VA.
1945: Basketball guard Walt Frazier is born in Atlanta. The future Hall of Famer will lead the New York Knicks to NBA championships in 1970 and 1973.

friday
30 89

1948: Trailblazing fashion model Naomi Sims is born in Oxford, MS.

saturday
31 90

1871: Jack Johnson, first African American heavyweight boxing champion, is born.
1988: Toni Morrison wins the Pulitzer Prize for her novel *Beloved*.

s	m	t	w	t	f	s
1	2	3	4	5	6	7
8	9	10	11	12	13	14
15	16	17	18	19	20	21
22	23	24	25	26	27	28
29	30					

APRIL

PALM SUNDAY

sunday
1 91

1930: Zawditu, first female monarch of Ethiopia, dies.

Noble Drew Ali
American, 1886–1929

Our limited knowledge of Noble Drew Ali's early life seems appropriate to his mystical persona. Born Timothy Drew in North Carolina, adopted and raised by Cherokee Indians, he began wandering as a circus magician at sixteen. He went to Egypt, where he studied esoteric teachings with a priest who, it is said, recognized him as a reincarnation of a former leader and saw a prophet in him.

And sure enough, back home he came to be viewed as a prophet: the last prophet of Islam. Ali set out to organize the black "people of Islam," teaching that Christianity kept them subservient. His goal was to instill pride and positive self-identity by teaching them of their Islamic origins. By 1928 he had started Moorish Science Temples across the country, with a national membership of 100,000.

Wallace Fard inspired Elijah Muhammad to found the Nation of Islam. But Fard's teachings derived from those of Noble Drew Ali, whose Islam was a combination of Eastern philosophy and religion, Christianity, Freemasonry, and metaphysics, all compiled in the Holy Koran of the Moorish Science Temple of America.

s	m	t	w	t	f	s
1	2	3	4	5	6	7
8	9	10	11	12	13	14
15	16	17	18	19	20	21
22	23	24	25	26	27	28
29	30					

APRIL

PASSOVER (BEGINS AT SUNSET)   *monday*
1796: Haitian revolt leader Toussaint L'Ouverture commands French forces at Santo Domingo.

◯ **2** 92

---

tuesday
1934: Richard Mayhew, highly respected and revolutionary landscape artist, is born in Amityville, NY.
1984: John Thompson of Georgetown University becomes the first African American coach to win an NCAA basketball tournament.

3 93

Independence Day (Republic of Senegal)   *wednesday*
1968: Martin Luther King Jr. is assassinated in Memphis.

4 94

---

thursday
1937: Colin Powell, first African American to serve as chairman of the Joint Chiefs of Staff and US secretary of state, is born in New York City.

5 95

GOOD FRIDAY   *friday*
1798: Noted scout James P. Beckwourth is born in Fredericksburg, VA. He will discover a pass in the Sierra Nevada that will later bear his name.
1905: W. Warrick Cardozo, physician and pioneering researcher in sickle cell anemia, is born in Washington, DC.

6 96

1867: Johnson C. Smith University is founded in Charlotte, NC.   *saturday*
1915: Jazz and blues legend Billie Holiday is born in East Baltimore, MD.

7 97

EASTER SUNDAY   *sunday*
1974: Hank Aaron breaks Babe Ruth's major league record with 715 home runs.
1990: Percy Julian and George Washington Carver are the first black inventors admitted into the National Inventors Hall of Fame.

8 98

Shirley Graham Du Bois
American, 1907–1977

Shirley Graham Du Bois, second wife of civil rights leader and author W. E. B. Du Bois, was a musicologist, novelist, playwright, and activist. Educated at Oberlin College and at the Sorbonne, Du Bois was the first to write and produce an all-black opera. *Tom-Toms: An Epic of Music and the Negro* was conceived to document and preserve the diverse and unique rhythms of black music. Produced by the Cleveland Opera Company in 1932, the opera was a resounding success, drawing an audience of ten thousand on the first night and fifteen thousand for the second, and final, performance.

Committed to uplifting her race and striving for world peace, Shirley Graham Du Bois remains as much a symbol of justice and world peace as her husband. Her life's mission is clear in the many plays she produced; in her biographies of W. E. B. Du Bois, Frederick Douglass, Paul Robeson, and others; and in her relentless fight to end injustice. Her awards and distinctions include a Guggenheim Fellowship and the National Institute of Arts and Letters Award.

s	m	t	w	t	f	s
1	2	3	4	5	6	7
8	9	10	11	12	13	14
15	16	17	18	19	20	21
22	23	24	25	26	27	28
29	30					

APRIL

---

monday

EASTER MONDAY (CANADA, UK)
National Day (Sierra Leone)
1898: Actor and singer Paul Robeson is born in Princeton, NJ.
1950: Juanita Hall is the first black to win a Tony Award, for her portrayal of Bloody Mary in *South Pacific.*

9 99

---

tuesday

1943: Arthur Ashe, first African American to win the US Open and men's singles title at Wimbledon, is born in Richmond, VA.

10 100

---

wednesday

1996: Forty-three African nations sign the African Nuclear Weapons Free Zone Treaty, pledging not to build, bury, stockpile, or test nuclear weapons.

11 101

---

thursday

1966: Emmett Ashford becomes the first African American major league umpire.
1968: Black students occupy the administration building at Boston University and demand black history courses and admission of more black students.

12 102

---

friday

1907: Harlem Hospital opens in New York City.
1997: Eldrick "Tiger" Woods wins the sixty-first Masters Tournament in Augusta, GA, at twenty-one, the youngest person and first black to win this tournament.

13 103

---

saturday

1775: The first US abolitionist society, the Pennsylvania Society for the Abolition of Slavery, is formed in Philadelphia by Quakers; Benjamin Franklin is its first president.

14 104

---

sunday

1889: Asa Philip Randolph, labor leader and civil rights advocate, is born in Crescent Way, FL.
1928: Norma Merrick (later Sklarek), first licensed female architect in the United States, is born in New York City.

15 105

Kimberly Cook
American

Kimberly Cook is a passionate artist who lives in New York City. In 1990 she received a BFA from University of the Arts, Philadelphia College of Art. She has also studied at the Studio Arts Center in Florence and at the Parsons School of Design and the American University in Paris.

Cook's subjects often represent the cultures of Africa, with particular attention to the Masai, Wodabe, Tuareg, and Ndebele cultures. She declares, "It has always been my attempt to try to preserve the cultures that quickly vanish due to economics, politics, and disease. I attempt to preserve the 'vanishing' by focusing on the immediate visual or physical distinctions that identify specific groups/tribes."

Masai Warrior, 2001
Collograph and chine colle, 30 x 22 in.
© Kimberly Cook

s	m	t	w	t	f	s
1	2	3	4	5	6	7
8	9	10	11	12	13	14
15	16	17	18	19	20	21
22	23	24	25	26	27	28
29	30					

APRIL

---

monday
16 106

1864: Acclaimed concert singer Flora Batson is born in Washington, DC.
1973: Leila Smith Foley is elected mayor of Taft, OK, becoming the first black woman to serve as mayor of a US city. She will hold the position thirteen years.

---

tuesday
17 107

1758: Frances Williams, first African American to graduate from college in the Western Hemisphere, publishes a collection of Latin poems.

---

wednesday
18 108

Independence Day (Zimbabwe)
1818: A regiment of Indians and blacks is defeated in the Battle of Suwanna, FL, ending the first Seminole War.

---

thursday
19 109

Republic Day (Sierra Leone)
1938: Nana Annor Adjaye, Pan-Africanist, dies in West Nzima, Ghana.

---

friday
20 110

1926: Harriet Elizabeth Byrd is born in Cheyenne, WY. A teacher, in 1981 she will become Wyoming's first black state legislator. .
1984: Popular English vocalist Mabel Mercer dies.

---

saturday
21 111

1966: PFC Milton Lee Olive is awarded the Medal of Honor posthumously for bravery during the Vietnam War.

---

sunday
22 112

EARTH DAY
1526: The first recorded New World slave revolt occurs in what is now South Carolina.
1922: Bassist, composer, and bandleader Charles Mingus is born in Nogales, AZ.

George Walker
American, b. 1922

A prodigy and future musical pioneer, George Walker began taking piano lessons at the age of five. He was born in Washington, DC, to a West Indian father and an American mother who supported his musical ambitions from the outset.

Walker graduated from Dunbar High School at just fourteen and gave his first public recital at Howard University that same year. At fifteen, he enrolled in Oberlin on a scholarship; two years later, he became the organist for the college's Graduate School of Theology. He graduated from Oberlin at eighteen with the highest honors of his class and, in 1945, earned artist diplomas in piano and composition from the Curtis Institute, becoming the first black to graduate from that renowned music school.

In 1954, Walker toured seven European countries—unprecedented for a black musician—playing in Stockholm, Copenhagen, The Hague, Amsterdam, Frankfurt, Lausanne, Berne, Milan, and London to great acclaim. In 1996, late in his long career, he became the first African American to win the Pulitzer Prize in music, for *Lilacs for Voice and Orchestra*.

Photograph by J. Abresch

s	m	t	w	t	f	s
1	2	3	4	5	6	7
8	9	10	11	12	13	14
15	16	17	18	19	20	21
22	23	24	25	26	27	28
29	30					

APRIL

---

monday
1856: Granville T. Woods, inventor of the steam boiler and automobile air brakes, is born.

23 113

---

tuesday
1993: Oliver Tambo, leader of the African National Congress, dies in Johannesburg.

☽ **24** 114

---

wednesday
1918: Ella Fitzgerald, "First Lady of Song," is born in Newport News, VA.
1945: The United Nations is founded at a San Francisco meeting attended by W. E. B. Du Bois, Mary McLeod Bethune, Ralph J. Bunche, and Walter White.

25 115

---

thursday
1991: Maryann Bishop Coffey becomes the first female African American cochair of the National Conference of Christians and Jews.

26 116

---

friday
1903: Maggie L. Walker becomes the first black woman to head a bank when she is named president of Richmond's St. Luke Penny Bank and Trust Company.
1994: South Africa's first all-races democratic elections are held.

27 117

---

saturday
1913: Political activist Margaret Just Butcher is born in Washington, DC.
1957: Chicago lawyer W. Robert Ming is elected chairman of the American Veterans Committee, becoming the first black to head a major national veterans organization.

28 118

---

sunday
1854: Ashmun Institute (later Lincoln University), the world's first institution founded "to provide a higher education in the arts and sciences for youth of African descent," opens in Oxford, PA.
1992: Four Los Angeles police officers are acquitted of charges stemming from the beating of Rodney King; rioting ensues.

29 119

Granville T. Woods
American, 1856–1910

Born in Columbus, Ohio, Granville Woods apprenticed in a machine shop at an early age, attended night school, and studied electricity in his spare time, preparing himself to be an engineer. He reached his goal in 1872, when he took a job as a fireman on the Danville and Southern Railroad in Missouri. In 1878 he obtained a job aboard the *Ironsides*, a British steamer, and two years later he was named chief engineer.

Eventually settling in Cincinnati, Woods became interested in improving the railway system. He invented the "third rail" system still used by electric trains. Perhaps his most important invention, however, was telegraphony, a system that allowed train operators to maintain contact with each other, significantly reducing accidents.

The owner of at least sixty patents, Woods has been called "the Black Edison." (Thomas Edison sued him for patent infringement over telegraphony, then offered him a job; the White Edison was unsuccessful in both endeavors.) Cincinnati's *Catholic Tribune* wrote that Woods was "equal, if not superior, to any inventor in the country."

Illustrator unknown; drawn from a photograph by Eddowes Brothers

s	m	t	w	t	f	s
			1	2	3	4	5
6	7	8	9	10	11	12
13	14	15	16	17	18	19
20	21	22	23	24	25	26
27	28	29	30	31		

MAY

---

monday
30 120

1951: Surgeons Rivers Frederick, Ulysses G. Dailey, and Nelson M. Russell are honored at the University of Italy.

---

tuesday
1 121

1901: Poet, literary critic, and editor Sterling Brown is born in Washington, DC.
1950: Gwendolyn Brooks becomes the first African American to win the Pulitzer Prize, for her book of poetry *Annie Allen.*

---

wednesday
2 122

1969: Record-breaking cricket batsman Brian Lara is born in Santa Cruz, Trinidad.

---

thursday
3 123

1855: Macon B. Allen becomes the first African American to be formally admitted to the bar in Massachusetts.
1902: Astride Alan-a-Dale, African American jockey Jimmy Winkfield wins his second Kentucky Derby in a row.

---

friday
4 124

1942: Songwriter Nickolas Ashford is born in Fairfield, SC. He and his wife, Valerie Simpson, will cowrite many pop hits.
1969: *No Place to Be Somebody* opens in New York. It will win the Pulitzer Prize the following year.

---

saturday
5 125

CINCO DE MAYO

1905: Robert Sengstacke Abbott founds the *Chicago Defender,* calling it "the world's greatest weekly."

---

sunday
6 126

1995: Ron Kirk becomes the first black mayor of Dallas, with 62 percent of the vote.

Claude McKay
American, b. Jamaica, 1890–1948

Claude McKay began writing poetry when he was only ten; he had already published two collections when he came to the United States at twenty-two. McKay was unprepared for the experience of American racism, and the subject would strongly inform his future work.

McKay was never very successful in worldly terms—poetry and poverty often seem to go together, and his sympathy with socialism could not have endeared him to people with money—but he did see a lot of the world. He lived in Alabama, Kansas, and New York, where he coedited the socialist *Liberator* magazine; making his way to London, he wrote for the *Worker's Dreadnought*. He led the expatriate life in France and North Africa, where his writings would fuel the later social-literary movement called negritude, and in Russia, where his essay collection *The Negroes in America* was published in 1923. McKay later denounced Communism, though he remained a socialist.

McKay's ideas, if not the sonnet form in which he expressed them, exerted major influence on Countee Cullen, Langston Hughes, and other poets and writers of the Harlem Renaissance.

Photograph by James L. Allen, 1930s

s	m	t	w	t	f	s
		1	2	3	4	5
6	7	8	9	10	11	12
13	14	15	16	17	18	19
20	21	22	23	24	25	26
27	28	29	30	31		

MAY

BANK HOLIDAY (UK)   *monday*

7   127

1941: Theodore Browne's play *Natural Man,* a production of the American Negro Theatre, premieres in New York City.
1946: William H. Hastie is inaugurated as the first black governor of the Virgin Islands.

---

tuesday

8   128

1965: The Association for the Advancement of Creative Musicians is founded by Muhal Richard Abrams.

---

wednesday

9   129

1800: John Brown, abolitionist and martyr at Harpers Ferry, is born.

---

thursday

10   130

1968: A public school in Brooklyn, NY, is named for noted scientist and inventor Lewis H. Latimer.

---

friday

11   131

1895: William Grant Still, dean of black classical composers, is born in Woodville, MS.

---

saturday

12   132

1926: Mervyn Dymally, California's first African American lieutenant governor, is born in Cedros, Trinidad.

MOTHER'S DAY   *sunday*

13   133

1914: Heavyweight boxer Joe Louis is born in Lexington, AL.
1990: George Stallings becomes the Black Catholic Church's first bishop. He had broken with the Roman Catholic Church in 1989, citing its failure to meet the needs of black Catholics.

Henry Ossawa Tanner
American, 1859–1937

Henry Ossawa Tanner was the first African American artist to receive international recognition. He studied with Thomas Eakins at the Pennsylvania Academy of the Fine Arts and painted two important works involving African American subjects, *The Banjo Lesson* and *The Thankful Poor,* before traveling to Paris for further study at the Académie Julian.

Later in his career Tanner turned his attention to landscapes and religious subjects; his painting *Daniel in the Lions' Den,* now in the Los Angeles County Museum of Art, received a silver medal at the 1900 Universal Exposition in Paris and another at the 1901 Pan American exhibition in Buffalo. The French government purchased his *Raising of Lazarus,* and in 1923 France awarded him its highest honor, making him a Chevalier of the Order of the Legion of Honor.

Tanner died in Paris, his adopted home. A collection of his work is in the Smithsonian American Art Museum in Washington, DC, and through the efforts of Hillary Clinton, a Tanner is the first painting by an African American to hang in the White House.

s	m	t	w	t	f	s
		1	2	3	4	5
6	7	8	9	10	11	12
13	14	15	16	17	18	19
20	21	22	23	24	25	26
27	28	29	30	31		

MAY

monday
14 134

1913: Clara Stanton Jones, first black president of the American Library Association, is born in St. Louis, MO.
1969: John B. McLendon becomes the ABA's first black coach when he signs a two-year contract with the Denver Nuggets.

tuesday
15 135

1918: PFCs Henry Johnson and Needham Roberts become the first Americans to win France's Croix de Guerre.
1946: Camilia Williams appears in the title role of *Madama Butterfly* with the New York City Opera, becoming the first black female singer to sign with a major US opera company.

wednesday
16 136

1929: John Conyers Jr., founder of the Congressional Black Caucus, is born.

thursday
17 137

1954: The US Supreme Court declares school segregation unconstitutional in *Brown v. Board of Education.*

friday
18 138

1946: New York Yankees baseball star Reggie Jackson is born in Wyncote, PA. He will set or tie seven World Series records.
1955: Mary McLeod Bethune, educator and founder of the National Council of Negro Women, dies in Daytona Beach, FL.

saturday
19 139

ARMED FORCES DAY

1993: University of Virginia professor Rita Dove is appointed US poet laureate.

sunday
20 140

National Holiday (United Republic of Cameroon)
1868: P. B. S. Pinchback and James J. Harris are named the first African American delegates to the Republican National Convention.

Florence Mills
American, 1895–1927

They called her "the Queen of Happiness." The Prince of Wales attended one of her revues more than twenty times. She rejected a major role with the Ziegfeld Follies—not a proposition to be taken lightly—in favor of appearing in an all-black production. An incomparable singer and dancer, a great beauty and a fine actor, a beacon of the Harlem Renaissance, and the gamest of Broadway troupers, Florence Mills used her celebrity as a podium from which to speak against racism.

The 1921 musical *Shuffle Along*—written, directed, and performed by African Americans, and featuring Ethel Waters, Josephine Baker, and Paul Robeson as well as Mills—was a massive success and a defining event in New York history; Langston Hughes wrote that "Manhattan's black Renaissance . . . began with *Shuffle Along*."

On the strength of that Broadway triumph, Mills worked in Paris and London and remained in great demand at home. She worked too hard, even putting off treatment for appendicitis, and it killed her at just thirty-one. More than 150,000 people turned out for her Harlem funeral procession.

s	m	t	w	t	f	s
		1	2	3	4	5
6	7	8	9	10	11	12
13	14	15	16	17	18	19
20	21	22	23	24	25	26
27	28	29	30	31		

MAY

---

monday
VICTORIA DAY (CANADA)
1833: African American students enroll in classes at the newly established Oberlin College in Oberlin, OH.
21 141

---

tuesday
1940: Bernard Shaw, journalist and principal Washington anchor for cable news network CNN, is born in Chicago.
1967: Noted poet Langston Hughes dies in New York City.
22 142

---

wednesday
1832: Jamaican national figure Samuel Sharpe is hanged.
☽ **23** 143

---

thursday
1905: Distinguished educator Hilda Davis is born in Washington, DC.
1954: Peter Marshall Murray becomes president of the New York County Medical Society, the first African American physician to head an AMA affiliate.
24 144

---

friday
1963: African Liberation Day is declared at the conference of the Organization of African Unity in Addis Ababa, Ethiopia.
25 145

---

saturday
1926: Renowned jazz trumpeter Miles Davis is born in Alton, IL.
26 146

---

sunday
1942: Dorie Miller, a messman, is awarded the Navy Cross for heroism at Pearl Harbor.
1958: Ernest Green becomes the first black to graduate from Central High School in Little Rock, AR.
27 147

Harry Thacker Burleigh
American, 1866–1949

Harry Thacker Burleigh was born in Erie, Pennsylvania. His mother, Elizabeth, was a domestic worker: she was unable to get a teaching position despite her college education and fluency in French and Greek. Burleigh's musical influences began with his maternal grandfather, Hamilton Waters, a partially blind ex-slave who worked as Erie's town crier and lamplighter. Waters sang to young Harry, passing on a music—the Negro spiritual—that his grandson would one day make known around the world.

Burleigh was probably the first successful African American classical composer. At twenty-four, he received a scholarship to the National Conservatory of Music in New York, whose director—the composer Antonin Dvořák—was deeply interested in American musical forms. "In the Negro melodies of America," Dvořák said, "I discover all that is needed for a great and noble school of music." Burleigh's spirituals influenced Dvořák's compositions.

Burleigh also sang in French, Italian, German, Latin, and Hebrew. He performed throughout the United States and Europe for various heads of state. Singers who studied with Burleigh include Roland Hayes, Paul Robeson, and Marian Anderson.

s	m	t	w	t	f	s
					1	2
3	4	5	6	7	8	9
10	11	12	13	14	15	16
17	18	19	20	21	22	23
24	25	26	27	28	29	30

JUNE

MEMORIAL DAY OBSERVED
BANK HOLIDAY (UK)
1981: Jazz pianist Mary Lou Williams dies in Durham, NC.

monday
28 148

1973: Tom Bradley becomes the first African American mayor of Los Angeles.

tuesday
29 149

MEMORIAL DAY
1822: Denmark Vesey's conspiracy to free slaves of Charleston, SC, and surrounding areas is thwarted by a slave who betrays the plot to whites.
1965: Vivian Malone becomes the first black to graduate from the University of Alabama.

wednesday
30 150

1931: Mezzo-soprano Shirley Verrett is born in New Orleans. She will become world famous for her performance in *Carmen*.
1955: The US Supreme Court orders school integration "with all deliberate speed."

thursday
31 151

National Day (Tunisia)
1919: Noted physician Caroline Virginia Still Wiley Anderson dies in Philadelphia.

friday
○ **1** 152

1948: Jamaican-born track star Herb McKenley sets a new world record for the 400-yard dash.
1999: South Africans vote to elect a president to succeed retiring eighty-year-old Nelson Mandela.

saturday
2 153

1904: Charles R. Drew, originator of blood plasma banks, is born in Washington, DC.

sunday
3 154

Georgia Douglas Johnson
American, 1877–1966

Musician, poet, playwright, columnist, short-story writer, wife, and mother, Georgia Douglas Johnson was an eminent figure of the Harlem Renaissance.

Georgia Blanche Douglas Camp was born in Atlanta to mixed parentage: her mother was Native American and black, her father a wealthy white musician. Throughout her school days, her racially mixed appearance kept her isolated and largely alone; she spent hours teaching herself to play the violin. She briefly studied music at Oberlin Conservatory, but left school to marry Henry Lincoln Johnson, a prominent attorney. The couple moved to Washington, DC, and her interest in writing poetry blossomed.

Johnson tried to avoid writing on racial themes, but they were prominent in her thoughts. To please her critics, she wrote on miscegenation in her book of poetry *Bronze: A Book of Verse*, but more than anything Johnson wanted to write about peace, love, and people coming together. She said, "If one can soar, he should soar, leaving his chains behind."

Artist unknown
Georgia Douglas Johnson, Poet, Playwright, Novelist, n.d.

s	m	t	w	t	f	s
					1	2
3	4	5	6	7	8	9
10	11	12	13	14	15	16
17	18	19	20	21	22	23
24	25	26	27	28	29	30

JUNE

---

monday
4 155

1946: Legislation is enacted authorizing establishment of Mississippi Valley State University in Itta Bena.
1967: Bill Cosby receives an Emmy Award for his work in the television series *I Spy*.

---

tuesday
5 156

Liberation Day (Republic of the Seychelles)
1973: Doris A. Davis, mayor of Compton, CA, becomes the first African American woman to govern a city in a major metropolitan area.

---

wednesday
6 157

1939: Marian Wright Edelman, the first female African American lawyer in Mississippi and founder of the Children's Defense Fund, is born.
1999: Nelson Mandela's successor, Thabo Mbake, is elected president of South Africa.

---

thursday
7 158

National Day (Chad)
1994: The Organization of African Unity formally admits South Africa as its fifty-third member.

---

friday
☽ 8 159

1939: Herb Adderley, Hall of Famer and defensive back for the Green Bay Packers, is born in Philadelphia.
1998: Nigerian military ruler Gen. Sani Abacha dies in the capital, Abuja.

---

saturday
9 160

1877: Sculptor Meta Vaux Warrick is born in Philadelphia.
2000: World-renowned artist Jacob Lawrence dies from lung cancer at eighty-two.

---

sunday
10 161

1854: James Augustine Healy, first African American Catholic bishop, is ordained a priest in Notre Dame Cathedral.
1997: Geronimo Pratt, former Black Panther Party member, is released from jail after serving twenty-seven years for a crime he did not commit.

Malvin Gray Johnson
American, 1896–1934

Malvin Gray Johnson was born in Greensboro, North Carolina; his family later moved to New York. His older sister Maggie gave him art lessons and materials. In 1906 Johnson drew his first picture that is still with us, in charcoal. Later he painted in oil and studied at the National Academy of Design.

Coming to prominence as an artist during the Harlem Renaissance, Johnson won a Harmon Foundation award in 1928 for his painting *Swing Low, Sweet Chariot*, a piece that received international attention. Johnson was one of the first African American artists to paint in the cubist style. He also used techniques derived from his studies of African sculpture.

Johnson gained sponsorship by the Artists' Aid Committee, and in 1934 he was employed by the Public Works of Art Project, developed by President Franklin D. Roosevelt to help artists survive the Depression. With the proceeds from his projects, Johnson traveled to rural Virginia, where he portrayed the African American farming community in a modern-folk style. One painting from that period, *Brothers*, is in the collection of the Smithsonian American Art Museum.

Negro Pharaoh (study), 1934
Oil on board, 12 x 16 in.

s	m	t	w	t	f	s
					1	2
3	4	5	6	7	8	9
10	11	12	13	14	15	16
17	18	19	20	21	22	23
24	25	26	27	28	29	30

JUNE

---

monday
11 162

1964: Nelson Mandela is sentenced to life imprisonment by the South African government.
2000: Earl T. Shinhoster, prominent civil rights activist who led the NAACP through a difficult period, is killed in a car accident in Alabama.

---

tuesday
12 163

1963: Civil rights leader Medgar Evers is killed in Jackson, MS.

---

wednesday
13 164

1967: Thurgood Marshall is appointed to the US Supreme Court by President Lyndon B. Johnson.
1992: Dominique Dawes makes the US Olympic Gymnastics Team.

---

thursday
14 165

FLAG DAY
1989: Congressman William Gray is elected Democratic whip of the House of Representatives, the highest leadership position in Congress held thus far by an African American.

---

friday
15 166

1927: Pianist and composer Natalie Hinderas is born in Oberlin, OH.

---

saturday
16 167

1976: Students riot in Soweto, South Africa.
1999: In Olympic Stadium, Athens, Greece, Maurice Greene, US track and field athlete, breaks the 100-meter dash world record, running 9.79.

---

sunday
17 168

FATHER'S DAY
1871: James Weldon Johnson, writer, poet, and first African American to be admitted to the Florida bar, is born.

Hubert Fauntleroy Julian
American, b. Trinidad, 1897–1983

No Harlem Renaissance personality was flashier, more charismatic, or more adventurous than Hubert Fauntleroy Julian. Born in Trinidad, Julian attended private school there, then studied in England. When World War I began, he left England and learned to fly from Canadian ace Billy Bishop. Julian missed the war, but became one of the first blacks in the United States to earn a pilot's license, and the first to fly across the country, coast to coast.

Julian became a stunt parachutist and headlined for pioneering aviator Bessie Coleman, jumping from planes, landing in predetermined spots, and delighting onlookers, who dubbed him "the Black Eagle." While in Harlem, Julian became involved with Marcus Garvey's Back to Africa movement.

In 1930, Julian flew to Ethiopia and impressed Emperor Haile Selassie I with his aerial exploits. He later returned to train Ethiopia's air force to resist Mussolini's invasion, but he was ordered to leave the country after publicly fighting with another pilot. Back in the United States, he continued barnstorming, served as private pilot for evangelist Father Divine, and invented a safety device for disabled aircraft.

s	m	t	w	t	f	s
					1	2
3	4	5	6	7	8	9
10	11	12	13	14	15	16
17	18	19	20	21	22	23
24	25	26	27	28	29	30

JUNE

---

monday

1942: The US Navy commissions its first black officer, Harvard University medical student Bernard Whitfield Robinson.
2000: "Tiger" Woods wins the 100th US Open Tournament.

18 169

---

tuesday

JUNETEENTH

1862: News of the Emancipation Proclamation reaches the South and Texas through Gen. Gordon Granger.

19 170

---

wednesday

National Holiday (United Republic of Cameroon)
1858: Charles Waddell Chesnutt, first African American writer to receive critical literary acclaim in the United States, is born.

20 171

---

thursday

SUMMER SOLSTICE 6:06 PM (GMT)

1859: Renowned painter Henry Ossawa Tanner is born.
1998: Marion Jones becomes the first athlete in fifty years to win the 100- and 200-meter events and long jump at the US Track and Field Championships in Indianapolis.

21 172

---

friday

1972: National Black MBA Association is incorporated, with over two thousand minority members.

☽ **22** 173

---

saturday

1899: Pvt. George Wanton is cited for bravery at Tayabacoa, Cuba, in the Spanish-American War.

23 174

---

sunday

1877: Bishop Josiah M. Kibira becomes the first black African leader of the Lutheran World Federation.

24 175

Walter Williams
American, 1920–1998

The painter, printmaker, and sculptor Walter Williams was born in Brooklyn. He attended public schools there and studied for four years at the Brooklyn Museum Art School, where he met artists who influenced his developing style. Gregorio Prestopino became a major influence on Williams' work.

In 1953, Williams earned a summer scholarship to the art school at Skowhegan, Maine, and won first prize in a painting competition. He first exhibited in 1954, and in the following year he received a Whitney Fellowship, on which he traveled and painted in Mexico. Williams traveled to many countries, attending workshops and exhibiting his work, throughout his artistic career. In 1960 he settled in Copenhagen, where he stayed for four years; he then moved to Rome and stayed there for two years, before returning to the United States to take a position as artist in residence at Fisk University in Nashville.

Williams' works are in the collections of the Metropolitan Museum of Art and the Schomburg Center in New York City and the National Gallery of Art in Washington.

Girl Jumping Rope, 1951
Oil on canvas, 40 x 30 in.
© Estate of Walter Williams
Courtesy M. Hanks Gallery,
Santa Monica, CA

s	m	t	w	t	f	s
1	2	3	4	5	6	7
8	9	10	11	12	13	14
15	16	17	18	19	20	21
22	23	24	25	26	27	28
29	30	31				

JULY

---

monday

National Day (Mozambique)
1792: Thomas Peters, an African American slave who led black emigrants from Nova Scotia to settle in Sierra Leone, dies.

25 176

---

tuesday

Independence Day (Democratic Republic of Madagascar and Republic of Somalia)
1993: Roy Campanella, legendary catcher for the Negro Leagues and the Los Angeles Dodgers, dies.

26 177

---

wednesday

National Day (Djibouti)
1833: Prudence Crandall, a white woman, is arrested for teaching black girls at her academy in Canterbury, CT.
1872: Prominent poet and writer Paul Laurence Dunbar is born in Dayton, OH.

27 178

---

thursday

1911: Samuel J. Battle becomes the first African American policeman in New York City.

28 179

---

friday

Independence Day (Republic of the Seychelles)
1886: Photographer James VanDerZee is born in Lenox, MA.
1998: Atlanta Hawks head coach Lenny Wilkens becomes the second person to be elected to the NBA Hall of Fame twice, as a player and a coach.

29 180

---

saturday

Independence Day (Republic of Zaire)
1917: Actor, singer, and civil rights advocate Lena Horne is born in Brooklyn, NY.

○ **30** 181

---

sunday

CANADA DAY (CANADA)
Independence Day (Burundi and Rwanda)
1899: Rev. Thomas Dorsey, father of gospel music, is born in Villa Rica, GA.
1975: Wallace D. Muhammad, head of the Nation of Islam, opens the group to members of all races.

1 182

Clayton "Peg Leg" Bates
American, 1907–1998

Born in rural Fountain Inn, South
Carolina, Clayton Bates was dancing at just five years of age, but at
twelve he lost a leg in a cotton mill
accident. That might have been the
end of his dancing. But Bates
turned pro, working his way up
from minstrel shows and carnivals
to the white vaudeville circuit and
eventually tap dancing in top
Harlem nightclubs such as the
Cotton Club, Connie's Inn, and Club
Zanzibar, and opening *The Ed
Sullivan Show* many times. He gave
two command performances for
the king and queen of England and
toured Europe, South America, and
Australia.

In 1951, Bates and his wife, Alice,
transformed their sixty-acre turkey
farm in the Catskills into a resort
for African Americans. This made
Bates the first black resort owner
in the Borscht Belt.

In 1998, on a Saturday night, Peg
Leg Bates danced once again in his
hometown of Fountain Inn, as part
of a celebration to raise money for
a statue of him to be erected. He
died of a heart attack the following
day, aged ninety-one.

Photograph by James J. Kriegsmann

s	m	t	w	t	f	s
1	2	3	4	5	6	7
8	9	10	11	12	13	14
15	16	17	18	19	20	21
22	23	24	25	26	27	28
29	30	31				

JULY

CANADA DAY OBSERVED (CANADA)
monday 2 183
1908: Thurgood Marshall, first African American US Supreme Court justice, is born.
1999: Alexandra Stevenson, daughter of NBA star Julius Erving, is the first qualifier to advance to the semifinals of the Wimbledon tennis tournament in England.

tuesday 3 184
1962: Jackie Robinson becomes the first African American to be inducted into the National Baseball Hall of Fame.

INDEPENDENCE DAY
wednesday 4 185
1881: Tuskegee Institute opens in Tuskegee, AL, with Booker T. Washington as its first president.

thursday 5 186
1809: Eighteen blacks under the leadership of Reverend Thomas Paul establish the Abyssinian Baptist Church in New York City.
1892: Andrew Beard is issued a patent for the rotary engine.

Independence Day (Republic of Malawi)
friday 6 187
1993: Eleven lives are lost in an antigovernment riot in Lagos, Nigeria.

Saba Saba Day (Tanzania)
saturday 7 188
1993: Political violence in South Africa continues after the declaration of the nation's first all-races democratic election.

sunday 8 189
1943: Women's rights advocate Faye Wattleton is born in St. Louis, MO.
2000: Venus Williams defeats Lindsay Davenport 6–3, 7–6, to win her first Wimbledon tennis championship.

Jesse Redmon Fauset
American, 1882–1961

As literary editor of *The Crisis,* the NAACP's magazine, from 1919 to 1926, Jessie Redmon Fauset was one of three people Langston Hughes credited with "mid-wif[ing] the so-called New Negro literature into being. Kind and critical ... they nursed us along until our books were born." Fauset, who was among the first African Americans to graduate from Cornell University (Phi Beta Kappa, in her case), nursed along books of her own as well. She produced four novels (*There Is Confusion, Plum Bun, The Chinaberry Tree,* and *Comedy, American Style*) dominated by a single theme: the fundamental importance of human relationships in a world rife with racial and sexual barriers. They were written in the midst of other jobs and other writing (poetry, essays, magazine articles, and material for *The Brownies' Book,* a children's magazine that she edited)—a fact that moved her to tell one interviewer of her longing to devote a year or two solely to a novel "just to see what I really could do if I had my full time and energy to devote to my work."

s	m	t	w	t	f	s
1	2	3	4	5	6	7
8	9	10	11	12	13	14
15	16	17	18	19	20	21
22	23	24	25	26	27	28
29	30	31				

JULY

1936: Poet and author June Jordan is born in Harlem, NY.

monday

9 190

Independence Day (Commonwealth of the Bahamas)
1993: Kenyan runner Yobes Ondieki becomes the first man to run ten thousand meters in less than twenty-seven minutes.

tuesday

10 191

President's Day (Republic of Botswana)
1915: Mifflin Wistar Gibbs, first African American to be elected a municipal judge, dies.

wednesday

11 192

BANK HOLIDAY (N. IRELAND)
1937: William Cosby, EdD, comedian, actor, educator, and humanitarian, is born in Philadelphia.

thursday

12 193

1928: Robert N. C. Nix Jr., first African American chief justice of a state supreme court (Pennsylvania), is born.

friday

13 194

1996: In Lapeenranta, Finland, Kenyan runner Daniel Komen shaves almost four seconds off the world mile record.

saturday

● **14** 195

1929: Francis Bebey, guitarist and author, is born.

sunday

15 196

Richmond Barthé
American, 1901–1989

Born in Bay St. Louis, Mississippi, Richmond Barthé was residing in New Orleans when, at the age of eighteen, he won his first prize for art. A local priest helped Barthé—who had little education and no formal training in art—to get into the Art Institute of Chicago. In his fourth year there, he began modeling in clay to gain a better understanding of his painting and discovered that he was more interested in three dimensions than in two.

Barthé opened his first studio in Harlem and became established as a sculptor. In 1934, he was awarded his first solo show. Barthé enjoyed broad critical success, but New York's tense environment and violence began to take their toll; he decided to abandon his life of fame and move to Jamaica. His career flourished on the island and he lived there until the mid-1960s.

Notable public works by Barthé include his Toussaint L'Ouverture monument and General Dessalines monument, both in Port-au-Prince, Haiti, and *Green Pastures: Walls of Jericho* for the Harlem River Housing Project.

Richmond Barthé
Toussaint L'Ouverture, n.d.
Pastel on paper, 15½ x 11 in.
© The Richmond Barthé Trust

s	m	t	w	t	f	s
1	2	3	4	5	6	7
8	9	10	11	12	13	14
15	16	17	18	19	20	21
22	23	24	25	26	27	28
29	30	31				

JULY

---

monday

1882: Violette Anderson, first African American woman to practice before the US Supreme Court, is born.
1998: Dr. John Henrik Clarke, historian and scholar, dies in New York City at eighty-three.

16 197

---

tuesday

1911: Frank Snowden, foremost scholar on African Americans in ancient history, is born in York County, VA.

17 198

---

wednesday

1896: First African American professional golfer, John Shippen, finishes fifth in the US Open.
1899: L. C. Bailey is issued a patent for the folding bed.

18 199

---

thursday

1979: In her second Cabinet-level appointment, Patricia Roberts Harris is named secretary of health and human services.

19 200

---

friday

1967: The first National Conference of Black Power opens in Newark, NJ.

20 201

---

saturday

1896: Mary Church Terrell founds the National Association of Colored Women in Washington, DC.

21 202

---

sunday

1939: Jane Bolin is appointed to New York City's Domestic Relations Court, becoming the first female African American judge.

☽ **22** 203

Caterina Jarboro
American, 1903–1986

Born in Wilmington, North Carolina, Caterina Jarboro, soprano extraordinaire, developed at an early age a consuming passion for opera, a passion that called her to New York at the age of thirteen. Five years later she joined a stellar cast—Eubie Blake, Noble Sissle, William Grant Still, Josephine Baker, Florence Mills, and Paul Robeson—in *Shuffle Along* (1921), the first all-black show to appear on Broadway in a decade.

Jarboro studied voice in Paris and Milan and was well received by the French and Italian opera communities. In 1930 she won the starring role in *Aida*, debuting at Milan's Puccini Opera House to standing ovations and rave reviews.

Back in the United States, Jarboro performed *Aida* with the Chicago Opera Company in 1933 at the Hippodrome in New York. Again, her performance was well received.

But Jarboro's fame was brief. Once the American opera establishment realized that she was not Italian but African American, her career came to an end. Still, she was the first African American woman to have a starring role in a major opera production.

s	m	t	w	t	f	s
1	2	3	4	5	6	7
8	9	10	11	12	13	14
15	16	17	18	19	20	21
22	23	24	25	26	27	28
29	30	31				

JULY

Anniversary of Revolution (Arab Republic of Egypt)
1900: The first Pan-African Congress, organized by Henry Sylvester Williams, is held in London.

monday
23 204

1925: Operatic soprano Adele Addison is born in New York City.

tuesday
24 205

1916: Wearing the protective mask he invented, Garrett Morgan enters a gas-filled tunnel with a rescue party after an underground explosion in Cleveland, OH; six lives are saved.

wednesday
25 206

Independence Day (Republic of Liberia)
1865: Catholic priest Patrick Francis Healy becomes the first African American to earn a PhD degree.

thursday
26 207

1996: Donovan Bailey, a Jamaican running for Canada, becomes the "world's fastest human" in the Atlanta Olympics, setting a world record of 9.84 in the 100-meter dash.

friday
27 208

1868: The Fourteenth Amendment is ratified, granting citizenship to African Americans.
1996: Ethiopian police officer Fatuma Roba becomes the first African woman to win a medal in an Olympic marathon.

saturday
28 209

1909: Crime novelist Chester Himes is born in Jefferson City, MO.

sunday
29 210

José Antonio Jarvis
American, 1901–1963

The historian, author, poet, journalist, and artist José Antonio Jarvis was born in the Virgin Islands. His *Brief History of the Virgin Islands* (1938) was written as a high school textbook, to teach students the history of their island culture. In 1930 he cofounded *The Daily News,* now the territory's most influential and widely distributed newspaper. Jarvis both painted his visions and expressed them in writing. *View from Fort Christian, Island Sloop,* and *Mahogany Trees* are among his best-known works.

Jarvis was deeply concerned with the well-being and future success of the islands' youth; he dedicated himself to teaching and writing in an effort to facilitate the progression of excellence in his people.

In 1970, the legislature of the Virgin Islands renamed the Abraham Lincoln School on St. Thomas: it became the José Antonio Jarvis Elementary School in appreciation of Jarvis' service as its principal.

Virgin Islands—Saturday Morning, 1940
Oil on canvas, 16 x 20 in.
Photograph by Manu Sassoonian

s	m	t	w	t	f	s
			1	2	3	4
5	6	7	8	9	10	11
12	13	14	15	16	17	18
19	20	21	22	23	24	25
26	27	28	29	30	31	

AUGUST

---

monday
30 211
1996: Three years after recovering from third-degree burns, Cuba's Ana Quirot wins a silver medal in the 800-meter run in the Atlanta Olympics.

---

tuesday
31 212
1921: Educator and civil rights activist Whitney Young Jr. is born in Lincoln Ridge, KY.

---

wednesday
1 213
Independence Day (Jamaica)
1996: Michael Johnson becomes the first man to win gold medals in both the 200- and 400-meter runs, breaking his own world record.

---

thursday
2 214
1847: William A. Leidesdorff launches the first steamboat in San Francisco Bay.
1997: Nigerian musician, composer, and political activist Fela Anikulapo-Kuti dies from AIDS in Lagos.

---

friday
3 215
Independence Day (Republic of Niger)
1996: Josia Thugwane becomes the first black South African to win an Olympic gold medal, completing the marathon in 2 hours, 12 minutes, 36 seconds.

---

saturday
4 216
1961: Barack Obama, future US senator from Illinois, is born in Honolulu.
1997: Australia's Cathy Freeman becomes the first aboriginal athlete to capture a world track title when she wins the 400-meter event in Greece.

---

sunday
5 217
1914: The first electric traffic lights (invented by Garrett Morgan) are installed in Cleveland.

Hubert Harrison
American, 1883–1927

Hubert Harrison was an important figure of the Harlem Renaissance. Born in the Virgin Islands, he came to New York City at seventeen and worked as a bellhop and elevator operator while studying sociology, science, psychology, drama, and literature.

Harrison joined the Industrial Workers of the World, and then the Socialist Party. There he met other African American radicals such as A. Philip Randolph, Chandler Owen, and Claude McKay. He had much to say about the condition of his race, often speaking on socialism and civil rights and sometimes attracting street corner crowds of more than ten thousand.

A profound influence on Marcus Garvey and Randolph, Harrison enjoyed the friendship of J. A. Rogers, who wrote about him in *The World's Great Men of Color.* He edited *The Masses* and *The Voice* and published two important books, *The Negro and the Nation* (1917) and *When Africa Awakes* (1920).

Harrison was instrumental in founding the New York Public Library's Division of Negro Literature, History, and Prints, which grew into the internationally known Schomburg Center for Research in Black Culture.

s	m	t	w	t	f	s
			1	2	3	4
5	6	7	8	9	10	11
12	13	14	15	16	17	18
19	20	21	22	23	24	25
26	27	28	29	30	31	

AUGUST

monday 6 218
CIVIC HOLIDAY (CANADA, MOST PROVINCES)
BANK HOLIDAY (SCOTLAND)
1965: President Lyndon B. Johnson signs the Voting Rights Act, outlawing the literacy test for voting eligibility in the South.

tuesday 7 219
1904: Ralph Bunche, first African American Nobel Prize winner, is born in Detroit.

wednesday 8 220
1865: Matthew A. Henson, first explorer to reach the North Pole, is born in Charles County, MD.

thursday 9 221
1936: Jesse Owens wins four gold medals in track and field events at the Berlin Olympics.
2003: Gregory Hines, actor and dancer, dies from cancer.

friday 10 222
1829: A race riot erupts in Cincinnati, prompting about one thousand blacks to leave for Canada, Michigan, western Pennsylvania, and New York.
1989: Gen. Colin Powell is nominated as chairman of the Joint Chiefs of Staff.

saturday 11 223
Independence Day (Republic of Chad)
1921: Alex Haley, author, is born in Ithaca, NY.

sunday 12 224
1890: Acclaimed soprano Lillian Evans Evanti, first African American to perform with an organized European opera company, is born in Washington, DC. In 1934 she will give a command performance for President Franklin Roosevelt at the White House.

Philippa Schuyler
American, 1931–1967

Philippa Duke Schuyler was the daughter of George Schuyler, a noted black journalist and an editor of the *Pittsburgh Courier,* and Josephine Cogdell, a white artist and Texas banking heiress. She is said to have crawled at four weeks, walked at eight months, read at two years, and played piano at three. By thirteen, Schuyler had composed more than a hundred songs and completed her first symphony, *Manhattan Nocturne,* which was performed at Carnegie Hall by the New York Philharmonic Orchestra. Her piano compositions *Six Little Pieces, Eight Little Pieces,* and *Rumpelstiltskin* were performed by the Boston Pops and the New York Philharmonic Orchestra.

Schuyler earned critical acclaim and collegial recognition as a mature concert pianist for her 1953 debut at New York's Town Hall. Fluent in French, Spanish, and Italian, she toured more than fifty countries as a goodwill ambassador for the United States. Her virtuoso performances were commanded by the rulers of Malaysia, Belgium, and Nigeria.

In May 1967, Schuyler died in a helicopter accident while helping to evacuate children from a Catholic school in Da Nang, Vietnam.

s	m	t	w	t	f	s
			1	2	3	4
5	6	7	8	9	10	11
12	13	14	15	16	17	18
19	20	21	22	23	24	25
26	27	28	29	30	31	

AUGUST

Independence Day (Central African Republic)
monday
1989: The wreckage of the plane that carried US Congressman Mickey Leland and others on a humanitarian mission is found on a mountainside in Ethiopia; there are no survivors.
13 225

---

tuesday
1990: Singer Curtis Mayfield is paralyzed in an accident at an outdoor concert in Brooklyn, NY.
14 226

National Day (Congo Republic)
wednesday
1938: Maxine Waters, second African American woman from California to be elected to Congress, is born.
15 227

Restoration Day (Dominican Republic)
thursday
1930: Innovative blues guitarist Robert Johnson dies in Greenwood, MS.
1998: Harlem Renaissance author Dorothy West dies at eighty-eight in Boston.
16 228

Independence Day (Republic of Gabon)
friday
1993: Jackie Joyner-Kersee wins her seventeenth consecutive heptathlon at the World Track and Field Championships in Stuttgart, Germany.
17 229

---

saturday
1963: James Meredith becomes the first African American to graduate from the University of Mississippi.
18 230

---

sunday
1989: Bishop Desmond Tutu defies apartheid laws by walking alone on a South African beach.
19 231

Lith de Villain

Nzinga, Queen of Matamba
Angolan, 1582–1663

In the days of the slave trade, the Portuguese turned their attention to a country named Ngola (now Angola). There they were confronted by a determined leader, a woman who swore never to succumb to their wishes.

Queen Nzinga's success in holding off the interlopers is legendary. Spies behind the Portuguese lines kept her abreast of the military's plans. Each time the Europeans tried to conquer Ngola, Nzinga rallied her troops to beat them back.

Queen Nzinga also fought intelligently against attempts to convert Ngolans to Christianity, knowing that conversion was a psychological ploy used to soften resistance. She led by example, renouncing the Christian name, Ann Nzinga, under which she had been baptized in the Catholic Church. Nzinga believed that to be baptized was to surrender soul and body not to Christ, but to the white man.

A respected leader and military strategist, Nzinga ruled Angola until her death at eighty.

Artist unknown
Ann Zingha: Queen of Matamba, n.d.
Etching, 11¼ x 17¼ in.

s	m	t	w	t	f	s
			1	2	3	4
5	6	7	8	9	10	11
12	13	14	15	16	17	18
19	20	21	22	23	24	25
26	27	28	29	30	31	

AUGUST

---

monday

1565: Black artisans and farmers aid the explorer Menendez in building St. Augustine, FL.
1619: The first group of twenty Africans is brought to Jamestown, VA.

☽ **20** 232

---

tuesday

1904: Bandleader and composer William "Count" Basie is born in Red Bank, NJ.

21 233

---

wednesday

1910: The famous Howard Theater in Washington, DC, opens for Broadway shows and musical entertainment.
1978: Kenyan president and revolutionary Jomo Kenyatta dies.

22 234

---

thursday

1900: Booker T. Washington forms the National Negro Business League in Boston.

23 235

---

friday

National Flag Day (Liberia)
1948: Edith Mae Irby becomes the first African American student at the University of Arkansas.

24 236

---

saturday

1989: Huey P. Newton, cofounder of the Black Panther Party, dies.

25 237

---

sunday

1946: Composer, singer, and producer Valerie Simpson Ashford is born in the Bronx, NY.

26 238

Etta Moten Barnett
American, 1901–2004

Etta Moten was born in Weiman, Texas, to a Methodist minister. She earned a degree in voice and drama from the University of Kansas and then moved to New York to pursue her career.

George Gershwin wrote the role of Bess in *Porgy and Bess* for Moten; she performed the role on Broadway, with Todd Duncan as Porgy. On the occasion of President Franklin D. Roosevelt's birthday, Moten became the first black woman to sing at the White House. Highlights of her stage career include Broadway performances in *Fast and Furious, Sugar Hill, Zombie,* and *Lysistrata*. Her film performances include *The Gold Diggers of 1933* and *Flying Down to Rio.* Moten hosted radio programs in San Francisco and at NBC in Chicago. As a concert artist, she toured Canada, Argentina, Brazil, England, and West Africa.

With her husband, Claude Barnett, Etta Moten Barnett represented Presidents Eisenhower, Kennedy, and Johnson on official visits to seven African countries. She belonged to numerous public service organizations, including the African American Institute, the Chicago Urban League, and the National Council of Negro Women.

s	m	t	w	t	f	s
						1
2	3	4	5	6	7	8
9	10	11	12	13	14	15
16	17	18	19	20	21	22
23	24	25	26	27	28	29
30						

SEPTEMBER

---

monday

BANK HOLIDAY (UK EXCEPT SCOTLAND)
1937: Alice Coltrane, musician, is born in Detroit.
1963: W. E. B. Du Bois, scholar, civil rights activist, and founding father of the NAACP, dies in Accra, Ghana.

27 239

---

tuesday

1963: A quarter million demonstrators take part in the March on Washington for Jobs and Freedom, the largest civil rights demonstration to date in US history.

28 240

---

wednesday

1920: Jazz saxophonist Charlie "Bird" Parker is born in Kansas City, KS.

29 241

---

thursday

Fete La Rose (Feast of St. Rose of Lima), Saint Lucia
1800: Gabriel Prosser, a slave, organizes a slave revolt in Virginia.
1983: Lt. Col. Guion S. Bluford Jr. becomes the first African American in space.

30 242

---

friday

Independence Day (Trinidad and Tobago)
1935: Baseball player and manager Frank Robinson is born in Beaufort, TX.

31 243

---

saturday

Heroes Day (United Republic of Tanzania)
1993: Condoleezza Rice is named provost at Stanford University, becoming the youngest person and the first black to hold this position.

1 244

---

sunday

1833: Ohio's Oberlin College, first US college to routinely enroll black students, is founded.
1975: Joseph W. Hatcher becomes Florida's first African American supreme court justice since Reconstruction.

2 245

Frederick Douglass
American, 1818–1895

Born a slave, Frederick Douglass escaped to freedom at twenty and spent his life thereafter speaking, writing, and working tirelessly for the cause of freedom. The American Anti-Slavery Society engaged him to undertake a lecture tour; a brilliant success thanks to his extraordinary oratorical powers and compelling personal presence, it made him known as the greatest African American speaker of his time. His fame increased upon the publication of his autobiography, in 1845, and of his abolitionist newspaper, *The North Star*.

Douglass advised President Lincoln during the Civil War, pressing for voting rights and other civil liberties for blacks and for the recruitment of black soldiers, a practice that was taken up in 1862. After the war, Douglass continued his public service career. He served in several capacities, but the rights of African Americans were always at the forefront of his powerful, effective activism.

Douglass' papers—some 7,400 pieces—are in the collection of the Library of Congress.

Bo Walker
Frederick Douglass Ikenga, 1978
Steel and wood, 50 x 20 x 16 in.
© Panya Walker

s	m	t	w	t	f	s
						1
2	3	4	5	6	7	8
9	10	11	12	13	14	15
16	17	18	19	20	21	22
23	24	25	26	27	28	29
30						

SEPTEMBER

LABOR DAY (US, CANADA)
1838: Frederick Douglass escapes from slavery, disguised as a sailor.

monday
3 246

1957: Arkansas governor Orval Faubus calls out the National Guard to bar African American students from entering a Little Rock high school.

tuesday
☾ 4 247

1960: Leopold Sedar Senghor, poet and politician, is elected president of Senegal.

wednesday
5 248

Independence Day (Kingdom of Swaziland)
1996: Eddie Murray joins Hank Aaron and Willie Mays as the only baseball players with at least 500 home runs and 3,000 hits.

thursday
6 249

Independence Day (Brazil)
1954: Integration of public schools begins in Washington, DC, and Baltimore.

friday
7 250

1766: Josephy Boulogne Saint-Georges participates in his first public fencing match in Paris.
1981: Roy Wilkins, executive director of the NAACP, dies.

saturday
8 251

1915: Dr. Carter G. Woodson founds the Association for the Study of Negro Life and History.
1999: A Texas jury imposes the death sentence on Lawrence Russell Brewer, the second white supremacist convicted of killing James Byrd Jr.

sunday
9 252

Ernest Crichlow
American, 1914–2005

Ernest Crichlow was born in Brooklyn to a family of nine children. He took an early interest in art, and intended to pursue commercial illustration until noted Harlem Renaissance sculptor and art educator Augusta Savage encouraged him toward fine art. That led Crichlow to studies at New York University and the Art Students League. He later taught at both.

Crichlow developed his social-realist style while working for the WPA during the Depression. He oberved of *White Fence*, "I always reacted to this business of the fencing in of people. Then there is the question of this white child, who is large and big and dominating the picture with her whiteness and these pressed-in groupings of Negro children who are in a barren whiteness and they become the only color there. Every time I react to this picture I react to it a little bit differently."

White Fence
Oil on canvas
© Ernest Crichlow

s	m	t	w	t	f	s
						1
2	3	4	5	6	7	8
9	10	11	12	13	14	15
16	17	18	19	20	21	22
23	24	25	26	27	28	29
30			SEPTEMBER			

monday 10 253
National Day (Belize)
1961: Jomo Kenyatta returns to Kenya from exile, during which he had been elected president of the Kenya National African Union.

tuesday 11 254
1974: Haile Selassie I is deposed from the Ethiopian throne.
1999: Seventeen-year-old Serena Williams defeats Martina Hingis to win her first major tennis championship, the US Open.

wednesday 12 255
ROSH HASHANAH (BEGINS AT SUNSET)
RAMADAN (BEGINS AT SUNSET)
Independence Day (Cape Verde)
1913: Track and field star Jesse Owens is born in Oakville, AL.
1977: Steven Biko, leader of the black consciousness movement in South Africa, dies in police custody.

thursday 13 256
1913: Dancer, Tony Award winner, and famed Motown choreographer Cholly Atkins is born in Pratt City, AL.

friday 14 257
1980: Dorothy Boulding Ferebee, physician and second president of the National Council for Negro Women, dies.

saturday 15 258
1830: The first national convention for blacks is held at Bethel Church, Philadelphia.
1943: Paul Robeson performs in *Othello* for the 269th time.

sunday 16 259
Independence Day (Papua New Guinea)
1925: Blues great B. B. King is born in Indianola, MS.

Oscar Micheaux
American, 1884–1951

Oscar Micheaux was born in Metropolis, Illinois, and educated in the public schools there. He worked as a Pullman porter and was a farmer and rancher in South Dakota before heading for Harlem, where he found distinction as a novelist and movie producer.

A pioneer in the moving-picture industry, Micheaux was probably the most prolific independent filmmaker of his time: he wrote, produced, and directed forty-four feature-length films between 1919 and 1948. Oscar Micheaux made films that featured all-black casts (he introduced Paul Robeson to the screen, in *Body and Soul*). They include *A Daughter of the Congo*, *Harlem After Midnight*, and *God's Stepchildren*.

Spurred by the release of the racist *Birth of a Nation*, Micheaux became the first filmmaker to portray blacks in a positive, nonstereotypical light. A great admirer of Booker T. Washington, Micheaux also published seven novels, including *Conquest: The Story of a Negro Pioneer*, *The Homesteader*, *The Story of Dorothy Stanfield*, and *The Wind from Nowhere*, which he promoted and sold through book-signing tours around the country.

s	m	t	w	t	f	s
						1
2	3	4	5	6	7	8
9	10	11	12	13	14	15
16	17	18	19	20	21	22
23	24	25	26	27	28	29
30			SEPTEMBER			

monday
National Heroes Day (Angola)
1983: Vanessa Williams, Miss New York, becomes the first black Miss America.
17 260

tuesday
1980: Cosmonaut Arnoldo Tamayo, a Cuban, becomes the first black to travel in space.
18 261

wednesday
1963: Iota Phi Theta fraternity is founded at Morgan State University, Baltimore.
1989: Gordon Parks' *Learning Tree* is among the first films listed on the National Film Registry of the Library of Congress.
☽ **19** 262

thursday
1664: Maryland takes the lead in passing laws against the marriage of English women to black men.
1830: The National Negro Convention convenes in Philadelphia with the purpose of abolishing slavery.
20 263

friday
YOM KIPPUR (BEGINS AT SUNSET)
Independence Day (Belize)
1998: Florence (Flo-Jo) Griffith-Joyner, Olympic gold medalist in track, dies at thirty-nine from an apparent heart seizure in Mission Viejo, CA.
21 264

saturday
Independence Day (Republic of Mali)
1828: Zulu leader Shaka the Great is assassinated.
1915: Xavier University, the first African American Catholic college, opens in New Orleans.
22 265

sunday
AUTUMNAL EQUINOX 9:51 AM (GMT)
1993: South Africa's parliament creates a multiracial body to oversee the end of exclusive white control of the nation.
23 266

Dr. William Augustus Hinton
American, 1883–1959

The son of former slaves, William Augustus Hinton enrolled at the University of Kansas in 1900, finished the school's premedical program in just two years, and went on to earn his bachelor's degree from Harvard University. Harvard offered him a medical school scholarship specifically for black students, but Hinton refused it and instead won two scholarships in competition with the whole student body. He graduated with honors (after only three years) and began teaching and conducting research in bacteriology and immunology at Wasserman Laboratory (then affiliated with Harvard).

His research led him to develop the Hinton Test for syphilis in 1927 and the improved Davies-Hinton Test in 1931. Both tests set the standard as the most accurate then available. In 1936, Hinton wrote *Syphilis and Its Treatment*, the first published medical textbook by an African American.

A giant in the field, Hinton taught bacteriology and immunology at Harvard for thirty-six years, becoming the first black professor in the school's history before retiring as professor emeritus in 1950.

s	m	t	w	t	f	s
						1
2	3	4	5	6	7	8
9	10	11	12	13	14	15
16	17	18	19	20	21	22
23	24	25	26	27	28	29
30						

SEPTEMBER

Republic Day (Port of Spain, Trinidad)
1923: Nancy Green, the world's first living trademark (Aunt Jemima), is struck and killed by an automobile in Chicago.

monday
24   267

Referendum Day (Rwanda)
1911: Dr. Eric Williams, future president of Trinidad and Tobago, is born.
1974: Barbara W. Hancock becomes the first African American woman to be named a White House Fellow.

tuesday
25   268

1937: Bessie Smith, "Empress of the Blues," dies.
1998: Betty Carter, jazz singer, dies from pancreatic cancer in her New York City home.

wednesday
○ 26   269

1944: Stephanie Pogue, artist and art professor, is born in Shelby, NC.

thursday
27   270

1829: David Walker, a freeborn black, publishes a provocative pamphlet calling for slaves worldwide to revolt against their white masters.
1912: W. C. Handy's "Memphis Blues" is published.

friday
28   271

1980: The Schomburg Center for Research in Black Culture opens a new $3.8 million building in New York City.
1997: Brazil mercifully agrees to accept thousands of African refugees fleeing war in Angola.

saturday
29   272

Independence Day (Republic of Botswana)
1935: Singer Johnny Mathis is born in Gilmer, TX.

sunday
30   273

Billy Dee Williams
American, b. 1937

Billy Dee Williams needs no intro-
duction, but his acting career has
overshadowed the fact that he is
an accomplished artist. He grew up
in Harlem with a family that
encouraged his artistic abilities,
and he began drawing at an early
age. Later he won scholarships to
the National Academy of Fine Arts
and Design in New York to study
the classical principles of painting.
Acting gave him the financial
resources to pursue painting, his
first love.

Williams' acting career has cen-
tered on Hollywood, and he makes
his home in California. But a return
to New York to star in a 1988
Broadway production put him back
in the center of the art world and
renewed his enthusiasm for working on canvas. He painted well over
one hundred pieces in the next
couple of years.

Since 1991, Williams has had solo
exhibitions across America and has
donated paintings to the National
Portrait Gallery and to the
Schomburg Center for Research in
Black Culture.

Summer Day on 110th Street, 1990
Acrylic on canvas, 72 x 48 in.
© Billy Dee Williams

Independence Day (Nigeria)
1903: Virginia Proctor Powell, the first female African American librarian, is born in Wilkinsburg, PA.
1996: Lt. Gen. Joe Ballard becomes the first African American to head the Army Corps of Engineers.

monday 1 274

1958: The Republic of Guinea, under Ahmed Sékou Touré, gains inde-pendence from France.

tuesday 2 275

1990: Rio de Janeiro's first black congresswoman, Benedita da Silva, sweeps the first round of the city's mayoral race.

wednesday 3 276

Independence Day (Kingdom of Lesotho)
1943: H. Rap Brown, chairman of the Student Nonviolent Coordinating Committee (SNCC), is born.

thursday 4 277

1878: George B. Vashon, first African American lawyer in the state of New York, dies in Rodney, MS.

friday 5 278

1917: Fannie Lou Hamer, founder of the Mississippi Freedom Democratic Party, is born in Montgomery County, MS.

saturday 6 279

1993: Author Toni Morrison becomes the first African American to win the Nobel Prize in literature.

sunday 7 280

s	m	t	w	t	f	s
	1	2	3	4	5	6
7	8	9	10	11	12	13
14	15	16	17	18	19	20
21	22	23	24	25	26	27
28	29	30	31			

OCTOBER

Adam Clayton Powell Sr.
American, 1865–1953

The Reverend Adam Clayton Powell Sr.'s legacy is overshadowed by his son's, but the elder Powell put into motion methods for blacks to achieve self-reliance.

Born in Soak Creek, Virginia, Powell attended Virginia Union University from 1888 to 1892 and graduated from its theological and academic schools. An avid churchman, he experienced racial prejudice at a New York church; in response, he cofounded the Abyssinian Baptist Church. (New York's oldest extant African American church, Abyssinian has one of the country's largest congregations.) During the Depression, Powell campaigned to feed the poor and for better jobs and city services. Active in the struggle against racism, he lectured on race relations at Colgate University, City College of New York, and Union Theological Seminary. He was a cofounder of the National Urban League and an early leader in the NAACP.

Powell described his congregation as "the electric current in the organized Christian church. Confine it to batteries, and this wild and frightful something could run our trains, drive our automobiles, and bring New York and South Africa within whispering distance of each other."

s	m	t	w	t	f	s
	1	2	3	4	5	6
7	8	9	10	11	12	13
14	15	16	17	18	19	20
21	22	23	24	25	26	27
28	29	30	31			

OCTOBER

monday 8 281
COLUMBUS DAY OBSERVED
THANKSGIVING DAY (CANADA)
1820: Henri Christophe, leader of Haitian independence from France, dies.
1941: Rev. Jesse L. Jackson, political activist and civil rights leader, is born in Greenville, SC.
1980: Bob Marley collapses during a concert in Pittsburgh; he will not perform again.

tuesday 9 282
Independence Day (Republic of Uganda)
1806: Mathematician and astronomer Benjamin Banneker dies in Ellicott City, MD.

wednesday 10 283
1901: Frederick Douglass Patterson, founder of the United Negro College Fund, is born.
1935: George Gershwin's Porgy and Bess premieres at Alvin Theater, New York City.

thursday 11 284
1792: Antoine Blanc founds the first black Catholic order of nuns.
1919: Jazz drummer and bandleader Art Blakey is born in Pittsburgh.

friday 12 285
COLUMBUS DAY
EID-AL-FITR (BEGINS AT SUNSET)
1932: Comedian and civil rights activist Dick Gregory is born in St. Louis, MO.

saturday 13 286
1902: Arna Bontemps, poet and librarian, is born in Alexandria, LA.
1925: Garland Anderson's Appearances, the first full-length Broadway play by an African American, opens at the Frolic Theater.

sunday 14 287
Young People's Day (Democratic Republic of the Congo)
1964: Dr. Martin Luther King Jr. is awarded the Nobel Peace Prize.

Black Judaism

Rabbi Wentworth A. Matthew (American, 1892–1973), pictured here, was the longtime leader of one of New York City's most prominent black Jewish groups. He founded the Commandment Keepers Congregation of the Living God. Like other black Jewish groups, the Commandment Keepers observe all the Judaic holy days and speak Hebrew in the practice of their religion.

Lawrence, Kansas, street preacher William Saunders Crowdy taught in 1896 that Christian churches were not pleasing to God and that a return to Judaism was in order. He founded the Church of God and Saints of Christ; the movement spread and spawned similar groups throughout the country. But black adherence to Judaism dates back to antiquity. There are blacks in West Africa today who still practice religious customs that are curiously identical to the Jewish faith's tenets.

The Falasha Jews of Ethiopia, the Black Hebrew Israelites of North America, and thousands of African Americans feel that Israel is their homeland; many have moved there.

s	m	t	w	t	f	s
	1	2	3	4	5	6
7	8	9	10	11	12	13
14	15	16	17	18	19	20
21	22	23	24	25	26	27
28	29	30	31			

OCTOBER

monday 15 288
1968: Wyomia Tyus becomes the first person to win a gold medal in the 100-meter race in two consecutive Olympic games.

tuesday 16 289
1995: The Million Man March, for "A Day of Atonement," takes place in Washington, DC.

wednesday 17 290
Mother's Day (Malawi)
1806: Jean-Jacques Dessalines, revolutionist and emperor of Haiti, is assassinated.

thursday 18 291
1903: Felix Houphouet-Boigny, president of Ivory Coast, is born.
1926: Rock 'n' roll legend Chuck Berry is born in San Jose, CA.

friday 19 292
1878: Dr. Frederick Victor Nanka Bruce, the first physician on the Gold Coast, is born in Accra, Ghana.
1936: Dr. Johnnetta Cole, the first black female president of Spelman College in Atlanta, is born.

saturday 20 293
1953: Jomo Kenyatta and five other Mau Mau leaders refuse an appeal of their prison terms.

sunday 21 294
1872: John H. Conyers Sr. becomes the first African American admitted to the US Naval Academy.

E. Franklin Frazier
American, 1894–1962

E. Franklin Frazier was a brilliant man who applied his intellect to analyzing the problems of our society, as it related to blacks, and to curing its ills. Like W. E. B. Du Bois, Ralph Bunche, Countee Cullen, George Schuyler, and others, he wrote well-respected critiques on resolving "the Negro problem."

Frazier attended the Baltimore public schools and graduated with honors from Howard University in 1916. A Fisk faculty member from 1931 until 1934, he became head of Howard's department of sociology, retiring as professor emeritus in 1959. He received a 1940 Guggenheim Fellowship and the John Anisfield Award for his work in sociology.

Frazier, Abram Harris, Sterling Brown, Emmet Dorsey, and Ralph Bunche represented a group of radical black intellectuals whom Du Bois called the Young Turks. They argued that focusing on issues of class, not race, was the key to solving the problems of African America, and they criticized the black community's preoccupation with sports and sports figures as an obstacle to higher cultural pursuits.

The prolific Frazier's books include the controversial *Black Bourgeoisie* (1957).

s	m	t	w	t	f	s
	1	2	3	4	5	6
7	8	9	10	11	12	13
14	15	16	17	18	19	20
21	22	23	24	25	26	27
28	29	30	31			

OCTOBER

monday
22 295

1936: Bobby Seale, cofounder of the Black Panther Party, is born in Dallas.

tuesday
23 296

1886: Wiley Jones opens the first streetcar line in Pine Bluff, AR.

wednesday
24 297

UNITED NATIONS DAY

1996: Robert M. Bell becomes the first African American to serve as chief judge of Maryland's Court of Appeals.

thursday
25 298

Independence Day (Republic of Zambia)

1992: Vivian Dandridge, dancer and sister of actor Dorothy Dandridge, dies.

friday
26 299

1899: Meta Vaux Warrick, African American sculptor, arrives in Paris to meet artist Henry Ossawa Tanner.
1962: Actor Louise Beavers dies in Los Angeles.

saturday
27 300

1891: D. B. Downing, inventor, is awarded a patent for the street letter box.
1924: Actor Ruby Dee is born in Cleveland.

sunday
28 301

SUMMER TIME ENDS (UK)

1981: Edward M. McIntrye is elected the first African American mayor of Augusta, GA.

Samella Lewis
American, b. 1924

Born in New Orleans, Samella Lewis is a scholar, artist, writer, and educator in the arts. Her art education began at Dillard University under the tutelage of the celebrated artist Elizabeth Catlett. She earned her BA from Hampton University, and in 1951 she became the first African American woman to earn a doctorate in fine arts and art history, from Ohio State University. Since then, she has taught at California State University, the University of New York, Florida A & M, Morgan State University in Maryland, and her undergraduate alma mater, Hampton, in Virginia.

Lewis has been drawing and painting for nearly all her life. Her art, which invariably reflects her personal experiences, can be seen at universities, galleries, and archives all over the country. It has been displayed at the Zora Neale Hurston Museum in Eatonville, Florida, the Museum of African American Art in Los Angeles, California, the Art Institute of Chicago, and the Brooklyn Museum, and it can be found in the permanent collections of the Metropolitan Museum of Art and Ohio State.

Celo, 1996
Lithograph, 21³/₄ x 30 in.
© Samella Lewis

s	m	t	w	t	f	s
				1	2	3
4	5	6	7	8	9	10
11	12	13	14	15	16	17
18	19	20	21	22	23	24
25	26	27	28	29	30	

NOVEMBER

---

monday
29 302

1949: Alonzo G. Moron of the Virgin Islands becomes the first African American president of Hampton Institute, VA.

---

tuesday
30 303

1831: Slave rebellion leader Nat Turner is captured in Virginia.
1966: Huey Newton and Bobby Seale found the Black Panther Party for Self-Defense in Oakland, CA.

---

wednesday
31 304

HALLOWEEN
1900: Actor and singer Ethel Waters is born in Chester, PA.

---

thursday
1 305

National Day (Antigua)
1945: John H. Johnson publishes the first issue of *Ebony.*
1999: Chicago Bears Hall of Fame running back Walter Payton succumbs to liver disease at forty-five.

---

friday
2 306

1983: President Ronald Reagan signs a law designating the third Monday in January as Martin Luther King Jr. Day.
1996: Toni Stone, the first woman to play baseball in the Negro Leagues, dies in California.

---

saturday
3 307

National Day (Dominica)
Independence Day (Panama)
1983: Jesse Jackson announces his candidacy for the office of president of the United States.

---

sunday
4 308

DAYLIGHT SAVING TIME ENDS
1974: Harold Ford is elected US congressman from Tennessee.
1992: Carol Moseley Braun becomes the first African American woman to be elected to the US Senate.

Ethel Waters
American, 1900–1977

The first African American to star in her own television series and to be nominated for an Emmy, Ethel Waters was raised by her grandmother in the slums of Philadelphia. Her singing skills were honed in the church, where she began performing at the age of five. At seventeen, already a versatile actor and singer, she moved to Baltimore. Billed as Sweet Mama Stringbean, Waters enthralled vaudeville and nightclub patrons with her gutsy blues; she was the first woman to perform W. C. Handy's famous "St. Louis Blues."

In the early days of the Harlem Renaissance, Waters sang the "lowdown" blues in New York nightclubs. She scored her first major hit in a 1925 musical revue at the Plantation Club. Waters appeared on Broadway in 1927 in *Africana*; that launched a series of Broadway hits for her, including *Cabin in the Sky*, *As Thousands Cheer*, and *Stormy Weather*. These led to movie contracts, among them the film version of *Cabin in the Sky*. Waters' 1950s television series was *Beulah*; her Emmy nomination, in 1962, was for an episode of *Route 66*.

s	m	t	w	t	f	s
				1	2	3
4	5	6	7	8	9	10
11	12	13	14	15	16	17
18	19	20	21	22	23	24
25	26	27	28	29	30	

NOVEMBER

---

monday
5 309

1862: Frazier A. Boutelle is commissioned as a second lieutenant in the 5th New York Cavalry.

---

tuesday
6 310

Green March Day (Morocco)
1983: Sgt. Farley Simon, a native of Grenada, becomes the first Marine to win the Marine Corps Marathon.
1989: Renowned attorney Sadie Tanner Mossell Alexander dies in Philadelphia.

---

wednesday
7 311

1989: Douglas Wilder of Virginia becomes the nation's first black governor since Reconstruction.
1999: Tiger Woods becomes the first golfer to win four consecutive tournaments since Ben Hogan in 1953.

---

thursday
8 312

1938: Crystal Bird Fauset of Pennsylvania becomes the first African American woman to be elected to a state legislature.

---

friday
9 313

1731: Benjamin Banneker, scientist and inventor, is born in Ellicott City, MD.
1997: The NBA announces the hiring of Dee Kantner and Violet Palmer as the first women to officiate in an all-male major sports league.

---

saturday
10 314

1917: Musician and writer Nora Holt joins the *Chicago Defender* as the writer of the feature article "Cultivating Symphony Concerts."
1995: Nigerian author and poet Ken Saro-Wiwa is executed.

---

sunday
11 315

VETERANS DAY
REMEMBRANCE DAY (CANADA)
Independence Day (Angola)
1989: The Civil Rights Memorial in Montgomery, AL, is dedicated.

Allan Rohan Crite
American, b. 1910

Allan Rohan Crite is both a fine artist and a reporter/historian; his secular paintings, drawings, and prints are detailed studies of the daily life of black Boston in the 1920s and 1930s. Working in the reportorial tradition, he recounted what he saw with fidelity but without comment or obvious partiality, leaving a valuable record of street games no longer played, fashions grown quaint, and buildings long since demolished.

A lifelong Episcopalian, Crite turned to religious themes in the forties and worked prolifically, presenting his subjects not as generic white people in robe-and-sandal outfits but as the Africans, Levanters, and Asians one might actually have found in Galilee two thousand years ago.

A shy man, Crite has shunned publicity—perhaps too much for his own good; he has not achieved the recognition of many of his contemporaries. "That's not my business. My business is to do my work to the best of my ability," he says. "If it has an impact, that's nice. I can't do my work worrying about what other people are going to think about it."

Saint Mark, 1950
Linocut with gold leaf
© Allan Rohan Crite

s	m	t	w	t	f	s
				1	2	3
4	5	6	7	8	9	10
11	12	13	14	15	16	17
18	19	20	21	22	23	24
25	26	27	28	29	30	

NOVEMBER

VETERANS DAY OBSERVED

1922: Sigma Gamma Rho sorority is organized by Mary Lou Allison and six other teachers at Butler University.
1941: Madame Lillian Evanti and Mary Cardwell Dawson establish the National Negro Opera Company.

monday
12 316

1940: In *Hansberry v. Lee* the Supreme Court rules that African Americans cannot be barred from white neighborhoods.
1998: Kenny Kirkland, jazz pianist with the Branford Marsalis band, dies at home in Queens, NY.

tuesday
13 317

Children's Day (India)
1954: Dr. James Joshua Thomas is installed as minister of the Mott Haven Reformed Church in the Bronx, NY.

wednesday
14 318

---

218 BC: Hannibal crosses the Alps with elephants and twenty-six thousand men to defeat Roman troops at the Ticino and Trebbia rivers.
1998: Kwame Ture (Stokely Carmichael) succumbs to prostate cancer at fifty-seven in his home in Ghana.

thursday
15 319

1873: W. C. Handy, father of the blues, is born in Florence, AL.

friday
16 320

1911: Omega Psi Phi fraternity is founded at Howard University.
1980: WHMM-TV in Washington, DC, becomes the first African American public-broadcasting television station.

saturday
☽ **17** 321

Independence Day (Morocco)
1900: Dr. Howard Thurman, theologian, educator, and civil rights leader, is born in Daytona Beach, FL.

sunday
18 322

Charles Alston
American, 1907–1977

Born in Charlotte, North Carolina, Charles Alston moved to New York with his family in 1915. He displayed early artistic talent, studied at the National Academy of Art, and earned a BFA from Columbia College. While earning his master's degree, he was introduced to African art and immediately came under its influence.

Alston worked at the Harlem Arts Workshop run by the sculptor Augusta Savage. He later founded 306, an art school that became the center of Harlem's creative community. He joined Arthur Schomburg, Augusta Savage, and others to found the Harlem Artists' Guild.

Alston's sculpture, paintings, and murals were influenced by the social realist art of the 1930s, the politically charged work of the Mexican muralists, and New York's nightclub culture. He once declined an invitation to participate in an all-black group exhibition: "The idea of separating artists on the basis of color is a repulsive affirmation of the racism and bigotry which permeate American society. . . . I would hate to think that I was in an exhibition because I'm Black, rather than because I am a good painter."

Big Sister, 1935
Oil on canvas, 24 x 19 in.

s	m	t	w	t	f	s
					1	2	3
4	5	6	7	8	9	10
11	12	13	14	15	16	17
18	19	20	21	22	23	24
25	26	27	28	29	30	

NOVEMBER

Discovery Day (Puerto Rico)
1797: Abolitionist and women's rights advocate Sojourner Truth is born in New York.
1997: Drs. Paula Mahone and Karen Drake head a team of forty specialists in the first successful delivery of septuplets, born in Carlisle, IA.

monday
19 323

1695: Zumbi dos Palmares, Brazilian leader of a hundred-year-old rebel slave group, is killed in an ambush.

tuesday
20 324

1866: Duse Mohammed Effendi, Egyptian Pan-Africanist, is born.
1893: Granville T. Woods, inventor, patents the Electric Railway Conduit.

wednesday
21 325

THANKSGIVING DAY
1994: Jazz musicians Herbie Hancock, Clark Terry, and Joshua Redman perform in a concert beamed by satellite to sixty schools nationwide.

thursday
22 326

1941: Musician and actor Henrietta Vinton Davis dies in Washington, DC.

friday
23 327

National Holiday (Democratic Republic of the Congo)
Independence Day (Republic of Zambia)
1868: Scott Joplin, originator of ragtime music, is born in Texarkana, TX.

saturday
24 328

Independence Day (Republic of Suriname)
1955: The Interstate Commerce Commission bans segregation in interstate travel.

sunday
25 329

Archibald J. Motley Jr.
American, 1891–1981

Born in New Orleans, Archibald Motley Jr. grew up in Chicago, where he studied at the Art Institute. Philosophically influenced by the likes of Alaine Locke and W. E. B. Du Bois, he devoted much of his early work to portraiture, capturing his subjects' dignity and grace in a restrained and formal style. But he is better known for images that celebrate high living, uptown style, and the sporting life—images of African Americans drinking, dancing, gambling, telling tall tales—as well as more refined pastimes: garden parties, domestic scenes, the easy talk among neighbors who have spilled out of their apartments to enjoy whatever breeze a hot city night might provide.

Like so many others, Motley struggled against being pigeonholed as a "Negro artist" (although, within his pigeonhole, he had found success and broad acclaim). Finally, toward the end of his life, the art world at large became more likely to think of him as a regionalist or painter of the American scene. In the meantime, he negotiated the preconceptions of both blacks and whites, subordinating expectations of racial identity by "just being honest."

Woman Peeling Apples, 1924
Oil on canvas, 32 1/2 x 28 in.
© Valerie Gerard Browne

s	m	t	w	t	f	s
						1
2	3	4	5	6	7	8
9	10	11	12	13	14	15
16	17	18	19	20	21	22
23	24	25	26	27	28	29
30	31					

DECEMBER

---

monday 26 330

1878: Marshall Walter "Major" Taylor, world's fastest bicycle racer for twelve years, is born in Indianapolis.
1927: Marcus Garvey, Pan-Africanist, is released from Tombs Atlanta Penitentiary.

---

tuesday 27 331

1942: Rock musician Jimi Hendrix is born in Seattle.

---

wednesday 28 332

Independence Day (Islamic Republic of Mauritania)
1961: Ernie Davis becomes the first African American to win the Heisman Trophy.

---

thursday 29 333

1908: Adam Clayton Powell Jr., politician and civil rights activist, is born in New Haven, CT.

---

friday 30 334

Independence Day (People's Republic of Benin)
1912: Gordon Parks, filmmaker and photographer, is born.

---

saturday 1 335

1955: Rosa Parks defies the segregated transportation ordinance in Montgomery, AL, igniting a 382-day bus boycott and launching the civil rights movement in America.

---

sunday 2 336

1968: Dial Press publishes Frank Yerby's *Judas My Brother*.
1998: Former secretary of agriculture Mike Espy is acquitted of all thirty charges of corruption levied against him by independent counsel Donald Smaltz.

Mamie Smith
American, 1893–1946

Mamie Smith was the first nationally successful black female blues singer; her million-selling "Crazy Blues" initiated a recording boom for other black artists.

Smith was born in Cincinnati, Ohio, but little else is known about her childhood or family. Her career in entertainment began at the age of ten, when she performed with the Four Dancing Mitchells. In 1910 she toured the Midwest and the East Coast, singing with a black minstrel troupe, the Smart Set Company. When she married William Smith, the couple moved to New York, where Mamie became a cabaret dancer, singer, and pianist.

Smith's break came when Perry Bradford, a black songwriter and show business entrepreneur, heard her. Impressed, he chose her to be in his musical, *Made in Harlem*. Through Bradford, Mamie broke the recording industry's color line, singing songs he wrote with her in mind. The band backing her on "Crazy Blues"—her biggest success—included the now-legendary musicians Willie "the Lion" Smith, Jimmy Dunn, Coleman Hawkins, Fats Waller, and Buster Bailey.

s	m	t	w	t	f	s
						1
2	3	4	5	6	7	8
9	10	11	12	13	14	15
16	17	18	19	20	21	22
23	24	25	26	27	28	29
30	31					

DECEMBER

1911: Distinguished educator and historian Helen Gray Edmonds is born in Lawrenceville, VA.

monday
3 337

HANUKKAH (BEGINS AT SUNSET)
1906: Alpha Phi Alpha Fraternity, the first Greek organization for African Americans, is founded at Cornell University.

tuesday
4 338

1870: Alexandre Dumas (père), French novelist and dramatist, dies.

wednesday
5 339

1960: Some five hundred store owners in Tucson, AZ, sign pledges vowing not to discriminate on the basis of race, color, or religion.
1997: Lee Brown defeats Rob Mosbacher to become Houston's first black mayor.

thursday
6 340

Independence Day (Republic of Ivory Coast)
1941: Dorie Miller, a messman, downs three Japanese planes in the attack on Pearl Harbor.

friday
7 341

1850: Lucy Ann Stanton of Cleveland graduates from Oberlin College with a BA in literature.
1987: Kurt Schmoke becomes the first African American mayor of Baltimore.

saturday
8 342

Independence Day (Republic of Tanzania)
1919: Roy DeCarava, the first African American photographer to be awarded a Guggenheim Fellowship, is born.

sunday
9 343

A'Lelia Walker
American, 1885–1931

A'Lelia Walker was the daughter of the famous millionaire Madam C. J. Walker. Born Lelia Walker, she accompanied Madam throughout her quest to establish a successful business and provide a good life for her only child. A'Lelia inherited the Walker empire and continued the legacy established by Madam. Known as a socialite, she used her wealth to sponsor parties, meetings, and other events for the promotion of Harlem literary figures.

In 1927 she established a salon in her 136th Street home (called "the Dark Tower") where artists could exhibit their paintings and discuss their work. Langston Hughes called her the "the joy goddess of Harlem's 1920s." Her parties, Hughes said, "were as crowded as the New York subway at the rush hour." They attracted everyone—European royalty, white New York socialites, black celebrities, Harlem numbers runners and bootleggers.

Walker's huge funeral reflected her popularity, with virtually all of Harlem attending to pay respects. Adam Clayton Powell Sr. gave the eulogy; Mary McLeod Bethune spoke of the Walker legacy, and Langston Hughes recited a poem, "To A'Lelia."

Richmond Barthé
Portrait of A'Lelia Walker, n.d.
Pastel on paper, 24 x 18 in.
Photograph by Manu Sassoonian
© The Richmond Barthé Trust

s	m	t	w	t	f	s
						1
2	3	4	5	6	7	8
9	10	11	12	13	14	15
16	17	18	19	20	21	22
23	24	25	26	27	28	29
30	31				DECEMBER	

Human Rights Day (Equatorial New Guinea)
Independence Day (Panama)
1950: Dr. Ralph J. Bunche becomes the first African American to win the Nobel Peace Prize.

monday
10 344

Republic Day (Republic of Burkina Faso)
1926: Blues singer Willie Mae "Big Mama" Thornton is born in Montgomery, AL.

tuesday
11 345

Independence Day (Kenya)
1995: Willie Brown defeats incumbent Frank Jordan to become the first African American mayor of San Francisco.

wednesday
12 346

1957: Daniel A. Chapman becomes Ghana's first ambassador to the United States.
1998: Former light-heavyweight boxing champion Archie Moore dies at eighty-four in San Diego.

thursday
13 347

1963: Dinah Washington, "Queen of the Blues," dies in Detroit.

friday
14 348

1883: William A. Hinton, developer of the Hinton Test for diagnosing syphilis, is born.

saturday
15 349

1976: President Jimmy Carter appoints Andrew Young ambassador to the United Nations.

sunday
16 350

Countee Cullen
American, 1903–1946

One of the strongest voices of the Harlem Renaissance, Countee Cullen was widely celebrated when his first book, *Color*, was published in 1925—the same year he graduated with honors from New York University. After receiving a master's degree from Harvard University, Cullen became an editor and critic, and traveled to Europe on a Guggenheim Fellowship. He wrote plays and novels, but it was his poetry—drawing on such influences as Keats, Housman, and Robinson—that singled him out as someone to be heard. He addressed universal themes like love, religion, and death, but he believed, too, in the richness and importance of the African American experience and wrote "of the heights and depths of emotion I feel as a Negro."

Cullen married Nina Yolande Du Bois (W. E. B.'s daughter) in 1928, but the marriage failed within a couple of years. As the decade and the Renaissance faded, the optimism of his early poetry diminished; sorrow and disappointment are evident in his work of the 1930s.

s	m	t	w	t	f	s
						1
2	3	4	5	6	7	8
9	10	11	12	13	14	15
16	17	18	19	20	21	22
23	24	25	26	27	28	29
30	31			DECEMBER		

---

monday
1760: Deborah Sampson Gannett, who will disguise herself as a man in order to fight in the Revolutionary War, is born in Plymouth, VA.

☽ **17** 351

---

tuesday
Republic Day (Republic of Niger)
1912: Gen. Benjamin O. Davis Jr. is born in Washington, DC.

18 352

---

wednesday
EID-AL-ADHA (BEGINS AT SUNSET)
1933: Acclaimed actor Cicely Tyson is born in New York City.

19 353

---

thursday
1988: Max Robinson, first African American news anchor for a major television network, dies.

20 354

---

friday
1911: Josh Gibson, Negro Leagues home run king, is born in Buena Vista, GA.

21 355

---

saturday
WINTER SOLSTICE 6:08 AM (GMT)
1883: Arthur Wergs Mitchell, first African American elected to Congress, is born in Lafayette, AL.
1898: Dr. Chancellor Williams, historian and author of *Destruction of Black Civilization*, dies in Bennetsville, SC.

22 356

---

sunday
1867: Madam C. J. Walker, first female African American millionaire, is born.

23 357

Three Well-Dressed Children Dancing

Art is a cultural expression of life. However detailed or abstract, it invariably reflects the life experience of the artist and/or the people within his view.

The indefatigable nature of the human spirit is conveyed in this artistic image of nineteenth-century African American life. Absent the society pages and documentation in the local newspapers, the quiet rendering of the mundane speaks volumes in this slice-of-life textile.

The handcrafted detail of *Three Well-Dressed Children* shows great care and affection. Studying the children's intricate dance, the eye can extrapolate what words do not say.

The existence of these young people is brought to life, and that life is elevated into an art piece that has survived anonymity, ambivalence, and time. A rite of passage into a social structure still being discovered is intriguingly indicated in this fine work.

Three Well-Dressed Children Dancing
Painted handkerchief, probably nineteenth century

s	m	t	w	t	f	s
						1
2	3	4	5	6	7	8
9	10	11	12	13	14	15
16	17	18	19	20	21	22
23	24	25	26	27	28	29
30	31					

DECEMBER

1853: Author and teacher Octavia Victoria Albert Rogers is born.

monday **24** 358

CHRISTMAS DAY

1907: Cab Calloway, bandleader and first jazz singer to sell a million records, is born in Rochester, NY.

tuesday **25** 359

BOXING DAY (CANADA, UK)

Kwanzaa begins: Umoja (Unity). *To strive for a principled and harmonious togetherness in the family, community, nation, and world African community.*

wednesday **26** 360

Kujichagulia (Self-Determination). *To define ourselves, name ourselves, create for ourselves, and speak for ourselves.*

thursday **27** 361

Ujima (Collective Work and Responsibility). *To build and maintain our community together; to make our sisters' and brothers' problems our problems and to solve them together.*

friday **28** 362

Ujamaa (Cooperative Economics). *To build our own businesses, control the economics of our own communities, and share in all our communities' work and wealth.*

saturday **29** 363

Nia (Purpose). *To make our collective vocation the building and development of our community; to restore our people to their traditional greatness.*

sunday **30** 364

Odetta
American, b. 1930

It's nearly six decades since she began performing, but the years have not caught up to Odetta yet.

Born in Birmingham, Alabama, Odetta Holmes (aka Odetta Felious) moved to Los Angeles with her mother and sister when she was six and began taking singing lessons at thirteen. Classical music was stressed in her home. "Saturday was spring cleaning day in my mother's house. Everything had to be washed and dusted and whatever. When it came time for the Metropolitan Opera to come on the radio, we would stop what we were doing. I would sit in front of the radio and listen to them. Then we could get up and finish our work."

Odetta has been a major influence on such musicians and groups as Janis Joplin, Bob Dylan, Joan Baez, Sweet Honey in the Rock, Judy Collins, Tracy Chapman, Carly Simon, Cassandra Wilson, and Jewel. She was nominated for a Grammy in 2000, and in 2001 she released the album *Lookin' for a Home*. In 2003, the Library of Congress presented her with its "Living Legend" award.

In this photograph, Odetta is seen with Harlem Renaissance poet Langston Hughes. Of the many poets and novelists from this rich cultural period, Hughes remains the most renowned.

s	m	t	w	t	f	s
		1	2	3	4	5
6	7	8	9	10	11	12
13	14	15	16	17	18	19
20	21	22	23	24	25	26
27	28	29	30	31		

JANUARY

---

monday

Kuumba (Creativity). *To do as much as we can, in whatever way we can, to leave our community more beautiful and beneficial than it was when we inherited it.*

☾ **31** 365

NEW YEAR'S DAY   **tuesday**

Kwanzaa ends: Imani (Faith). *To believe with all our hearts in our people, our parents, our teachers, our leaders, and the righteousness and victory of our struggle.*
1804: Haiti declares its independence.
1937: Lou Stovall, artist and master printmaker, is born in Athens, GA.

1 1

BANK HOLIDAY (SCOTLAND)   **wednesday**

1898: Sadie Tanner Mossell Alexander, first African American to earn a PhD in economics, is born in Philadelphia.
1915: John Hope Franklin, historian, educator, and author of *From Slavery to Freedom: A History of Negro Americans,* is born.

2 2

---

thursday

1621: William Tucker is the first known African child to be born in America.
1956: Colored Methodist Church, established in 1870, officially changes its name to Christian Methodist Episcopal Church.

3 3

---

friday

1787: Prince Hall, founder of the first black Masonic lodge, and others petition the Massachusetts legislature for funds to return to Africa, the first recorded effort by blacks to do so.
1920: Andrew "Rube" Foster organizes the first black baseball league, the Negro National League.

4 4

---

saturday

1911: Kappa Alpha Psi Fraternity is chartered as a national organization.

5 5

---

sunday

1993: Jazz trumpeter John Birks "Dizzy" Gillespie dies.
1996: Recycling Black Dollars, an organization of black businesses, campaigns for "Change Bank Day" to benefit black-owned financial institutions.

6 6

2007 INTERNATIONAL HOLIDAYS

Following are the observed dates of major (bank-closing) holidays for selected countries in 2007. Islamic observances are subject to adjustment. Holidays for the US, UK, and Canada and major Jewish holidays appear on this calendar's grid pages. Pomegranate is not responsible for errors or omissions in this list. Users of this information should confirm dates with local sources before making international travel or business plans.

ARGENTINA

1 Jan	New Year's Day
2 Apr	Malvinas Islands Memorial
5 Apr	Holy Thursday
6 Apr	Good Friday
8 Apr	Easter
1 May	Labor Day
25 May	Revolution Day
18 Jun	Flag Day
9 Jul	Independence Day
20 Aug	General San Martín Anniversary
15 Oct	Día de la Raza
8 Dec	Immaculate Conception
25 Dec	Christmas

AUSTRALIA

1 Jan	New Year's Day
26 Jan	Australia Day
5 Mar	Labor Day (WA)
12 Mar	Labor Day (Vic) Eight Hours Day (Tas)
19 Mar	Canberra Day (ACT)
6 Apr	Good Friday
7–9 Apr	Easter Holiday
25 Apr	Anzac Day
7 May	Labor Day (Qld) May Day (NT)
4 Jun	Foundation Day (WA)
11 Jun	Queen's Birthday
6 Aug	Bank Holiday (NSW, NT)
1 Oct	Labor Day (NSW, ACT, SA)
25 Dec	Christmas
26 Dec	Boxing Day

BRAZIL

1 Jan	New Year's Day
20 Jan	São Sebastião Day (Rio de Janeiro)
25 Jan	São Paulo Anniversary (São Paulo)
19–20 Feb	Carnival
6 Apr	Good Friday
8 Apr	Easter
21 Apr	Tiradentes Day
1 May	Labor Day
7 Jun	Corpus Christi
9 Jul	State Holiday (São Paulo)
7 Sep	Independence Day
12 Oct	Our Lady of Aparecida
2 Nov	All Souls' Day
15 Nov	Proclamation of the Republic
20 Nov	Zumbi dos Palmares Day (Rio de Janeiro)
25 Dec	Christmas

CHINA (SEE ALSO HONG KONG)

1 Jan	New Year's Day
18–20 Feb	Lunar New Year
8 Mar	Women's Day
1–3 May	Labor Day Holiday
4 May	Youth Day
1 June	Children's Day
1 Aug	Army Day
1–3 Oct	National Holiday

FRANCE

1 Jan	New Year's Day
8–9 Apr	Easter Holiday
1 May	Labor Day
8 May	Armistice Day (WWII)
17 May	Ascension Day
27–28 May	Pentecost/Whitmonday
14 Jul	Bastille Day
15 Aug	Assumption Day
1 Nov	All Saints' Day
11 Nov	Armistice Day (WWI)
25 Dec	Christmas

GERMANY

1 Jan	New Year's Day
6 Jan	Epiphany*
6 Apr	Good Friday
8–9 Apr	Easter Holiday
1 May	Labor Day
17 May	Ascension Day
27–28 May	Pentecost/Whitmonday
7 Jun	Corpus Christi*
15 Aug	Assumption Day*
3 Oct	Unity Day
31 Oct	Reformation Day*
1 Nov	All Saints' Day*
21 Nov	Penance Day*
24–26 Dec	Christmas Holiday
31 Dec	New Year's Eve

*Observed only in some states

HONG KONG

1 Jan	New Year's Day
17–20 Feb	Lunar New Year
5 Apr	Ching Ming Festival
6–9 Apr	Easter Holiday
1 May	Labor Day
24 May	Buddha's Birthday
19 Jun	Tuen Ng Day
2 Jul	SAR Establishment Day
26 Sep	Mid-Autumn Festival
1 Oct	Chinese National Holiday
19 Oct	Chung Yeung Festival
25–26 Dec	Christmas Holiday

INDIA

20 Jan	Muharram (Islamic New Year)
26 Jan	Republic Day
31 Mar	Prophet Muhammad's Birthday Mahavir Jayanthi
6 Apr	Good Friday
2 May	Buddha Purnima
15 Aug	Independence Day
2 Oct	Mahatma Gandhi's Birthday
13 Oct	Ramzan Id (Eid-al-Fitr)
21 Oct	Dussehra
9 Nov	Diwali (Deepavali)
24 Nov	Guru Nanak's Birthday
20 Dec	Bakr-Id (Eid-al-Adha)
25 Dec	Christmas

Additional holidays to be declared

IRELAND

1 Jan	New Year's Day
17 Mar	St. Patrick's Day
8–9 Apr	Easter Holiday
7 May	May Holiday
4 Jun	June Holiday
6 Aug	August Holiday
29 Oct	October Holiday
25 Dec	Christmas
26 Dec	St. Stephen's Day

ISRAEL

4 Mar	Purim
3 Apr	First day of Pesach
9 Apr	Last day of Pesach
22 Apr	Memorial Day
23 Apr	Independence Day
23 May	Shavuot
24 Jul	Fast of Av
13–14 Sep	Rosh Hashanah
21–22 Sep	Yom Kippur
27 Sep	First day of Sukkot
4–5 Oct	Shemini Atzeret/Simhat Torah

ITALY

1 Jan	New Year's Day
6 Jan	Epiphany
8–9 Apr	Easter Holiday
25 Apr	Liberation Day
1 May	Labor Day
2 Jun	Republic Day
29 Jun	Sts. Peter and Paul (Rome)
15 Aug	Assumption Day
1 Nov	All Saints' Day
8 Dec	Immaculate Conception
25 Dec	Christmas
26 Dec	St. Stephen's Day

Japan

1 Jan	New Year's Day
8 Jan	Coming of Age Day
12 Feb	National Foundation Day
21 Mar	Vernal Equinox Holiday
30 Apr	Greenery Day
3 May	Constitution Day
4 May	National Holiday
5 May	Children's Day
16 Jul	Marine Day
17 Sep	Respect for the Aged Day
24 Sep	Autumnal Equinox Holiday
8 Oct	Health and Sports Day
3 Nov	Culture Day
23 Nov	Labor Thanksgiving Day
24 Dec	Emperor's Birthday

Kenya

1 Jan	New Year's Day
6 Apr	Good Friday
8–9 Apr	Easter Holiday
1 May	Labor Day
1 Jun	Madaraka Day
10 Oct	Moi Day
13 Oct	Eid-al-Fitr
20 Oct	Kenyatta Day
12 Dec	Jamhuri Day
25 Dec	Christmas
26 Dec	Boxing Day

Mexico

1 Jan	New Year's Day
5 Feb	Constitution Day
21 Mar	Benito Juárez's Birthday
5 Apr	Holy Thursday
6 Apr	Good Friday
8 Apr	Easter
1 May	Labor Day
5 May	Battle of Puebla
16 Sep	Independence Day
1 Nov	All Saints' Day
2 Nov	Day of the Dead
20 Nov	Revolution Day
12 Dec	Our Lady of Guadalupe
25 Dec	Christmas

Netherlands

1 Jan	New Year's Day
6 Apr	Good Friday
8–9 Apr	Easter Holiday
30 Apr	Queen's Birthday
4 May	Remembrance Day
5 May	Liberation Day
17 May	Ascension Day
27–28 May	Pentecost/Whitmonday
25–26 Dec	Christmas Holiday

New Zealand

1–2 Jan	New Year's Holiday
22 Jan	Provincial Anniversary (Wellington)
29 Jan	Provincial Anniversary (Auckland)
6 Feb	Waitangi Day
6 Apr	Good Friday
8–9 Apr	Easter Holiday
25 Apr	Anzac Day
4 Jun	Queen's Birthday
22 Oct	Labor Day
16 Nov	Provincial Anniversary (Canterbury)
25 Dec	Christmas
26 Dec	Boxing Day

Norway

1 Jan	New Year's Day
1 Apr	Palm Sunday
5 Apr	Holy Thursday
6 Apr	Good Friday
8–9 Apr	Easter Holiday
1 May	Labor Day
17 May	Ascension Day
	Constitution Day
27–28 May	Pentecost/Whitmonday
25–26 Dec	Christmas Holiday

Puerto Rico

1 Jan	New Year's Day
6 Jan	Three Kings Day (Epiphany)
8 Jan	Eugenio María de Hostos' Birthday
22 Mar	Emancipation Day
6 Apr	Good Friday
8 Apr	Easter
16 Apr	José de Diego's Birthday
16 Jul	Luís Muñoz Rivera's Birthday
25 Jul	Constitution Day
27 Jul	José Celso Barbosa's Birthday
8 Oct	Día de la Raza
19 Nov	Discovery of Puerto Rico
25 Dec	Christmas

All US federal holidays also observed.

Russia

1–2 Jan	New Year's Holiday
7 Jan	Orthodox Christmas
23 Feb	Soldiers Day
8 Mar	International Women's Day
8 Apr	Orthodox Easter
1–2 May	Spring and Labor Day
9 May	Victory Day
12 Jun	Independence Day
7 Nov	Reconciliation Day
12 Dec	Constitution Day

Singapore

1 Jan	New Year's Day
2 Jan	Hari Raya Haji (Eid-al-Adha)
18–20 Feb	Lunar New Year
6 Apr	Good Friday
8 Apr	Easter
1 May	Labor Day
31 May	Vesak Day (Buddha's Birthday)
9 Aug	National Day
13 Oct	Hari Raya Puasa (Eid-al-Fitr)
9 Nov	Deepavali
20 Dec	Hari Raya Haji (Eid-al-Adha)
25 Dec	Christmas

South Africa

1 Jan	New Year's Day
21 Mar	Human Rights Day
6 Apr	Good Friday
8 Apr	Easter
9 Apr	Family Day
27 Apr	Freedom Day
1 May	Labor Day
16 Jun	Youth Day
9 Aug	National Women's Day
24 Sep	Heritage Day
17 Dec	Day of Reconciliation
25 Dec	Christmas
26 Dec	Day of Goodwill

Spain

1 Jan	New Year's Day
6 Jan	Epiphany
19 Mar	St. Joseph's Day
5 Apr	Holy Thursday
6 Apr	Good Friday
8 Apr	Easter
1 May	Labor Day
25 Jul	St. James the Apostle Day
15 Aug	Assumption Day
12 Oct	National Holiday
1 Nov	All Saints' Day
6 Dec	Constitution Day
8 Dec	Immaculate Conception
25 Dec	Christmas

Switzerland

1 Jan	New Year's Day
2 Jan	Berchtold's Day
6 Apr	Good Friday
8–9 Apr	Easter Holiday
17 May	Ascension Day
27–28 May	Pentecost/Whitmonday
1 Aug	National Day
25 Dec	Christmas
26 Dec	St. Stephen's Day

Thailand

1 Jan	New Year's Day
2 Mar	Makha Bucha Day
6 Apr	Chakri Day
13–15 Apr	Songkran Festival
1 May	Labor Day
	Visakha Bucha Day (Buddha's Birthday)
7 May	Coronation Day
31 Jul	Buddhist Lent Day
13 Aug	Queen's Birthday
23 Oct	Chulalongkorn Day
5 Dec	King's Birthday
10 Dec	Constitution Day
31 Dec	New Year's Eve

2008

JANUARY
s	m	t	w	t	f	s
		1	2	3	4	5
6	7	8	9	10	11	12
13	14	15	16	17	18	19
20	21	22	23	24	25	26
27	28	29	30	31		

FEBRUARY
s	m	t	w	t	f	s
					1	2
3	4	5	6	7	8	9
10	11	12	13	14	15	16
17	18	19	20	21	22	23
24	25	26	27	28	29	

MARCH
s	m	t	w	t	f	s
						1
2	3	4	5	6	7	8
9	10	11	12	13	14	15
16	17	18	19	20	21	22
23	24	25	26	27	28	29
30	31					

APRIL
s	m	t	w	t	f	s
		1	2	3	4	5
6	7	8	9	10	11	12
13	14	15	16	17	18	19
20	21	22	23	24	25	26
27	28	29	30			

MAY
s	m	t	w	t	f	s
				1	2	3
4	5	6	7	8	9	10
11	12	13	14	15	16	17
18	19	20	21	22	23	24
25	26	27	28	29	30	31

JUNE
s	m	t	w	t	f	s
1	2	3	4	5	6	7
8	9	10	11	12	13	14
15	16	17	18	19	20	21
22	23	24	25	26	27	28
29	30					

JULY
s	m	t	w	t	f	s
		1	2	3	4	5
6	7	8	9	10	11	12
13	14	15	16	17	18	19
20	21	22	23	24	25	26
27	28	29	30	31		

AUGUST
s	m	t	w	t	f	s
					1	2
3	4	5	6	7	8	9
10	11	12	13	14	15	16
17	18	19	20	21	22	23
24	25	26	27	28	29	30
31						

SEPTEMBER
s	m	t	w	t	f	s
	1	2	3	4	5	6
7	8	9	10	11	12	13
14	15	16	17	18	19	20
21	22	23	24	25	26	27
28	29	30				

OCTOBER
s	m	t	w	t	f	s
			1	2	3	4
5	6	7	8	9	10	11
12	13	14	15	16	17	18
19	20	21	22	23	24	25
26	27	28	29	30	31	

NOVEMBER
s	m	t	w	t	f	s
						1
2	3	4	5	6	7	8
9	10	11	12	13	14	15
16	17	18	19	20	21	22
23	24	25	26	27	28	29
30						

DECEMBER
s	m	t	w	t	f	s
	1	2	3	4	5	6
7	8	9	10	11	12	13
14	15	16	17	18	19	20
21	22	23	24	25	26	27
28	29	30	31			

WHO
DONE IT?

Publications International, Ltd.

Puzzle creators: Myles Callum, Barry Clarke, Julie Cohen, Don Cook, Caroline Delbert, Harvey Estes, Josie Faulkner, Adrian Fisher, Connie Formby, Luke Haward, Stephen Ryder, Pete Sarjeant, Paul Seaburn, Terry Stickels, Nicole Sulgit

Puzzle illustrators: Helem An, Caroline Delbert, Elizabeth Gerber, Pat Hagle, Robin Humer, Nick LaShure, Nicole H. Lee, Lou Newton, Shavan R. Spears, Jen Torche

Additional images from Shutterstock.com

Louis Weber, CEO
Publications International, Ltd.
8140 Lehigh Avenue
Morton Grove, IL 60053

Permission is never granted for commercial purposes.

ISBN: 978-1-64030-009-5

Manufactured in U.S.A.

8 7 6 5 4 3 2 1

INVESTIGATE, DEDUCE, SOLVE!

Did you want to be a detective when you were a kid? Do you read mystery novels and know the culprit before page 25? If so, this is the book for you! The mind stretchers in this book will let you test your deductive skills against more than 300 puzzles.

You'll find a variety of puzzles here. Some will test your logical acumen, others your memory, others your observational skills. You'll have to remember what you saw in crime scene photographs, match fingerprints, crack codes to reveal intercepted messages, and more. You'll solve some mysteries with bursts of inspiration, while others will require hard work as you track down a chain of logic.

Don't worry if you find yourself getting stuck from time to time. Answers are located at the back of the book when you need a helpful boost.

So when you're ready to untangle alibis, crack cryptograms, and track down criminals, just open the book to any page and start solving!

FINGERPRINT MATCH

There are 4 sets of fingerprints. Find each match.

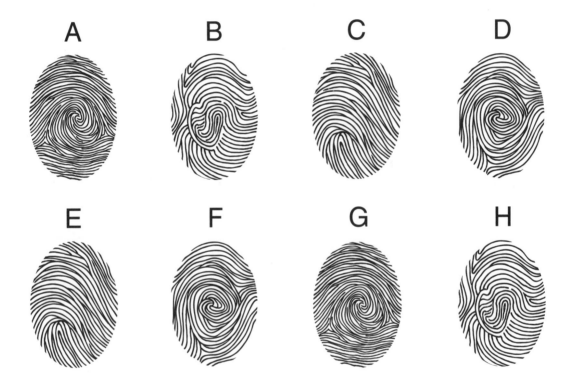

A B C D

E F G H

QUICK CRIME QUIZ

1. The first fingerprint classification system was created by a police officer working in this country.

____ United States

____ Great Britain

____ Argentina

2. Do identical twins have identical fingerprints?

____ Yes

____ No

3. Can someone be born without fingerprints?

____ Yes

____ No

4. Can you lose or erode fingerprints?

____ Yes

____ No

5. Can you lift fingerprints from fabric?

____ Easily

____ Sometimes, but it is difficult

____ Never

Answers on page 374.

CODES AND CIPHERS

Every word listed is contained within the group of letters. Words can be found in a straight line horizontally, vertically, or diagonally. They may be read either forward or backward.

ALGORITHM	ENCRYPTION
BLOCK	HIDDEN
CAESAR SHIFT	KEY
CODE	PLAINTEXT
CIPHERTEXT	STREAM
CRYPTANALYST	SUBSTITUTION
CRYPTOGRAM	TRANSPOSITION
DECRYPTION	VIGENÈRE

```
S  U  B  S  T  I  T  U  T  I  O  N  F  P  N
G  I  C  R  Y  P  T  A  N  A  L  Y  S  T  O
C  N  I  R  U  Y  O  J  N  K  C  Q  Q  N  I
A  O  P  Z  E  B  Q  E  F  S  C  V  Q  Z  T
E  I  H  K  D  L  C  Z  T  M  N  O  P  W  P
S  T  E  M  Q  R  B  R  H  M  U  L  L  U  Y
A  I  R  N  G  V  E  T  A  P  A  X  H  B  R
R  S  T  H  C  A  I  R  H  I  D  D  E  N  C
S  O  E  X  M  R  G  G  N  L  J  R  N  L  E
H  P  X  Q  O  O  Y  T  E  B  U  U  S  Z  D
I  S  T  G  F  E  P  S  N  P  Q  M  C  C  C
F  N  L  P  H  X  Q  N  T  L  È  M  K  O  P
T  A  Y  Q  T  B  N  Q  E  I  T  R  D  X  G
J  R  M  L  A  J  C  Z  U  S  O  E  E  Z  G
C  T  A  Z  U  M  X  D  Q  P  M  N  B  E  L
```

CRACK THE CODE

The 4 symbols each represent a different number between 1 and 9. The numbers to the right and below the grid show the totals of that row or column. Can you deduce the numerical value of each symbol?

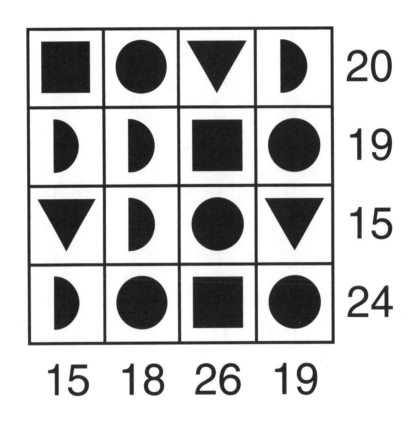

Answers on page 374.

IT'S IN THE BLOOD (PART 1)

Information about blood types can help investigators narrow down who could have left blood at the scene of a crime. Read the following information about blood types, then turn the page for a quiz.

Scientists have discovered eight major blood types; some are compatible, but others are not.

1. O+: 38 percent

O+ blood is needed more often than any other blood type because it's the most common. O+ blood can be given to a person with A+, B+, AB+, or O+ blood. A person with O+ blood can receive blood from O+ or O- donors.

2. A+: 34 percent

A person with A+ blood can receive A+, A-, O+, or O- blood. However, A+ blood can be given only to a person with the A+ or AB+ blood types.

3. B+: 9 percent

B+ blood can be given only to those with either AB+ or B+ blood. This blood type can receive blood from B+, B-, O+, or O- donors.

4. O-: 7 percent

O- is considered the universal donor because it can be given to anyone, regardless of blood type. However, a person with the O- blood type can receive blood only from other O- donors.

5. A-: 6 percent

A- blood can be given to a person with AB-, A-, AB+, or A+. This blood type can only receive blood from O- or A- donors.

6. AB+: 3 percent

AB+ is considered a universal receiver because people with this blood type can receive blood of any type. But AB+ blood can only be given to a person who also has AB+ blood.

7. B-: 2 percent

B- blood can be given to those with B-, AB-, B+, or AB+ blood. A person with B- blood can receive blood from O- or B- blood types.

8. AB-: 1 percent

AB- is the least common blood type. A person with this type can give blood to AB+ or AB- blood types, but must receive blood from O-, A-, B-, and AB- blood types.

IT'S IN THE BLOOD (PART II)

(Do not read this until you have read the previous page!)

1. Which blood type is more common?

____ A+

____ A-

2. Is O positive or O negative the universal donor?

____ O+

____ O-

3. People with this blood type are considered the universal recipient.

____ A-

____ AB+

____ AB-

____ O+

4. This is the least common blood type.

____ A-

____ AB+

____ AB-

____ O+

5. People with O+ blood can receive blood from O- donors.

____ True

____ False

Answers on page 374.

Study this picture of the crime scene for 1 minute, then turn the page.

WHAT DO YOU SEE? (PART II)

(Do not read this until you have read the previous page!) Which
image exactly matches the crime scene?

1.

2.

3.

4.

Answers on page 374.

BURIED DIAMONDS

The thief has buried stolen diamonds in various locations and left a list as a memory aid; however, she has mixed up her list. Although each item is in the correct column, only one item in each column is correctly positioned. The following facts are true about the correct order:

1. River is two places above dogwood and three places above 7 diamonds.
2. Neither lake nor wood are fifth.
3. The 10 diamonds amount is one place below beech and one place above lake.
4. Fifth place is occupied by neither 10 nor 15 diamonds
5. Neither ash nor elm is second.
6. The 8 diamonds amount is one place below garden and three places above fir.

Can you give the tree, location, and number of diamonds buried for each position?

	Tree	Location	No. Diamonds
1	ash	park	5
2	beech	garden	7
3	cedar	river	8
4	dogwood	wood	10
5	elm	fence	12
6	fir	lake	15

FIND THE WITNESS

On Box Street, there are 5 adjacent houses that are identical to each other. You've been asked to interview Mr. Jones, but without any addresses on the doors you are not sure which house to approach. At the local coffee shop, you ask the waitress for help. She is able to provide the following information:

A. Mr. Jones has 2 neighbors.

B. The house in the middle is occupied by an elderly woman.

C. Mary lives between the elderly woman and a family of 3 children.

D. The 3 children live in House A.

Can you determine which is Mr. Jones's house?

| House A | House B | House C | House D | House E |

Answers on page 374.

MOTEL HIDEOUT

A thief hides out in one of the 45 motel rooms listed in the chart below. The motel's in-house detective received a sheet of four clues, signed "The Logical Thief." Using these clues, the detective found the room number within 15 minutes—but by that time, the thief had fled. Can you find the thief's motel room quicker?

1. The sum of the digits is less than 8.
2. The number is divisible by 3.
3. It is not divisible by 5 or 7.
4. Both digits are greater than 2.

51	52	53	54	55	56	57	58	59
41	42	43	44	45	46	47	48	49
31	32	33	34	35	36	37	38	39
21	22	23	24	25	26	27	28	29
11	12	13	14	15	16	17	18	19

Answers on page 375.

CRIMINAL WORDS

Set each of the tile sets into the empty spaces below to create 3 nine-letter words related to investigation. Each tile set is used only once.

T I C	S U S	T E D
B A L	E X A	L I S
M I N	E R S	P E C

Answers on page 375.

IDENTITY PARADE

Oops! Four mugshots accidentally got sent through the shredder, and Officer Cuse is trying to straighten them out. Currently, only one facial feature in each row is in its correct place. Officer Cuse knows that:

1. C's eyes are one place to the right of his hair and 2 places to the right of D's nose.

2. A's mouth is one place to the right of B's eyes and one place to the left of D's hair.

3. C's mouth is 2 places to the left of his nose.

4. B's hair is one place to the right of C's eyes.

Can you find the correct hair, eyes, nose, and mouth for each person?

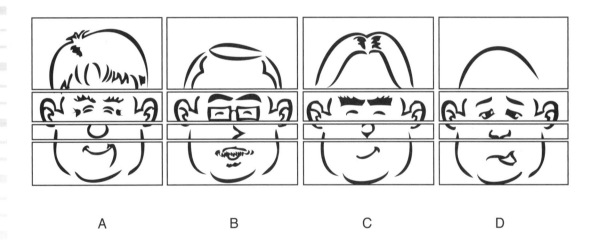

A   B   C   D

Answers on page 375.

INTERCEPTION

Can you complete the sequence below?

The detective is tracking down some stolen gems. She has found the pearls in the city of Edinburgh, the opals in the city of Oslo, and the garnets in the city of Athens. Where are the rubies most likely to be found?

A. Ulan Bator

B. Reykjavik

C. Yerevan

D. Bern

SCIENCE WINS!

The words SCIENCE OVER FIEND are an anagram for this two-word phrase related to crime scene investigation. What is it?

_____ _____

Answers on page 375.

BUILDING BLUEPRINTS

You enter a building, tracking a suspect. Can you make your way through the building as quickly as possible, before the suspect leaves it?

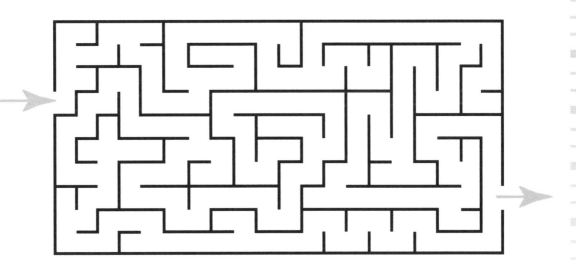

Answers on page 375.

ART THEFTS

The city of Arbourg is on high alert after a series of brazen art thefts. Four different artworks were stolen in the past several months, each by a different artist, and each housed in a different museum. Help the police track down clues by matching each stolen artwork to its artist and the museum in which it was housed, and determining the month in which each was stolen.

1. The painting by Laurent Lafayette was stolen sometime after *City Dreams.*

2. *Apple Cart* was stolen one month before the piece by Pedro Pocalini went missing.

3. The painting by Stephan Strauss went missing sometime before June.

4. The Tendrille museum was robbed in May, just one month after the painting by Don De Lorenzo was stolen.

5. The Givernelle museum was robbed 2 months before *Elba at Dawn* went missing.

6. The Beaufort museum was robbed sometime before July.

	Titles				Artists				Museums			
	Apple Cart	City Dreams	Elba at Dawn	Madame V.	De Lorenzo	Lafayette	Pocalini	Strauss	Beaufort	Givernelle	Millefoi	Tendrille
Months April												
May												
June												
July												
Museums Beaufort												
Givernelle												
Millefoi												
Tendrille												
Artists De Lorenzo												
Lafayette												
Pocalini												
Strauss												

Months	Titles	Artists	Museums
April			
May			
June			
July			

CAN A CLUE SET YOU FREE?

Change just one letter on each line to go from the top word to the bottom word. Do not change the order of the letters. You must have a common English word at each step.

C L U E

———

———

———

F R E E

TELL A TALE, GO TO JAIL

Change just one letter on each line to go from the top word to the bottom word. Do not change the order of the letters. You must have a common English word at each step.

T A L E

———

———

———

J A I L

Answers on page 375.

ROBBER RIDDLE

Cryptograms are messages in substitution code. Break the code to read the riddle and its answer. For example, THE SMART CAT might become FVO QWGDF JGF if **F** is substituted for **T, V** for **H, O** for **E,** and so on.

SDU SWO PDA PDEAB WHH SAP?

DA PNEAZ PK NKX A NERANXWJG.

NUMBER NOGGIN-SCRATCHER (PART I)

Look at the list of numerals below for 1 minute, and then turn the page.

634563312377896

Answers on page 375.

NUMBER NOGGIN-SCRATCHER (PART II)

(Do not read this until you have read the previous page!)

What was the longest string of consecutive numbers in the
string of numbers on the previous page?

A. 123

B. 1234

C. 345

D. 3456

E. 6789

F. 789

UNSCRAMBLE THE DETECTIVE

Sometimes the scrambled detective gets so excited when he's on the case that his words get scrambled. Help his assistant figure out what to do next. Fill in the blanks in the detective's instructions with words that are anagrams (rearrangements) of the capitalized words.

"To VOLES _____ this dastardly crime, we need to look for EVEN DICE

_____. Let's start by looking for FERN STRIPING _____,

PROTON FITS _____, and BRIEFS _____."

Answers on page 376.

Read the story below, than turn the page and answer the questions.

The detective overheard the jewelry thief tell her accomplice about the different places where she stashed the loot. She said, "Two of the diamonds are taped underneath a loose floorboard in the master bedroom. The other three are taped to the light fixture in the bathroom. The pearls are in a can of cornmeal in the kitchen. The gold bars are behind the laundry machine in the basement."

HELP THE DETECTIVE (PART II)

(Do not read this until you have read the previous page!)

The investigator overheard the information about where the stolen loot was stored, but didn't have anywhere to write it down! Answer the questions below to help the investigator remember.

1. How many diamonds are there altogether?

A. 2

B. 3

C. 4

D. 5

2. Some of the diamonds are taped to a light fixture in this room.

A. Master bedroom

B. Bathroom

C. Kitchen

D. Basement

3. What is found in the basement?

A. Gold bars

B. Gold coins

C. Pearls

D. Diamonds

4. The pearls are found in a can of this.

A. Baking powder

B. Oatmeal

C. Cornmeal

D. Baking soda

Answers on page 376.

CRACK THE CODE

The 4 symbols each represent a different number between 1 and 9. The numbers to the right and below the grid show the totals of that row or column. Can you deduce the numerical value of each symbol?

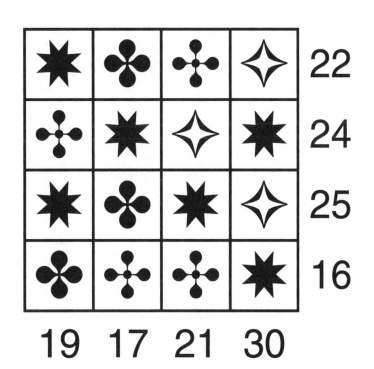

FINGERPRINT MATCH

Which fingerprint matches the one in the box?

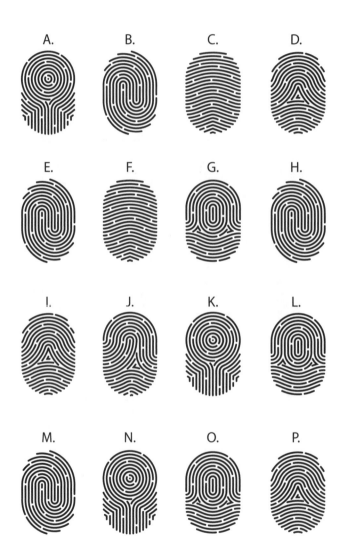

A.   B.   C.   D.

E.   F.   G.   H.

I.   J.   K.   L.

M.   N.   O.   P.

Answers on page 376.

Read the following information about acronyms used in forensic science, then turn the page for a quiz.

AAFS: American Academy of Forensic Sciences

ABO: ABO blood group system

ADME: absorption, distribution, metabolism, and excretion

ALS: alternate light source

ASTM: American Society for Testing Materials

BAC: blood alcohol concentration

CE: capillary electrophoresis

FID: flame ionization detector for gas chromatography

GLP: good laboratory practice

GSR: gunshot residue

MO: modus operandi

NASH: natural, accidental, suicidal, homicidal (cause of death)

PDQ: paint data query

RMNE: random man not excluded

ACRONYM QUIZ (PART II)

(Do not read this until you have read the previous page!)

1. In the context of forensic investigation, PDQ stands for:

a) pretty darn quick

b) paint data query, a database of vehicle paint colors

c) people deserve quality

2. GLP stands for:

a) gunshot

b) guided laser probe

c) good laboratory practice

3. The professional society for people in the forensic professions is:

a) American Academy of Forensic Sciences (AAFS)

b) Academy of American Forensic Investigators (AAFI)

c) American Society for Forensic Professionals (ASFP)

4. Light sources such as ultraviolet and fluorescent light are referred to as:

a) unfamiliar light sources (ULS)

b) alternate light sources (ALS)

c) non-standard light sources (NSLS)

5. Pharmaceutical compounds go through four phases:

a) absorption, distribution, metabolism, and excretion (ADME)

b) ingestion, distribution, affect, excretion (IDAE)

c) ingestion, metabolism, distribution, absorption (IMDA)

Answers on page 376.

HOT PURSUIT

You're in hot pursuit of a suspect, but rain has swept through the entire county, flooding all the bridges indicated by circles. Your job is to travel to each location where the criminal has been seen—A through I, in any order—by restoring only 2 of the bridges.

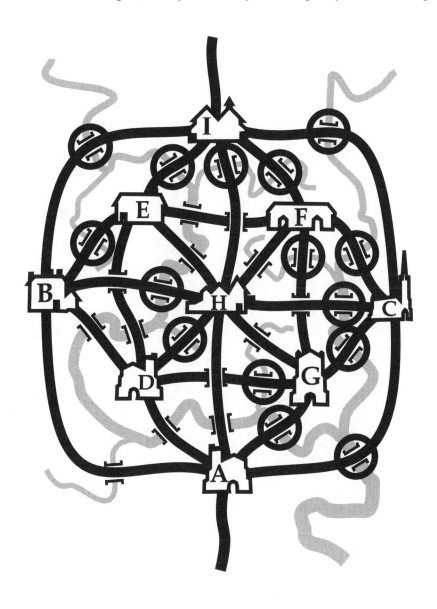

SPY FLY

As an international spy, your mission is to travel from your headquarters at Seth Castle to your safe house at Faro. To disguise your trail, you must stop once—and only once—at each airport. See if you can find the cheapest route for your trip. Less than $220 would make you a Steady Sleuth; less than $190, a Cool Operator; less than $160, a Crafty Agent. If you can make it on $130, then you're a Super Spy!

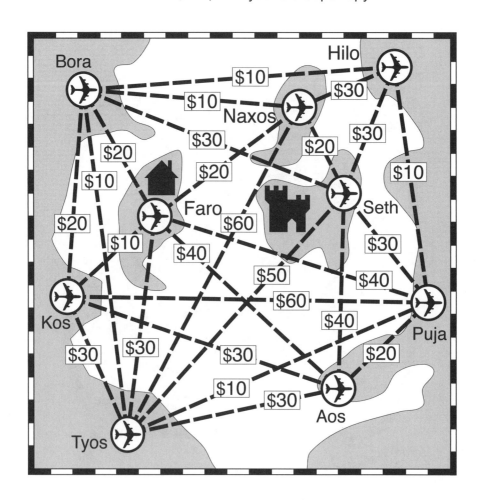

Answers on page 376.

INTERCEPTION

You've intercepted a message that is meant to reveal a location for an upcoming meeting between two criminal masterminds. The only problem is, the message shows many place names. Can you figure out the right location?

ICELAND

LESOTHO

TONGA

INDIA

COMOROS

BENIN

Answers on page 377.

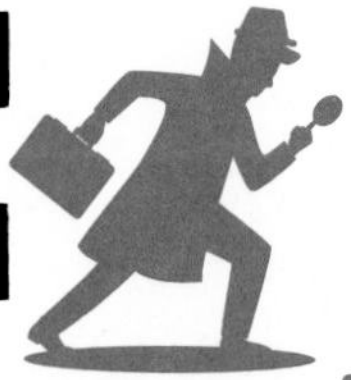

MOTEL HIDEOUT

A thief hides out in one of the 45 motel rooms listed in the chart below. The motel's in-house detective received a sheet of four clues, signed "The Logical Thief." Using these clues, the detective found the room number within 15 minutes—but by that time, the thief had fled. Can you find the thief's motel room quicker?

1. The second digit is larger than the first by at least 3.
2. Both digits are prime numbers.
3. The number itself is not prime.
4. The number can be divided by 3 but not 9.

51	52	53	54	55	56	57	58	59
41	42	43	44	45	46	47	48	49
31	32	33	34	35	36	37	38	39
21	22	23	24	25	26	27	28	29
11	12	13	14	15	16	17	18	19

Answers on page 377.

FIND THE WITNESS

On Box Street, there are 5 adjacent houses that are identical to each other. You've been asked to interview Mr. Linus, but without any addresses on the doors you are not sure which house to approach. At the local coffee shop, you ask the waitress for help. She is able to provide the following information:

A. Mr. Linus does not like dogs.

B. The dog living next door to Mr. Linus often tunnels under his other neighbor's fence to chase their cat.

C. There are no animals at House B.

D. House A owns a cat.

E. House C owns a cat.

| House A | House B | House C | House D | House E |

PASSING BAD CHECKS

Someone has been writing forged checks that have been bouncing all over San Pedro County! Four such checks have been reported so far, each in a different store and in a different town. None of the checks were for the same amount, and no two checks were written on the same day. Help Detective Punderson collect evidence by matching all four bad checks to the store and town in which they were used, and determining the date and total amount of each forged check.

1. Of the two checks written before October 8th, one was for $125.12 and the other was used in Georgetown.

2. The most expensive check was written eight days before the one used in Appleton.

3. The bad check passed at David's Deli was for either $125.12 or $35.15.

4. The check used in Georgetown was written four days before the one used at the Quick-Stop, and sometime after the one used at Carpet City.

5. The check for $52.89 was written 4 days before the one for $35.15.

6. The check passed in Lincoln was written sometime after the one for $125.12.

	Stores				Towns				Amounts			
	Carpet City	David's Deli	Quick-Stop	Well Mart	Appleton	Georgetown	Lincoln	Rio Pondo	$35.15	$52.89	$85.50	$125.12
Dates October 2												
October 6												
October 10												
October 14												
Amounts $35.15												
$52.89												
$85.50												
$125.12												
Towns Appleton												
Georgetown												
Lincoln												
Rio Pondo												

Dates	Stores	Towns	Amounts
October 2			
October 6			
October 10			
October 14			

ELEVATOR WORDS

Like an elevator, words move up and down the "floors" of this puzzle. Starting with the first answer, the second part of each answer carries down to become the first part of the following answer. With the clues given, complete the puzzle.

1. Crime _____

2. _____

3. _____ _____

4. _____

5. _____

6. _____ _____

7. _____ scene

1. An uptick in crime incidents
2. A graphic image of a wave's frequency
3. Companies send these
4. A company logo shows up on this
5. Holds hair back from your face
6. Grade school music classes might teach this
7. Groupies are part of this.

Answers on page 377.

AUTHORS AND DETECTIVES

The left column contains the scrambled names of five famous fictional detectives. The right column contains the authors who created them. Unscramble the names and then match each detective to its creator!

Detectives:

1. HEMLOCKS RESLOSH
2. SLAM SIMPER
3. D. AUSPICE UNTUG
4. FOOL NEWER
5. MONKEY ILLSHINE

Authors:

A. TEX TOURS
B. FORAGES NUT
C. AGHAST CHAIRTIE
D. ADAGE LONER LAP
E. ATRULY HONOR DANCE

DETECT THE WORDS

This puzzle functions exactly like an anagram with an added step: In addition to being scrambled, each word below is missing the same letter. Discover the missing letter, then unscramble the words. When you do, you'll reveal four words related to detection.

CONFERS

HEFT

AXE MEN

STATE GIVEN

Answers on page 377.

DETECTIVES

Complete the word search below to reveal a hidden message related to the puzzle's topic. Every word listed below is contained within the group of letters. Words can be found in a straight line horizontally, vertically, or diagonally. They may read either forward or backward. Once you find all the words, you can read the hidden message from the remaining letters, top to bottom, left to right.

LEFTOVER LETTERS SPELL 2 OF THE MOST FAMOUS NAMES IN DETECTIVE FICTION, AND THE AUTHOR WHO CREATED THEM (6 WORDS).

BANACEK

BARETTA

BARNABY (Jones)

CANNON

DICK TRACY

FRIDAY (Sgt.)

HAMMER (Mike)

HARDY BOYS

HERCULE POIROT

JIM ROCKFORD

McGEE (Travis)

MILLER (Barney)

NANCY DREW

QUEEN (Ellery)

QUINCY

SPADE (Sam)

THE HARTS

THE SAINT

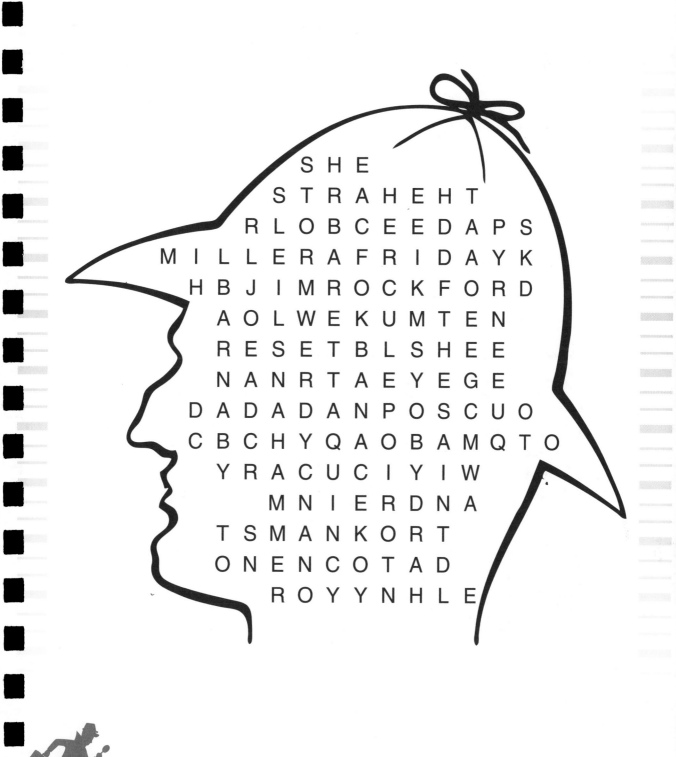

```
        S H E
        S T R A H E H T
        R L O B C E E D A P S
    M I L L E R A F R I D A Y K
    H B J I M R O C K F O R D
    A O L W E K U M T E N
    R E S E T B L S H E E
    N A N R T A E Y E G E
    D A D A D A N P O S C U O
    C B C H Y Q A O B A M Q T O
    Y R A C U C I Y I W
        M N I E R D N A
    T S M A N K O R T
    O N E N C O T A D
    R O Y Y N H L E
```

MOTEL HIDEOUT

A thief hides out in one of the 45 motel rooms listed in the chart below. The motel's in-house detective received a sheet of four clues, signed "The Logical Thief." Using these clues, the detective found the room number within 15 minutes—but by that time, the thief had fled. Can you find the thief's motel room quicker?

1. The second digit is larger than the first.

2. The first digit is the sum of two prime numbers.

3. The sum of the digits is greater than 10.

4. The number can be divided by 8 but not 6.

51	52	53	54	55	56	57	58	59
41	42	43	44	45	46	47	48	49
31	32	33	34	35	36	37	38	39
21	22	23	24	25	26	27	28	29
11	12	13	14	15	16	17	18	19

Answers on page 378.

HELP THE DETECTIVE (PART 1)

Read the story below, than turn the page and answer the questions.

The investigator overheard the thief telling his accomplice where the stolen loot was stored—on 41 S. 6th Street, on the 4th floor, in the 2nd room on the left, in a safe with the combination 34-43-434.

HELP THE DETECTIVE (PART II)

(Do not read this until you have read the previous page!)

The investigator overheard the information about where the stolen loot was stored, but didn't have anywhere to write it down! Answer the questions below to help him remember.

1. What was the street address?

A. 41 N. 6th St.

B. 41 S. 6th St.

C. 6 N. 41st St.

D. 6 S. 41st St.

2. What floor?

A. 1st

B. 2nd

C. 3rd

D. 4th

3. Was the room on the left or the right side of the hallway?

A. Left

B. Right

4. What was the combination to the safe?

A. 43-34-434

B. 34-34-434

C. 34-43-434

D. 34-43-343

Answers on page 378.

SPY FLY

As an international spy, your mission is to travel from your headquarters at Seth Castle to your safe house at Faro. To disguise your trail, you must stop once—and only once—at each airport. See if you can find the cheapest route for your trip. Less than $240 would make you a Steady Sleuth; less than $230, a Cool Operator; less than $220, a Crafty Agent. If you can make it on $200, then you're a Super Spy!

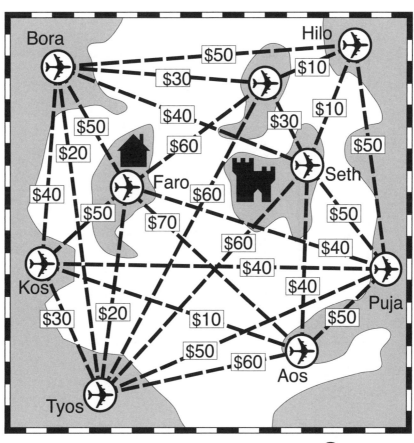

⊕ = Airport
🏰 = Start
🏠 = Finish

CRACK THE CODE

The 4 symbols each represent a different number between 1 and 9. The numbers to the right and below the grid show the totals of that row or column. Can you deduce the numerical value of each symbol?

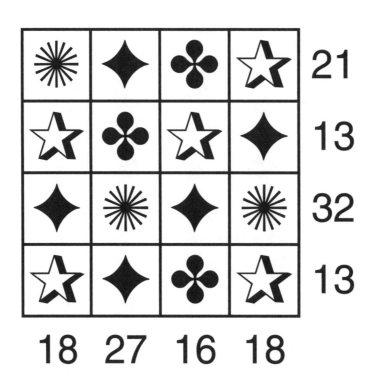

Answers on page 378.

Study this picture of the crime scene for 1 minute, then turn the page.

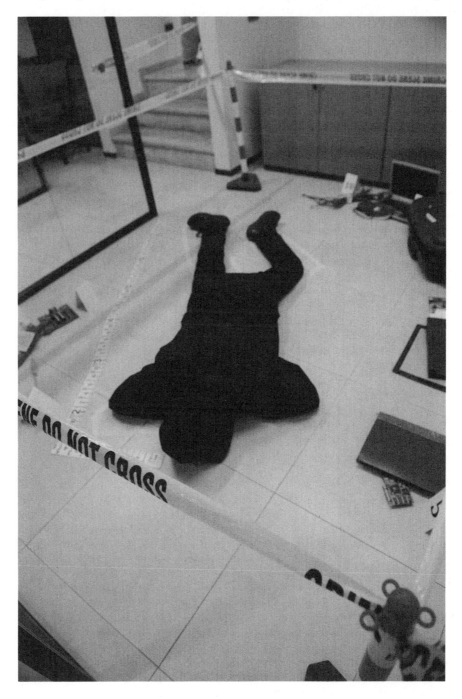

WHAT DO YOU SEE (PART II)

(Do not read this until you have read the previous page!)
Which image exactly matches the crime scene?

1.

2.

3.

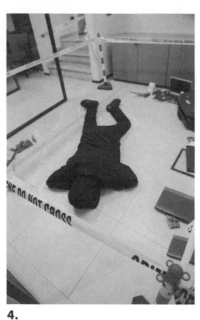

4.

Answers on page 378.

HOT PURSUIT

You're in hot pursuit of a suspect. Rain has swept through the entire county, flooding all the bridges indicated by circles. Your job is to travel to each location where the criminal has been seen—A through I, in any order—by restoring only 2 of the bridges.

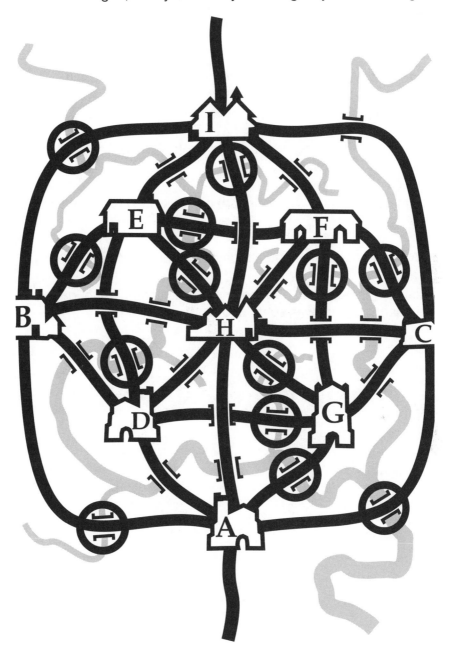

THE MISSING MILLIONAIRE

A wealthy oil tycoon named Allen Avery has gone missing, and his family has put up a huge reward for his safe return. Four different witnesses claim to have seen a man matching Avery's description in the past week, each in a different city and state. Using only the clues below, help track down Mr. Avery's whereabouts by matching each witness's sighting to its city, state, and date.

1. The California sighting occurred sometime after Edna Eddel's.

2. Avery was seen in Oregon 2 days after someone saw him in the town of Tetley.

3. Avery was seen in Ballingford sometime before Susie Seuss's reported sighting (which wasn't on Wednesday).

4. The sighting in Nevada was either the one by Hilda Hayes or the one on Tuesday (but not both).

5. Allen Avery was seen in Ventura 2 days after Edna Eddel's sighting.

6. Of Friday's witness report and the one in Washington state, one was in the city of Ventura and the other was submitted by Walt Wolsen.

	Witnesses				Cities				States			
	Edna Eddel	Hilda Hayes	Susie Seuss	Walt Wolsen	Ballingford	Pescadero	Tetley	Ventura	California	Nevada	Oregon	Washington
Days Tuesday												
Wednesday												
Thursday												
Friday												
States California												
Nevada												
Oregon												
Washington												
Cities Ballingford												
Pescadero												
Tetley												
Ventura												

Days	Witnesses	Cities	States
Tuesday			
Wednesday			
Thursday			
Friday			

Answers on page 378.

CRIME RHYMES

Each clue leads to a 2-word answer that rhymes, such as BIG PIG or STABLE TABLE. The numbers in parentheses after the clue give the number of letters in each word. For example, "cookware taken from the oven (3, 3)" would be "hot pot."

1. Murder amongst Neanderthals (10, 7): _____

2. Person who wants to be a PI (11, 9): _____

3. When the police officer likes to play hockey in spare time (6, 12): _____

4. An investigator who specializes in crimes involving dental work (5, 6): _____

5. A line of people waiting at the detective's door (7, 5): _____

6. The detective called the fingerprint found on the candy cane this (10, 5): _____

7. The local ornithological society was horrified when a member was killed in what was later called this (6, 6): _____

8. The case of the poison being found in the toothpaste was called this (8, 8): _____

Answers on page 378.

COLD CASE

Change just one letter on each line to go from the top word to the bottom word. Do not change the order of the letters. You must have a common English word at each step.

COLD

_____

_____

_____

_____

CASE

NUMBER NOGGIN-SCRATCHER (PART I)

Look at the list of numerals below for 1 minute, and then turn the page.

543209879099554

Answers on page 379.

NUMBER NOGGIN-SCRATCHER (PART II)

(Do not read this until you have read the previous page!)

Which one of the following groups of 3 numbers ended the
sequence on the previous page?

A. 543 B. 098 C. 954 D. 554 E. 544

CRIME CRYPTOGRAM

Cryptograms are messages in substitution code. Break the code to read the
message. For example, THE SMART CAT might become FVO QWGDF JGF
if **F** is substituted for **T,** V for **H, O** for **E,** and so on.

**ZNK GIZUX'Y IUYZGX GIIAYKJ NOS UL G JGYZGXJRE
IXOSK, HAZ ZNK VUROIK XKLAYKJ ZU OTBKYZOMGZK.**

CNGZ JOJ NK JU?

NK YZURK ZNK YIKTK!

MOTEL HIDEOUT

A thief hides out in one of the 45 motel rooms listed in the chart below. The motel's in-house detective received a sheet of four clues, signed "The Logical Thief." Using these clues, the detective found the room number within 15 minutes—but by that time, the thief had fled. Can you find the thief's motel room quicker?

1. The number is divisible by 3.

2. The digits add up to 6.

3. Both digits are prime numbers.

4. The first number is larger than the second.

51	52	53	54	55	56	57	58	59
41	42	43	44	45	46	47	48	49
31	32	33	34	35	36	37	38	39
21	22	23	24	25	26	27	28	29
11	12	13	14	15	16	17	18	19

Answers on page 379.

On Police Officer Appreciation Day at the Bear Clause Donut Shop and Law Firm, all local officers who came in uniform got to eat as many donuts as they wanted. Thirty men and women in blue showed up and chowed down. When the cloud of powdered sugar finally settled and the satisfied officers left, the clerk realized she had forgotten to write down how many donuts each officer had eaten. The legal branch of the Bear Clause Donut Shop and Law Firm informed her that by some obscure law, she must report the total number of officers who ate 6, 7, 8, or 9 donuts so they can be written off as a charitable donation (or in this case, a "donution"). All the poor clerk can remember is that 10 of the officers ate fewer than 6 donuts, 8 ate more than 7 donuts, 5 ate more than 8 donuts, and one ate more than 9 donuts. Can you help the clerk stay out of trouble with her bosses and figure out how many officers ate 6, 7, 8, or 9 donuts?

Answers on page 379.

TUT'S TOMB

Those bars of gold at the center of the maze are worth millions—but they're encased in the tomb. Can you find the only way to the riches?

HOT PURSUIT

You're in hot pursuit of a suspect. But rain has swept through the entire county, flooding all the bridges indicated by circles. Your job is to travel to each location where the criminal has been seen—A through I, in any order—by restoring only 2 of the bridges.

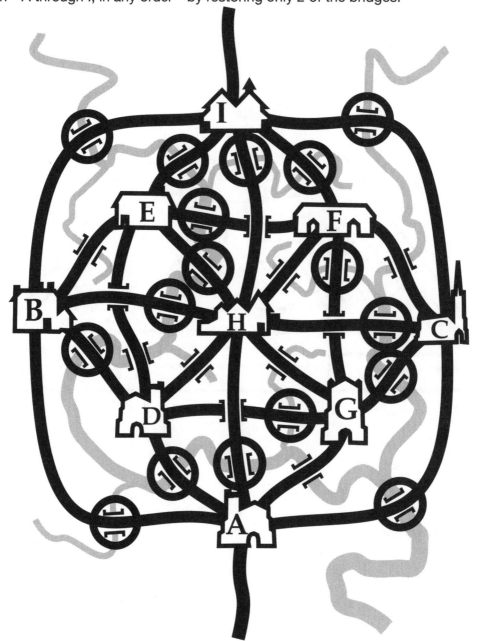

Answers on page 379.

HELP THE DETECTIVE (PART I)

Read the story below, than turn the page and answer the questions.

The detective overheard the jewelry thief tell his accomplice about the different places where he stashed the loot. He said, "The sapphire is tucked in a running shoe in the spare closet. The diamond necklace is behind the mirror in the dining room. The ruby is at the bottom of the salt shaker. The emeralds are in a waterproof bag in the toilet tank."

HELP THE DETECTIVE (PART II)

(Do not read this until you have read the previous page!)

The investigator overheard the information about where the stolen loot was stored, but didn't have anywhere to write it down! Answer the questions below to help the investigator remember.

1. The sapphire is found in this location.

A. The toe of a slipper

B. The toe of a running shoe

C. The bottom of the salt shaker

D. In the refrigerator

2. What is found behind the mirror in the dining room?

A. The sapphire

B. The diamond ring

C. The diamond necklace

D. The emeralds

3. How many emeralds are there?

A. 1

B. 2

C. 3

D. We are not told.

4. What kind of gem is found in the salt shaker?

A. Sapphire

B. Diamond

C. Ruby

D. Emerald

Answers on page 379.

POP QUIZ: TERMINOLOGY

1. What is the difference between a coroner and a medical examiner?

A. No difference. These are two different terms for the same role.

B. Coroners are elected and may not be physicians; medical examiners are physicians appointed to the job.

C. Medical examiners can only perform exams like blood tests and visual examinations, while autopsies must be performed by coroners.

2. In American law, the terms robbery, burglary, and theft are used to describe three slightly different crimes. Which statement below describes each crime?

A. This term refers to the act of wrongfully taking property from someone without their consent.

B. If you use force or the threat of force to take someone else's property without consent, this term is used.

C. If you enter a structure or dwelling with the intent of committing a crime, this term is used.

3. A forensic dentist is also called by this term.

A. Entomologist

B. Odontologist

C. Pathologist

4. This word is used by arson investigators to describe a substance that promotes or spreads a fire.

A. Accelerant

B. Combustant

C. Flammable

Answers on page 380.

Read the account of the crime, then turn the page to answer questions.

On Saturday December 9th at 3:17 AM, a passing trucker made a call to 911 to report a blaze at a structure on Faraday Road. (Faraday Road is in an office park; the trucker was on route 56, which runs parallel.) Firefighters, on arriving, found a fire at the empty office building at 514 E. Faraday Road. It had not yet spread to the surrounding office buildings. Building owned by PilotBuilding Enterprises. The office building houses three businesses: one dentist's office (Dr. Thomas Wexworth, DDS); one app developer (Games to Infinity); one therapists' office (Dr. Wendy Yaxley, PhD; Dr. Rashida Brown, PhD). Each renter had five rooms (entry room, three offices, bathroom) and one storage closet.

The blaze was set in the app developer's office, specifically the storage closet. It spread throughout the office and through the shared wall to the dentist's office, which incurred extensive damage in one room and minimal damage in the others. It did not affect the therapists' office other than some smoke and water damage.

The app developer was a local branch of a larger company. Four employees worked out of this branch: Tomas Villanueva, lead developer; Rembert Whitehead, audio developer; Rachel Smith, junior developer; Yvette Washington, marketing. Another junior developer had been recently fired for cause: Thomas Greene.

The building owner provided cleaning once a week. Cleaning supplies for small spills were kept in the bathroom cabinet. All four employees interviewed attested that the storage closet was used minimally, primarily for paper materials, and that they could not remember chemicals or flammable materials being housed there.

Further investigation revealed that turpentine was used as an accelerant; all employees agreed that none was found anywhere in the office.

There were no signs of forced entry. The external door to the building and the main door to each set of offices were opened by electronic keycard. Current keycards were in the possession of current employees, the building owner, and the cleaning crew.

Attention focused on current and ex-employees of the app developers. All professed to be happy with their employment and to work well together. Washington brought up an ex-boyfriend (Tim Tresworth, one charge of drunk and disorderly at age 21, one dropped charge of shoplifting at the age of 22, no record of arson) who had gotten "borderline stalkery" when they broke up 6 months ago. She had broken up with him partly because he had previously accused her of spending too much time at work and flirting with her male colleagues. He no longer had access to her keycard, but he would have had access to her purse while they were dating, and might have duplicated it then.

When interviewed, Tresworth expressed anger at Washington for "trying to get him involved." He attested that she "went crazy" after their breakup and accused him of stalking her when he was just trying to return some items. He was "dating someone right now" and "didn't need to be reminded of his crazy ex." He professed to have been at her house the night of the fire. His current girlfriend, Janet Parkinson, confirmed. She also said (after asking that "this not get back to him") that she could see him doing something stupid ("he, uh, doesn't have great impulse control") right after a breakup, but she couldn't see him doing something that required a lot of planning 6 months after a breakup. ("Like, he wouldn't plan ahead and get her keycard or anything. He might, like, bang on the door to her office building to yell at her or those guys.")

Thomas Greene, former employee, no prior convictions, was let go for not meeting deadlines, not responding well to feedback, and not working well with outside clients. Greene said that he had not been given clear directions or support and that he'd been set up to fail, and that by the time he was fired he was glad to leave the company. He had since been doing freelance work. He had turned in his keycard to Villanueva (Villanueva confirmed).

A half-full container of turpentine was found in his apartment, in a closet in the guest bedroom, behind a stack of blank canvases. He attested that it was left behind from a girlfriend who had painted oils. There was no dust on the canister; no fingerprints were found.

A CASE OF ARSON (PART II)

(Do not read this until you have read the previous page!)

1. The fire could have been accidental.

_____ Likely

_____ Unlikely

2. There were signs of forced entry.

_____ True

_____ Unconfirmed

_____ False

3. Thomas Greene had a working keycard for the building.

_____ True

_____ Unconfirmed

_____ False

4. Tresworth had an alibi for the time of the crime.

_____ True

_____ Unconfirmed

_____ False

5. The turpentine found in Greene's apartment was left behind by an ex-girlfriend.

_____ True

_____ Unconfirmed

_____ False

Answers on page 380.

CRACK THE CODE

The 5 symbols each represent a different number between 1 and 9. The numbers to the right and below the grid show the totals of that row or column. Can you deduce the numerical value of each symbol?

❖	☀	▲	☀	✳	30
✿	❖	✿	❖	✿	14
☀	✿	▲	✳	☀	28
✿	✳	✿	▲	✳	27
❖	☀	▲	✳	☀	30
17	23	31	32	26	

THE KINGS OF KHAFAR

The tiny island nation of Khafar has had a tumultuous history. Five of its kings have been poisoned in the past century alone, each by a different relative and with a different type of poison. Using only the clues below, determine the year in which each king died, who killed him, and the name of the poison that was used.

1. Of King Taton-on and whoever was poisoned with hemlock, one died in 1938 and the other was murdered by his uncle.

2. The arsenic poisoning occurred 17 years before King Kaponi's untimely end.

3. The king who was poisoned by his eldest son died 34 years before the one who died of oleander poisoning.

4. Of King Anjiwat and whoever was killed in 1921, one was poisoned by his wife and the other by hemlock.

5. King Lilamaku, who died sometime after 1910, wasn't murdered by either his cousin or his uncle.

6. King Anjiwat died of strychnine poisoning in 1972.

		Kings					Killers					Poisons				
		Anjiwat	Kaponi	Lilamaku	Taton-on	Veri'ma	Brother	Cousin	Son	Uncle	Wife	Arsenic	Cyanide	Hemlock	Oleander	Strychnine
Years	1904															
	1921															
	1938															
	1955															
	1972															
Poisons	Arsenic															
	Cyanide															
	Hemlock															
	Oleander															
	Strychnine															
Killers	Brother															
	Cousin															
	Son															
	Uncle															
	Wife															

Years	Kings	Killers	Poisons
1904			
1921			
1938			
1955			
1972			

FIND THE WITNESS

On Persimmon Street, there are 5 houses. You need to gather a witness statement from Anjali Patel, but without any address on the doors you are not sure which house to approach. You know that Patel is a single woman who lives by herself. The staff at the coffee shop around the corner and your own observations give you some clues. From the information given, can you find the right house?

A. One member of the wait staff says Ms. Patel lives at one of the two green houses on the street.

B. Another member of the wait staff knows that a family lives in house C.

C. House D is yellow.

D. The house at one end of the street is blue; the house at the other end is white.

| House A | House B | House C | House D | House E |

Answers on page 380.

MOTEL HIDEOUT

A thief hides out in one of the 45 motel rooms listed in the chart below. The motel's in-house detective received a sheet of four clues, signed "The Logical Thief." Using these clues, the detective found the room number within 15 minutes—but by that time, the thief had fled. Can you find the thief's motel room quicker?

1. The number is divisible by 4.

2. The second digit is larger than the first.

3. The second digit is divisible by 4.

4. The first digit is not a prime number.

51	52	53	54	55	56	57	58	59
41	42	43	44	45	46	47	48	49
31	32	33	34	35	36	37	38	39
21	22	23	24	25	26	27	28	29
11	12	13	14	15	16	17	18	19

INTERCEPTION

You've intercepted a message that is meant to reveal a location for an upcoming meeting between two criminal masterminds. The only problem is, the message shows many place names. Can you figure out the right location?

WASHINGTON D.C.

PHNOM PENH

HELSINKI

FOND DU LAC

ATLANTA

PHILIPSBURG

OSLO

Answers on page 380.

SPY FLY

As an international spy, your mission is to travel from your headquarters at Seth Castle to your safe house at Faro. To disguise your trail, you must stop once—and only once—at each airport. See if you can find the cheapest route for your trip. Less than $260 would make you a Steady Sleuth; less than $240, a Cool Operator; less than $220, a Crafty Agent. If you can make it on $200, then you're a Super Spy!

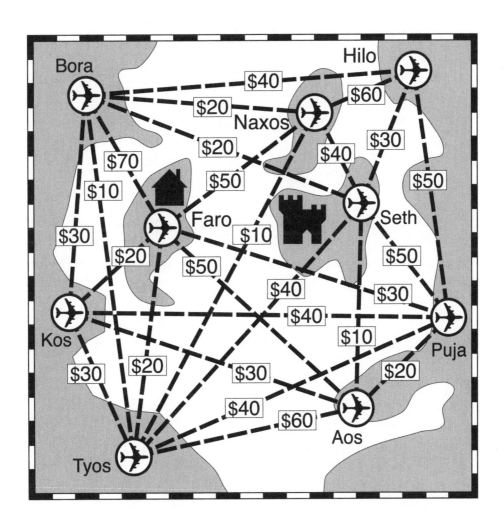

= Airport
= Start
= Finish

71

CATCH THE THIEF

The detective found a list from the burglar and thinks it might indicate what the burglar plans to steal. But in addition to being scrambled, each word or phrase below is missing the same letter. Discover the missing letter, then unscramble the words. When you do, you'll find out what the burglar's targets are.

MAD NODS

A RAT

ADD ME

FINE RUG

CRYPTO-LOGIC

Each of the numbers in the sequence below represents a letter. Use the mathematical clues to determine which number stands for which letter, and then reveal the encrypted word.

4 9 3 1

Clues:

S = 5

2S = I

I / 10 = T

S - T = N

N - A = T

3A = E

Study this picture of the crime scene for 1 minute, then turn the page.

WHAT DO YOU SEE? (PART II)

(Do not read this until you have read the previous page!)

1. There was a small placard on the floor with a number on it. What was that number?

A. 1

B. 2

C. 3

D. 4

2. How many markers were on the table?

A. 1

B. 2

C. 3

D. 4

3. Was there any writing on any of the papers?

____ Yes

____ No

4. A chair had been overturned.

____ Yes

____ No

Answers on page 381.

Read the story below, than turn the page and answer the questions.

The detective overheard the thief tell her accomplice about the different places where she stashed the loot. She said, "The ruby bracelet and the sapphire ring are both found in the summer house in Claremont Heights. The pearl necklace is hidden in the penthouse suite of the condo building in New York. The vintage wine is in the crawlspace of the farmhouse in Trevalyn. The gold coins are in the safety deposit box in the bank in Potosie."

HELP THE DETECTIVE (PART II)

(Do not read this until you have read the previous page!)

The investigator overheard the information about where the stolen loot was stored, but didn't have anywhere to write it down! Answer the questions below to help the investigator remember.

1. Two items are found at the summer house. What are they?

A. Ruby bracelet and sapphire ring

B. Ruby ring and sapphire bracelet

C. Ruby bracelet and pearl necklace

D. Ruby bracelet and gold coins

2. The pearl necklace is found in this location.

A. Claremont Heights

B. New York

C. Trevalyn

D. Potosie

3. The vintage wine is found in this part of the farmhouse.

A. Attic

B. Basement

C. Crawlspace

D. Safe

4. The bank is found in this location.

A. Claremont Heights

B. New York

C. Trevalyn

D. Potosie

Answers on page 381.

FINGERPRINT MATCH

There are six sets of fingerprints. Find each match.

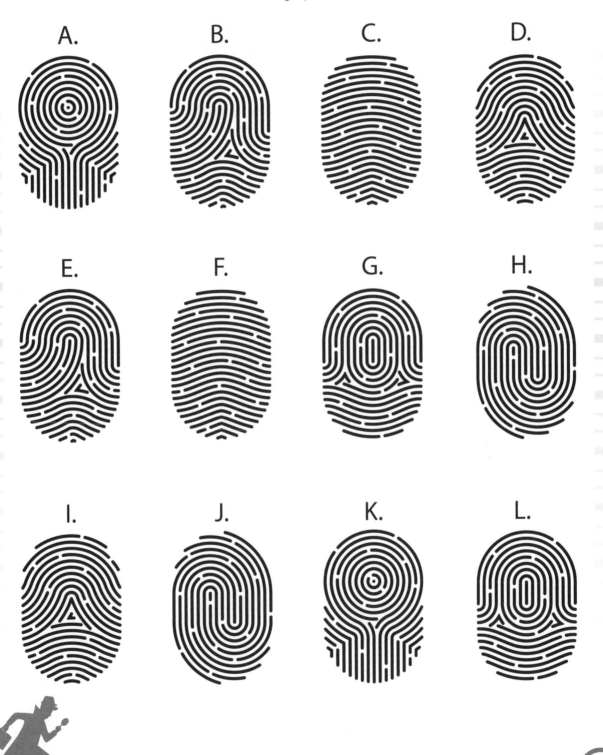

A.　B.　C.　D.

E.　F.　G.　H.

I.　J.　K.　L.

Answers on page 381.

LOST LUGGAGE

George works at the "Lost Luggage" desk at Teterboro Airport, and he's just been given five different bags that need to be rerouted. Each bag is a different color and a different weight, and each of the five bags need to be routed to a different destination. Using only the clues below, help George sort everything out by matching each bag's color and size to its proper owner and destination.

1. Of the 20-pound bag and the one headed to Albuquerque, one is Wendell's and the other Sierra's.

2. Charlie's bag weighs 23 pounds.

3. The five owners are Wendell, Sierra, whoever has the orange bag, and the two people headed to Denver and Calgary.

4. The blue bag is 6 pounds lighter than the yellow one.

5. Sierra's bag doesn't weight exactly 17 pounds.

6. Of the heaviest bag and the yellow one, one belongs to Charlie and the other is headed to Calgary.

7. The pink bag weighs 26 pounds.

8. Felicia isn't headed to Calgary, and Sierra isn't going to Emeryville.

		Owners					Colors					Destinations				
		Charlie	Felicia	Sierra	Wendell	Yolanda	Blue	Green	Orange	Pink	Yellow	Albuquerque	Boston	Calgary	Denver	Emeryville
Weights	14 lbs															
	17 lbs															
	20 lbs															
	23 lbs															
	26 lbs															
Destinations	Albuquerque															
	Boston															
	Calgary															
	Denver															
	Emeryville															
Colors	Blue															
	Green															
	Orange															
	Pink															
	Yellow															

Weights	Owners	Colors	Destinations
14 lbs			
17 lbs			
20 lbs			
23 lbs			
26 lbs			

Answers on page 381.

79

SHE'S A COP!

Find the answers in the grid in which police drama you would see the list of actresses. (Hint: this list is in alphabetical order of the TV show titles). Every word listed is contained within the group of letters. Words can be found in a straight line horizontally, vertically, or diagonally. They may be read either forward or backward.

Kathryn Morris as Lilly Rush

Marg Helgenberger as Catherine Willows

Mary McCormack as Mary Shannon

Mariska Hargitay as Olivia Benson

Vivica A. Fox as Nicole Scott

Angie Dickinson as Suzanne "Pepper" Anderson

Holly Hunter as Grace Hanadarko

Heather Locklear as Stacy Sheridan

Kyra Sedgwick as Brenda Leigh Johnson

Peggy Lipton as Julie Barnes

Poppy Montgomery as Samantha Spade

```
C T M D N R E L T O T I C E W
L S H P O L E J S D I O L I P
R A A G W M H S R C D A T W O
P C W T I O I S O A C H U I L
I O Q A O S V S U L O S E T I
S H L K N S N Q S U C C O S C
T H E I P D S I T I A E C O E
E R C I C D O A A R N G H U W
P S A P O E T R G L S G T T R
O E A M H R W G D P P W H M T
L H E C A O N O U E Q N E I H
I H W C D I L C M O R C I S O
T C E H V L T J H A N S A S U
I I I A I C O T E C N S V I S
A C S L N P L C W I T H O U W
```

MOTEL HIDEOUT

A thief hides out in one of the 45 motel rooms listed in the chart below. The motel's in-house detective received a sheet of four clues, signed "The Logical Thief." Using these clues, the detective found the room number within 15 minutes—but by that time, the thief had fled. Can you find the thief's motel room quicker?

1. It is a prime number.

2. At least one of its digits is not prime.

3. The first digit is greater than the second digit.

4. The sum of the digits is less than 6.

51	52	53	54	55	56	57	58	59
41	42	43	44	45	46	47	48	49
31	32	33	34	35	36	37	38	39
21	22	23	24	25	26	27	28	29
11	12	13	14	15	16	17	18	19

Answers on page 381.

IDENTITY PARADE

Oops! Four mugshots accidentally got sent through the shredder, and Officer Burns is trying to straighten them out. Currently, only one facial feature in each row is in its correct place. Officer Burns knows that:

1. C's nose is one place to the left of D's mouth.
2. C's eyes are one place to the right of C's hair.
3. B's nose is not next to C's nose.
4. A's eyes are 2 places to the left of A's mouth.
5. C's eyes are not next to A's eyes.
6. D's hair is one place to the right of B's nose.

Can you find the correct hair, eyes, nose, and mouth for each person?

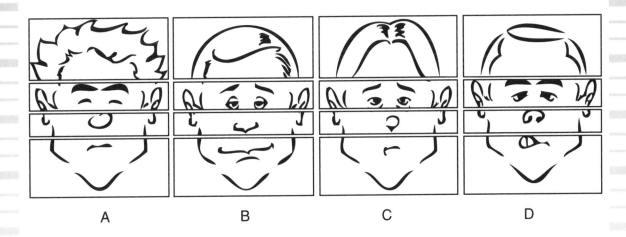

A   B   C   D

Answers on page 381.

TREASURE HUNT

The treasure hunter found six treasures in a row. At each find, he found a clue for the next treasure. Can you put the list of the six treasures he found in order, using the information below?

1. He did not search out the gold coins immediately after finding the rubies.

2. The clue buried with the silver necklace led him immediately to the bronze tiara.

3. He found the three stashes of gemstones (pearls, rubies, and sapphires) in the first three spots, but pearls were not first, rubies were not second, and sapphires were not third.

4. The gold coins were neither the first nor the last things he found.

Answers on page 382.

The 5 symbols each represent a different number between 1 and 9. The numbers to the right of and below the grid show the totals of that row or column. Can you deduce the numerical value of each symbol?

❖	✿	☀	❖	✳	30
☀	▲	❖	☀	▲	23
✳	☀	▲	✿	✳	16
✿	☀	❖	✿	▲	30
▲	❖	✿	✳	✳	21
24	27	32	28	9	

HOT PURSUIT

You're in hot pursuit of a suspect, but rain has swept through the entire county, flooding all the bridges indicated by circles. Your job is to travel to each location where the criminal has been seen—A through I, in any order—by restoring only 2 of the bridges.

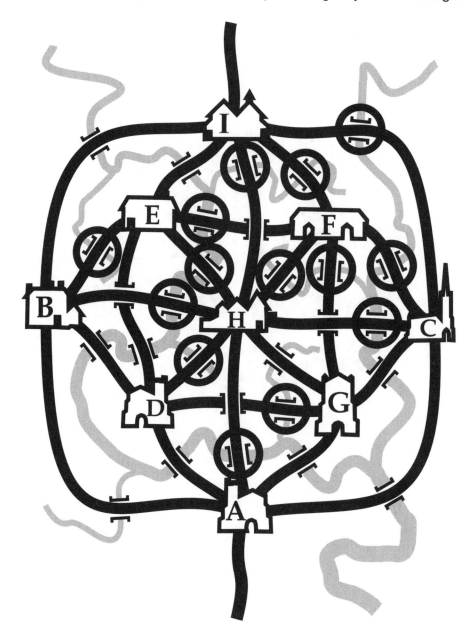

Answers on page 382.

SPY FLY

As an international spy, your mission is to travel from your headquarters at Seth Castle to your safe house at Faro. To disguise your trail, you must stop once—and only once—at each airport. See if you can find the cheapest route for your trip. Less than $280 would make you a Steady Sleuth; less than $260, a Cool Operator; less than $240, a Crafty Agent. If you can make it on $220, then you're a Super Spy!

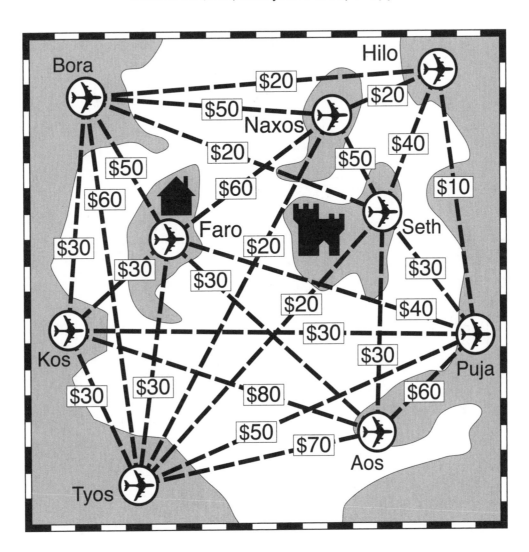

BUILDING BLUEPRINTS

You've found a set of the building blueprints for the criminal's lair. But there are some false ones in the pile, too! Only one of the 3 pieces (labeled A, B, and C) will allow you to go from start to finish without getting stuck. Which one is it?

START

A

← END

B

← END

C

← END

Answers on page 382.

TREASURE HUNT

The treasure hunter found six treasures in a row. At each find, she found a clue for the next treasure. Can you put the list of the six treasures she found in order, using the information below?

1. The sapphires did not lead her immediately to the pearls or rubies; the rubies did not lead her immediately to the sapphires or pearls; the pearls did not lead her immediately to the sapphires or rubies.

2. The bronze tiara was found sometime after the gold coins, but not immediately after.

3. The rubies were found two spots after the bronze tiara.

4. The pearls were one of the first three things found, but not the first.

5. The silver necklace was one of the last three things found, but not the last.

CATCH THE THIEF

The detective found a list that the burglar left behind. She knows that the burglar likes to scramble words, then remove one letter. To help the detective, discover the missing letter, then unscramble the words. When you do, you'll reveal the burglar's plans on a specific city and day, as well as his method of transport.

ERRED PUT

RIPS

DYED NEWS

PRALINE

CRYPTO-LOGIC

Each of the numbers in the sequence below represents a letter. Use the mathematical clues to determine which number stands for which letter and reveal the encrypted word.

812563

Clues:

T=12

1/3 T=(P-1)

2P=O

O-2=S

O-S=M

M/2=I

M+I=E

2E=L

ROBBER RIDDLE

Cryptograms are messages in substitution code. Break the code to read the riddle and its answer. For example, THE SMART CAT might become FVO QWGDF JGF if **F** is substituted for **T**, **V** for **H**, **O** for **E**, and so on.

OZQ VAV LZW LZAWX GFDQ KSQ "EWGO" LG LZW HGDAUW?

TWUSMKW ZW OSK S USL TMJYDSJ.

GEMSTONE MATH

There are 6 types of gems. There is 1 gem of the first type, 2 of the second type, 3 of the third type, 4 of the fourth type, 5 of the fifth type, and 6 of the sixth type. From the information given below, can you tell how many gemstones there are of each kind?

There are at least 4 pearls. There are fewer than 3 zircons. There are more garnets than diamonds, but more sapphires than garnets. There are 2 more diamonds than aquamarines. There are fewer sapphires than pearls.

CAN'T BUY ME LUNCH

Four friends met for lunch. When the check came, Cass, who had steak and potatoes, insisted that it could be fairly split into four equal parts. John, Denny, and Michelle, who ate three small but pricey salads, felt cheated. The check totaled 84 dollars, so Cass told each friend to put exactly four bills in front of them. Together, the 16 bills consisted of 4 ones, 8 fives, and 4 ten dollar bills. John had the least amount of money but had just one dollar less than Michelle. Cass had no ones but had the most money. Denny and Michelle were the only ones who had at least one of each bill. Each friend's four bills paid for their portion of the lunch. How much money did each person have?

INTERCEPTION

You've intercepted two messages. One had the date of a meeting. The other must be the location—but the intercepted list has 13 place names on it. Can you decipher where the meeting is?

THAILAND

ECUADOR

ITALY

YORK, ENGLAND

FAROE ISLANDS

U.S. VIRGIN ISLANDS

TIPPERARY, IRELAND

NIGERIA

NAMIBIA

BIG LAKE

GHANA

OTTAWA

EL SALVADOR

Answers on page 383.

WAYWARD HIKERS

Five hikers were reported as missing this morning in various parts of Canada's Northwest Territories. Thankfully local rescue workers found all of them safe and sound! Using only the clues below, determine when each hiker was rescued, and determine the latitude and longitude of the location at which each was found.

1. Of Randall and whoever was rescued at 5:05pm, one was at latitude 64.19 and the other at 64.38.

2. The hiker found at longitude -110.29 was rescued 90 minutes after the person found at longitude -109.99.

3. Kari wasn't picked up at latitude 64.08.

4. The hiker found at longitude -110.42 was found 45 minutes after the one rescued at latitude 64.38.

5. Of Edna and whoever was found at longitude -110.01, one was located at latitude 64.61 and the other was picked up at 5:05pm.

6. Victoria was the first hiker to be rescued (but she wasn't at either latitude 64.61 or 64.08).

7. The hiker found at longitude -110.01 was either Victoria or whoever was rescued at 5:50pm.

		Hikers					Latitudes					Longitudes				
		Edna	Kari	Luke	Randall	Victoria	64.08	64.19	64.38	64.61	64.73	-110.42	-110.29	-110.22	-110.01	-109.99
Times	4:20pm															
	5:05pm															
	5:50pm															
	6:35pm															
	7:20pm															
Longitudes	-110.42															
	-110.29															
	-110.22															
	-110.01															
	-109.99															
Latitudes	64.08															
	64.19															
	64.38															
	64.61															
	64.73															

Times	Hikers	Latitudes	Latitudes
4:20pm			
5:05pm			
5:50pm			
6:35pm			
7:20pm			

FIND THE WITNESS

On Trevalyn Street, there are 5 houses that are identical to each other. You need to gather a witness statement from Henry Riggins, but without any address on the doors you are not sure which house to approach. You know that Riggins lives with his girlfriend and her teenaged son. The staff at the coffee shop around the corner and your own observations give you some clues. From the information given, can you find the right house?

A. The people who live in the house in the middle always help the elderly couple next door, whose children live far away, shovel their walkway.

B. The elderly couple also get help from Matthew and Jonas, who live on the other side of the elderly couple and drive them to the grocery store each week.

C. The couple in house D just put out a stork figurine to celebrate their new baby.

D. One house is vacant while it's being sold.

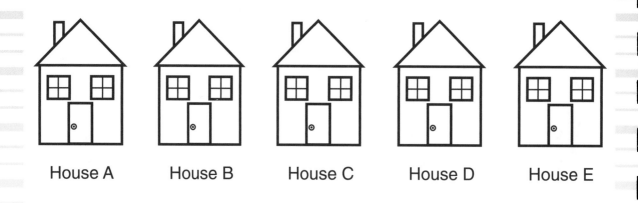

House A   House B   House C   House D   House E

Answers on page 383.

Read the story below, than turn the page and answer the questions.

The detective overheard the thief tell her accomplice about the different places where she stashed the loot. She said, "I left the largest diamond taped to the drainpipe underneath the upstairs sink. The four smaller diamonds are tucked in a pair of pantyhose in the third drawer down in the dresser. The gold necklace is wrapped up in the rose-patterned pillowcase in the linen closet. The gold bars are in a locked trunk in the attic."

HELP THE DETECTIVE (PART II)

(Do not read this until you have read the previous page!)

The investigator overheard the information about where the stolen loot was stored, but didn't have anywhere to write it down! Answer the questions below to help the investigator remember.

1. What is found in the drainpipe?

A. The largest diamond

B. The four smaller diamonds

C. The gold necklace

D. The pearl

2. The gold necklace is wrapped in this.

A. Pantyhose

B. Plain pillowcase

C. Rose-patterned pillowcase

D. Sock

3. The gold bars are in this.

A. The linen closet

B. A locked trunk in the attic

C. A trunk in the crawlspace

D. A trunk in the basement

4. Which item or items are found in the top dresser drawer?

A. The largest diamond

B. The four smaller diamonds

C. The gold necklace

D. None of them

Answers on page 383.

MOTEL HIDEOUT

A thief hides out in one of the 45 motel rooms listed in the chart below. The motel's in-house detective received a sheet of four clues, signed "The Logical Thief." Using these clues, the detective found the room number within 15 minutes—but by that time, the thief had fled. Can you find the thief's motel room quicker?

1. The second digit is more than twice the first digit.
2. The number is not prime.
3. The number is not divisible by 2, 5, or 7
4. The sum of the digits is 10 or greater.

51	52	53	54	55	56	57	58	59
41	42	43	44	45	46	47	48	49
31	32	33	34	35	36	37	38	39
21	22	23	24	25	26	27	28	29
11	12	13	14	15	16	17	18	19

Answers on page 383.

You're in hot pursuit of a suspect, but rain has swept through the entire county, flooding all the bridges indicated by circles. Your job is to travel to each location where the criminal has been seen—A through I, in any order—by restoring only 2 of the bridges.

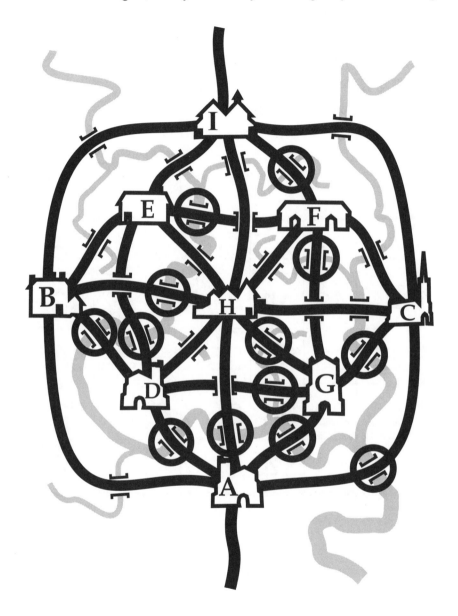

Answers on page 383.

SPY FLY

As an international spy, your mission is to travel from your headquarters at Seth Castle to your safe house at Faro. To disguise your trail, you must stop once—and only once—at each airport. See if you can find the cheapest route for your trip. Less than $280 would make you a Steady Sleuth; less than $270, a Cool Operator; less than $260, a Crafty Agent. If you can make it on $230, then you're a Super Spy!

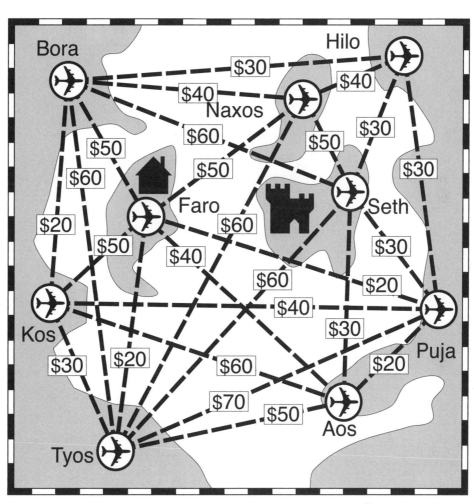

⊕ = Airport
🏰 = Start
🏠 = Finish

SPY SCRAMBLE

You're tracking down a mole. You know when he's meeting with his contact to relay information, and the city, but not the exact street or building. However, you've found a list of random words that you think might combine to form an anagram of the location. Can you unscramble the letters and find the meetup details?

NOR FORCE AM DIN FAN STIR

CRYPTO-LOGIC

Each of the numbers in the sequence below represents a letter. Use the mathematical clues to determine which number stands for which letter and reveal the encrypted word.

Hint: Remember that a / indicates divided by, and that all sums in parentheses must be done first.

6 4 1 3

Clues:

2=F

4F=U

U/2=A

A-E=C

F/2=C

2E=P

Answers on page 384.

CRYPTO-LOGIC

Each of the numbers in the sequence below represents a letter. Use the mathematical clues to determine which number stands for which letter and reveal the encrypted word.

Hint: Remember that a / indicates divided by, and that all sums in parentheses must be done first.

7 9 4 5 2

Clues:

$R=E+A$

$E=2T$

$T=S-1$

$R=3S$

$S=\frac{1}{2}U$

$U=6$

$R-T=G$

MEALTIME CRIME

Cryptograms are messages in substitution code. Break the code to read the message. For example, THE SMART CAT might become FVO QWGDF JGF if **F** is substituted for **T, V** for **H, O** for **E,** and so on.

ZKDW GLG WKH KHDGOLQH UHDG IRU WKH EDNHUB WKHIW WKDW WRRN SODFH GXULQJ WKH VROVWLFH LQ MXQH?

WKH VXPPHUWLPH NHB OLPH FULPH.

Answers on page 384.

CRACK THE CODE

The 5 symbols each represent a different number between 1 and 9. The numbers to the right and below the grid show the totals of that row or column. Can you deduce the numerical value of each symbol?

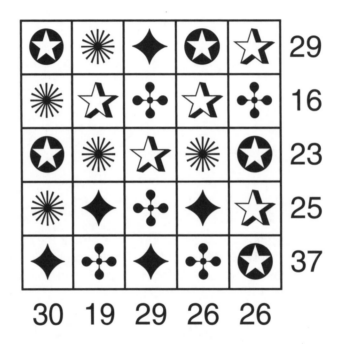

Answers on page 384.

Study this picture of the crime scene for 1 minute, then turn the page.

WHAT DO YOU SEE? (PART II)

(Do not read this until you have read the previous page!) Which image exactly matches the crime scene?

1

2

3

4

Answers on page 384.

A SET OF 13 CRYPTOGRAMS

Cryptograms are messages in substitution code. Break the code to read the message. For example, THE SMART CAT might become FVO QWGDF JGF if **F** is substituted for **T, V** for **H, O** for **E,** and so on. These cryptograms share a common cipher and a common theme. Can you decipher them all?

1. GUR SRNE BS GUR AHZORE GUVEGRRA VF PNYYRQ GEVFXNVQRXNCUBOVN.

2. GUR GUVEGRRAGU CERFVQRAG JNF ZVYYNEQ SVYYZBER.

3. N ONXRE'F QBMRA PBAGNVAF GUVEGRRA YBNIRF.

4. GUVEGRRA VF N CEVZR AHZORE.

5. ZHFVPVNA GNLYBE FJVSG JNF OBEA BA QRPRZORE GUVEGRRAGU.

6. GUR CT-GUVEGRRA ENGVAT QROHGRQ VA 1984.

7. ERQ QNJA JNF GUR SVEFG ZBIVR ERYRNFRQ JVGU GUNG ENGVAT.

8. GURER NER GUVEGRRA FGEVCRF BA GUR NZREVPNA SYNT.

9. GUR NCBYYB GUVEGRRA ZVFFVBA UNCCRARQ VA 1970.

10. GUR ZBIVR SEVQNL GUR GUVEGRRAGU QROHGRQ VA 1980.

11. GURER NER GJRYIR SVYZF VA GUR SENAPUVFR NF BS 2016.

12. GUR GUVEGRRAGU NZRAQZRAG NOBYVFURQ FYNIREL.

13. NYY GURFR NER RAPELCGRQ JVGU N ZRGUBQ PNYYRQ EBG-GUVEGRRA.

CRIME RHYMES

Each clue leads to a 2-word answer that rhymes, such as BIG PIG or STABLE TABLE. The numbers in parentheses after the clue give the number of letters in each word. For example, "cookware taken from the oven (3, 3)" would be "hot pot."

1. Theft of a sushi ingredient (3, 5): _____

2. Fingerprint found at a cheese store robbery (4, 4): _____

3. Shoplifter from a butcher (4, 5): _____

4. Citrus-related robbery (4, 5): _____

5. Robber of drinks (8, 5): _____

6. Plans to steal boat (5, 4): _____

7. Thoughtful investigator (10, 9): _____

8. Foot impression found in the herbal garden (4, 5): _____

MOTEL HIDEOUT

A thief hides out in one of the 45 motel rooms listed in the chart below. The motel's in-house detective received a sheet of four clues, signed "The Logical Thief." Using these clues, the detective found the room number within 15 minutes—but by that time, the thief had fled. Can you find the thief's motel room quicker?

1. The second digit is larger than the first.

2. The sum of the digits is less than 9.

3. The first digit is odd, and the second even.

4. The first number is greater than 1.

51	52	53	54	55	56	57	58	59
41	42	43	44	45	46	47	48	49
31	32	33	34	35	36	37	38	39
21	22	23	24	25	26	27	28	29
11	12	13	14	15	16	17	18	19

TYPES OF EVIDENCE (PART I)

Just walk through a room, let alone commit a crime, and you'll leave a trace that will detail your every action. Read the information below about forensic evidence, then turn the page.

1. Tool marks: If you use any sort of object to commit your crime—a pickax on a door lock, a ladder to reach a window, a knife or a rag (for any purpose)—it will be traceable. Tools used in any capacity create tiny nicks that can be detected, identified, and tracked by a crime scene investigator.

2. Paint: A paint chip left at a crime scene reveals volumes. If it's from the vehicle you used in committing the crime, it indicates the make and model. If paint is found on the tool you used to break into a house, it could place you at the scene. Think it's too hard to distinguish specific paint colors? There are 40,000 types of paint classified in police databases.

3. Broken glass: Microscopic glass fragments cling to your clothes and can't be laundered out easily. Crime labs examine tint, thickness, density, and refractive index of the fragments to determine their origins.

4. Dust and dirt: Even if you're a neat-and-tidy sort of criminal, dust and dirt are often missed by the most discerning eye. These particles can reveal where you live and work and if you have a pet (and what kind). If you've trudged through fields or someone's backyard, researchers can use palynology—the science that studies plant spores, insects, seeds, and other microorganisms—to track you down.

5. Fibers: The sources include clothing, drapes, wigs, carpets, furniture, blankets, pets, and plants. Using a compound microscope, an analyst can determine if the fibers are manufactured or natural, which often indicates their value as evidence. The more specific the fiber, the easier it will be to identify (consider the differences between fibers from a white cotton T-shirt and those from a multicolored wool sweater). There are more than a thousand known fibers, as well as several thousand dyes, so if an exact match is found, you will be too.

6. Blood: A victim's blood tells investigators a lot, but they're also looking for different kinds of blood—including yours if you were injured at the scene—and the patterns of blood distribution. Detectives are well trained in collecting blood evidence to estimate when the crime occurred and who was involved. By the way, don't bother to clean up any blood, because investigators use special lights that reveal your efforts.

7. Bodily fluids: Saliva, urine, vomit, and semen are a crime-scene investigator's dream, providing DNA evidence that will implicate even the most savvy criminal. Saliva is commonly found left behind by a criminal who took time out for a beverage, a snack, or a cigarette.

8. Fingerprints: One of the best ways to identify a criminal is through fingerprints left at the scene. But you kept track of what you touched and then wiped everything down, right? It doesn't matter: You still left smeared prints that can be lifted and analyzed. Investigators enter fingerprint evidence into national databases that can point directly to you.

9. Shoe prints: If you have feet (and assuming you're not a "barefoot burglar"), you left behind shoe prints. They could be in soil or snow or perhaps on a carpet or across a bare floor. The particular treads on the soles of shoes make them easy to trace, and the bottoms of most shoes have nicks or scratches that make them easy to identify.

10. Hair: Humans shed a lot of hair from all parts of their bodies, so bald bandits have no advantage. Hairs as tiny as eyelashes and eyebrows have unique characteristics that reveal a lot about a person, including race, dietary habits, and overall health. And don't forget: While your hair is dropping all over the crime scene, the victim's hair is clinging to your clothing.

TYPES OF EVIDENCE (PART II)

(Do not read this until you have read the previous page!)

1. There are 40,000 types of paint classified in police databases.

____ True

____ False

2. The study of fibers is called palynology.

____ True

____ False

3. Investigators can only lift perfect fingerprints.

____ True

____ False

4. A bald criminal could still be convicted on evidence of hair.

____ True

____ False

5. Broken glass cannot easily be laundered out of clothes.

____ True

____ False

Answers on page 385.

FINGERPRINT MATCH

There are eight sets of fingerprints. Find each match.

A.

B.

C.

D.

E.

F.

G.

H.

I.

J.

K.

L.

M.

N.

O.

P.

Answers on page 385.

THE ESCAPE ARTIST

Marco Antonini, an infamous jewel thief, has made a name for himself over the years as something of an escape artist. He's broken his way out of five different prisons, each in a different state, and each using a different method (such as a tunnel or a guard's uniform). Using only the clues below, match each of his successful escape attempts to the correct year, jail, and state, and determine the method he used during each.

1. Marco broke out of Tulveride prison 4 years after he escaped from Middle Fork.

2. His most recent escape, the Pennington break-out, and the escape where he wore a guard's uniform occurred in three different states.

3. The 2009 escape didn't involve wire cutters.

4. Marco used a guard's uniform as a disguise 4 years after he broke out of Middle Fork prison.

5. The Alabama escape was 12 years before the one in Virginia.

6. Marco broke out of Lexington prison 12 years after his Middle Fork escape.

7. Of the two break-outs where Marco used a rope and a guard's uniform, one was at Calahatchee prison and the other was in 2005.

9. Marco wasn't in Montana in 2005, and he used neither wire cutters nor a tunnel for his Virginia escape.

	Prisons					States					Methods				
	Calahatchee	Lexington	Middle Fork	Pennington	Tulveride	Alabama	Colorado	Idaho	Montana	Virginia	Ladder	Rope	Tunnel	Uniform	Wire cutters
Years 2001															
2005															
2009															
2013															
2017															
Methods Ladder															
Rope															
Tunnel															
Uniform															
Wire cutters															
States Alabama															
Colorado															
Idaho															
Montana															
Virginia															

Years	Prisons	States	Methods
2001			
2005			
2009			
2013			
2017			

Answers on page 385.

CRYPTOGRAM

Cryptograms are messages in substitution code. Break the code to read the message. For example, THE SMART CAT might become FVO QWGDF JGF if **F** is substituted for **T, V** for **H, O** for **E,** and so on. This cryptogram concerns a figure from American history.

GJSOFRNS KWFSPQNS BFX F RFS TK RFSD UZWXZNYX.
MJ XJWAJI TS YMJ HTRRNYYJJ TK XJHWJY
HTWWJXUTSIJSHJ KTW YMJ XJHTSI HTSYNSJSYFQ
HTSLWJXX. NY YWNJI YT XBFD KTWJNLS HTZSYWNJX
YT YMJ FRJWNHFS HFZXJ.

QUOTABLE CRYPTOGRAMS

Cryptograms are messages in substitution code. Break the code to read the message. For example, THE SMART CAT might become FVO QWGDF JGF if **F** is substituted for **T, V** for **H, O** for **E,** and so on. This cryptogram contains quotes by a person named in the previous cryptogram.

BPWAM EPW EWCTL OQDM CX MAAMVBQIT TQJMZBG,
BW XCZKPIAM I TQBBTM BMUXWZIZG AINMBG,
LMAMZDM VMQBPMZ TQJMZBG VWZ AINMBG.

TWDM GWCZ MVMUQMA, NWZ BPMG BMTT GWC GWCZ
NICTBA.

Q EQAP BPM JITL MIOTM PIL VWB JMMV KPWAMV IA
BPM ZMXZMAMVBIBQDM WN WCZ KWCVBZG; PM QA I
JQZL WN JIL UWZIT KPIZIKBMZ; TQSM BPWAM IUWVO
UMV EPW TQDM JG APIZXQVO IVL ZWJJQVO, PM QA
OMVMZITTG XWWZ, IVL WNBMV DMZG TWCAG. BPM
BCZSMG QA I UCKP UWZM ZMAXMKBIJTM JQZL.

Read the story below, than turn the page and answer the questions.

The detective overheard the thief tell his accomplice about the different places where he stashed the loot. He said, "I left the jewels at the apartment on 4th Street, the gold bars at the condo on 48th Street, the $235,000 in unmarked bills in a safety deposit box at the bank on Pearson Avenue, and the art forgery at the townhome on Reardon Street."

HELP THE DETECTIVE (PART II)

(Do not read this until you have read the previous page!)

The investigator overheard the information about where the stolen loot was stored, but didn't have anywhere to write it down! Answer the questions below to help the investigator remember.

1. The jewels are found on this street.

A. 4th Street

B. 48th Street

C. Pearson Avenue

D. Reardon Street

2. The gold bars are found in this type of building.

A. Apartment

B. Condo

C. Townhome

D. Office

3. How much money did the thief stash?

A. $205,000

B. $215,000

C. $225,000

D. $235,000

4. What is found on Reardon Street?

A. Jewels

B. Gold bars

C. Unmarked bills

D. Art forgery

Answers on page 385.

FIND THE WITNESS

On Webster Street, there are 5 houses that are identical to each other. You need to gather a witness statement from Savannah Jenkins, but without any address on the doors you are not sure which house to approach. You know that Jenkins lives by herself but that she was out walking her dog when she saw the crime. The staff at the coffee shop around the corner and your own observations give you some clues. From the information given, can you find the right house?

A. One barista says she has definitely heard barking from both houses A and C when she walks past them to get to the bus stop. She's not sure about the other houses.

B. Another barista know the single woman who lives in house D has allergies that keep her from owning any pets.

C. The coffee shop's manager says that a retired couple lives in house C. They consider the kids who live in the house next door to them "honorary grandkids."

D. The coffee shop's manager also says that the retired couple on the other side of the family wish the kids wouldn't trek across their lawn to get to the nearby park, but they don't feel comfortable bringing it up to the parents.

House A

House B

House C

House D

House E

Answers on page 385.

HOMICIDE: LIFE ON THE STREETS

Every word listed is contained within the group of letters. Words can be found in a straight line horizontally, vertically, or diagonally. They may be read either forward or backward.

BALTIMORE

BAYLISS

CAREER

CONFLICT

CRIME

DETECTIVE

EVIDENCE

GIARDELLO

INEQUALITY

INTERVIEW

JUDGMENT

JUSTICE

LEWIS

MUNCH

PARTNERS

PEMBLETON

PHILOSOPHY

POLICE

RACE

SUSPECT

```
B E P T A H A H T S Y Y A Y B
Z K S E E V I T C E T E D H L
T L Q S M C Q U O M C C O P G
P C I S G B A H C Z E I W O N
A E I I H C L R C L P L I S G
R C A L D Z I E U N S O N O I
T E K Y F M B O T H U P T L A
N V U A E N S X P O S M E I R
E I V B M J O Q O G N I R H D
R D V V Y L H C G P B J V P E
S E C I T S U J J L E W I S L
I N E Q U A L I T Y V I E I L
U C B A L T I M O R E L W E O
O E X Y M W M T R O A V T E P
R E E R A C A J U D G M E N T
```

MOTEL HIDEOUT

A thief hides out in one of the 45 motel rooms listed in the chart below. The motel's in-house detective received a sheet of four clues, signed "The Logical Thief." Using these clues, the detective found the room number within 15 minutes—but by that time, the thief had fled. Can you find the thief's motel room quicker?

1. Each digit is a prime number.

2. The number itself is not prime.

3. The second digit is larger than the first digit by 2.

4. The sum of the digits is less than 10.

51	52	53	54	55	56	57	58	59
41	42	43	44	45	46	47	48	49
31	32	33	34	35	36	37	38	39
21	22	23	24	25	26	27	28	29
11	12	13	14	15	16	17	18	19

Answers on page 386.

TREASURE HUNT

The treasure hunter visited eight cities, finding a clue in each one that led her to the treasure in the final city. Can you put the list of the eight cities she visited in order, using the information below?

The three cities with names that began with the letter C were visited one after the other.

Dakar was one of the first four cities visited; the other African capital on the list was one of the final four cities.

Budapest was visited immediately before Vientiane, which was not where the treasure was found.

Copenhagen was one of the first three cities visited.

Neither Caracas nor Dakar was the first city visited.

Nairobi was visited immediately after Kingston.

One city separated the visit to Canberra and the later visit to Budapest.

Three cities separated the visit to the Jamaican capital from the earlier visit to the city in Australia.

Answers on page 386.

CRACK THE CODE

The 6 symbols each represent a different number from 1 through 10. The numbers to the right and below the grid show the totals of that row or column. Can you deduce the numerical value of each symbol?

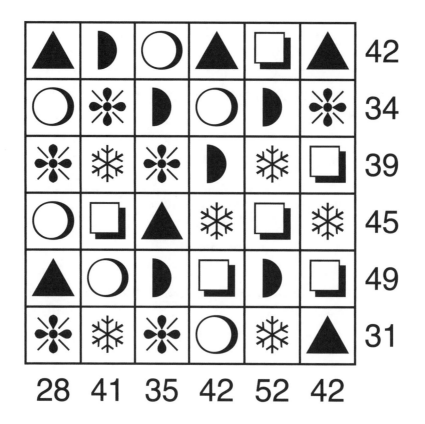

Answers on page 386.

FIND THE MOLE

Be a superspy and track down the mole! Change just one letter on each line to go from the top word to the bottom word. Do not change the order of the letters. You must have a common English word at each step.

FIND

———

———

———

MOLE

FROM CLUES TO TRIAL

Change just one letter on each line to go from the top word to the bottom word. Do not change the order of the letters. You must have a common English word at each step.

CLUES

———

———

———

———

———

TRIAL

Answers on page 386.

You're in hot pursuit of a suspect, but rain has swept through the entire county, flooding all the bridges indicated by circles. Your job is to travel to each location where the criminal has been seen—A through I, in any order—by restoring only 2 of the bridges.

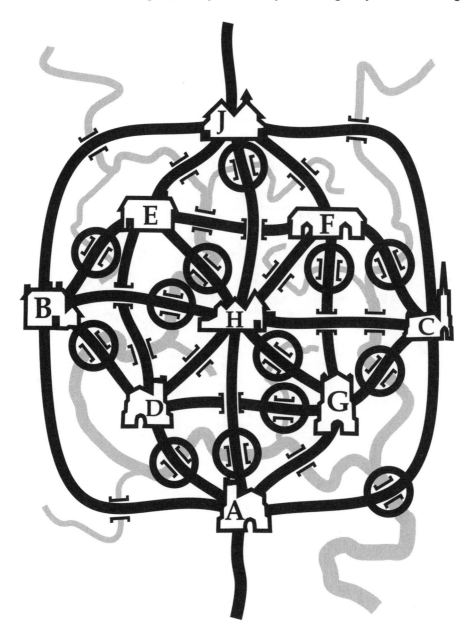

Answers on page 386.

SPY FLY

As an international spy, your mission is to travel from your headquarters at Seth Castle to your safe house at Faro. To disguise your trail, you must stop once—and only once—at each airport. See if you can find the cheapest route for your trip. Less than $240 would make you a Steady Sleuth; less than $230, a Cool Operator; less than $220, a Crafty Agent. If you can make it on $210, then you're a Super Spy!

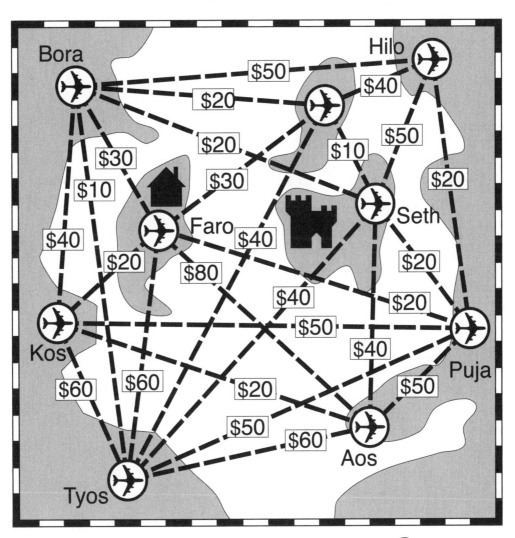

⊕ = Airport
♜ = Start
🏠 = Finish

SPY SCRAMBLE

You will be contacted by a mysterious stranger seeking to pass information. The coded information below gives an identifying characteristic and what the stranger will say to prove their identity. Can you unscramble the letters and find the details about your contact?

MOW TWIN AHA SORE BOOR CHILL COW MOM TEN THEN US SENT

CRYPTO-LOGIC

Each of the numbers in the sequence below represents a letter. Use the mathematical clues to determine which number stands for which letter and reveal the encrypted word.

Hint: Remember that a / indicates divided by, and that all sums in parentheses must be done first.

5723

Clues:

L = 10

L / N = D

D − 4 = S

S = 1

D + 2 = O

L − O = E

SPY SCRAMBLE

You're tracking down a mole. You know where she meets with her contact to relay information, but you don't know when. However, you've found a list of random words that you think might combine to form an anagram of the day and time. Can you unscramble the letters and find the meetup details?

RID THAT DUES TOY HEM FONT THAT WON TITHE FARE NO NO

A HEATED CRIME

Cryptograms are messages in substitution code. Break the code to read the message. For example, THE SMART CAT might become FVO QWGDF JGF if **F** is substituted for **T, V** for **H, O** for **E,** and so on.

EPIB LQL BPM IZAWVQAB AIG BW PQA AEMMBPMIZB?

K'UWV, JIJG, TQOPB UG NQZM.

Answers on page 387.

PARKING TICKETS

Susan works as a parking enforcement officer in downtown Charlotte. Today she wrote tickets for five illegally-parked cars. Help her sort out her paperwork by matching each ticket to the correct car (model and color), street location, and the time at which it was written.

1. The Toyota was ticketed one hour after the green car.

2. Of the Toyota and the Chevrolet, one was silver and the other was the last to be ticketed.

3. The ticket on Tawny Terrace was written at 12:00pm. Susan wrote the ticket for the silver car sometime before that.

4. The brown car was ticketed 2 hours after the Nissan.

5. Susan wrote the ticket on Sandy Street sometime before the one for the double-parked Chevrolet.

6. The Mazda was ticketed 2 hours after the black car.

7. Susan was on Apple Avenue sometime before 12:30pm.

8. The ticket on Lantern Lane wasn't written at 1:00pm.

		Models					Colors					Locations				
		Chevrolet	Honda	Nissan	Mazda	Toyota	Black	Blue	Brown	Green	Silver	Apple Ave.	Lantern Ln.	Raffle Rd.	Sandy St.	Tawny Terr.
Times	10:00am															
	11:00am															
	12:00pm															
	1:00pm															
	2:00pm															
Locations	Apple Ave.															
	Lantern Ln.											
	Raffle Rd.											
	Sandy St.											
	Tawny Terr.											
Colors	Black						
	Blue						
	Brown						
	Green						
	Silver						

Times	Models	Colors	Locations
10:00am			
11:00am			
12:00pm			
1:00pm			
2:00pm			

Answers on page 387.

MOTEL HIDEOUT

A thief hides out in one of the 45 motel rooms listed in the chart below. The motel's in-house detective received a sheet of four clues, signed "The Logical Thief." Using these clues, the detective found the room number within 15 minutes—but by that time, the thief had fled. Can you find the thief's motel room quicker?

1. The second digit is at least twice as large as the first digit.

2. One digit is even and the other is odd.

3. The digits add up to the number 9.

4. The number is not divisible by 6.

51	52	53	54	55	56	57	58	59
41	42	43	44	45	46	47	48	49
31	32	33	34	35	36	37	38	39
21	22	23	24	25	26	27	28	29
11	12	13	14	15	16	17	18	19

Answers on page 387.

INTERCEPTION

You've intercepted a message between two spies. At first glance it doesn't seem to make sense, but can you decipher the true message to reveal the date and location of a meeting?

TEN WAS ASP ATE

PAN AND ADD

AFT NOR PUT ART ATE AHA

PAT ATE

TEN TIN AGE THE ETA

APE IMP

Answers on page 387.

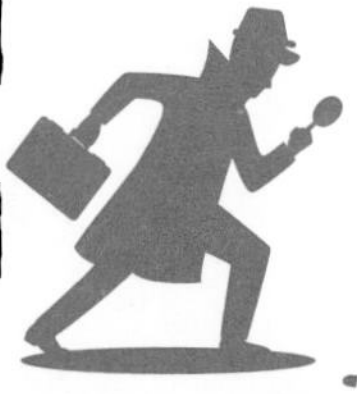

HELP THE DETECTIVE

The detective is putting together the tools she needs. Can you determine the order of the 6 tools gathered from the information below?

The magnifying glass was one of the first three things gathered.

The notepad was not gathered immediately before or after the pencil, nor was it found last.

The fingerprint kit was found right before the flashlight.

The pencil was found third or fourth.

The magnifying glass was put in the kit, then three other items, and then the measuring tape.

The flashlight was found right before the measuring tape.

Answers on page 387.

WHAT DO YOU SEE? (PART I)

Study this picture of the crime scene for 1 minute, then turn the page.

WHAT DO YOU SEE? (PART II)

(Do not read this until you have read the previous page!) Which image exactly matches the crime scene?

1

2

3

4

Answers on page 387.

HELP THE DETECTIVE (PART 1)

Read the story below, than turn the page and answer the questions.

The detective overheard the jewelry thief tell his accomplice about the different places where he stashed the loot. He said, "The pearls are inside the egg carton in the fridge. The opals are in the ice cube tray in the freezer. The rubies are in the cereal box. The garnets are in the medicine cabinet in the upstairs bathroom."

HELP THE DETECTIVE (PART II)

(Do not read this until you have read the previous page!)

The investigator overheard the information about where the stolen loot was stored, but didn't have anywhere to write it down! Answer the questions below to help the investigator remember.

1. The garnets are found in this room.

A. Kitchen

B. Upstairs bathroom

C. Downstairs bathroom

D. We are not told.

2. The pearls are found in this location.

A. Refrigerator

B. Freezer

C. Kitchen cabinet

D. Medicine cabinet

3. What is found in the ice cube tray?

A. Pearls

B. Opals

C. Rubies

D. Garnets

4. What is found in the cereal box?

A. Pearls

B. Opals

C. Rubies

D. Garnets

Answers on page 387.

INVESTIGATE THE ANAGRAM

This puzzle functions exactly like an anagram with an added step: In addition to being scrambled, each word below is missing the same letter. Discover the missing letter, then unscramble the words to reveal five terms related to crime scene investigation.

LOSE

NEED ICE

EAT SING TIE

TEE EDICT

HE TIES

NUMBER NOGGIN-SCRATCHER (PART I)

Look at the list of numerals below for 1 minute, and then turn the page.

672333434987012212

Answers on page 388.

NUMBER NOGGIN-SCRATCHER (PART II)

(Do not read this until you have read the previous page!)

Which one of the following groups of 3 numbers began the sequence on the previous page?

A. 723

B. 673

C. 672

D. 434

E. 212

A FAMOUS MYSTERY WRITER

Cryptograms are messages in substitution code. Break the code to read the message. For example, THE SMART CAT might become FVO QWGDF JGF if **F** is substituted for **T, V** for **H, O** for **E,** and so on.

**LTHQ TATPBT UBNCOPCQ'O YCUPCJITG LQPQUPCSQO
CIUGRLQL HCOO DTIQ HTNKGQ TIL BQNURGQ KJCNJP.**

Answers on page 388.

BUILDING BLUEPRINTS

Using the building blueprints, can you chart a course to the safe at the center of the building before the thief absconds with the loot?

MOTEL HIDEOUT

A thief hides out in one of the 45 motel rooms listed in the chart below. The motel's in-house detective received a sheet of four clues, signed "The Logical Thief." Using these clues, the detective found the room number within 15 minutes—but by that time, the thief had fled. Can you find the thief's motel room quicker?

1. The first digit is a prime number.

2. Both digits are even.

3. The second digit cannot be divided by 3.

4. The second digit is not larger than the first digit.

51	52	53	54	55	56	57	58	59
41	42	43	44	45	46	47	48	49
31	32	33	34	35	36	37	38	39
21	22	23	24	25	26	27	28	29
11	12	13	14	15	16	17	18	19

Answers on page 388.

CRACK THE CODE

The 6 symbols each represent a different number between 1 and 9. The numbers to the right and below the grid show the totals of that row or column. Can you deduce the numerical value of each symbol?

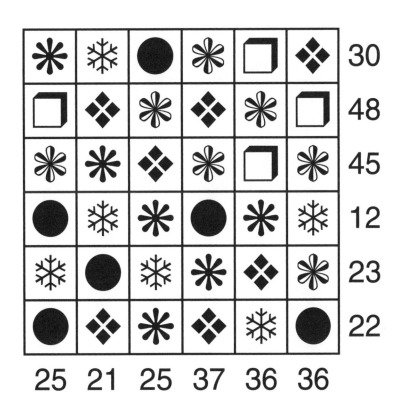

THE SUSPECT LIST

There's been a murder at the Forsyth Mansion! It happened sometime last evening during a fancy dinner party, and five guests who were present at the time are now considered possible suspects. Each has a different profession and is from a different town. None of the five men are the same age. Help the police sort out their investigation by matching each suspect to his age, profession, and home town.

1. Albert isn't the oldest of the five men.

2. The Flagstaff native is 3 years older than the suspect from Midvale (who isn't the dentist), and six years younger than the architect.

3. The engineer is older than Vincent.

4. Nicholas, who is from Billings, is 3 years older than Michael. Of the two of them, one is 26 years old and the other is the tennis pro.

5. The dentist isn't from Flagstaff.

6. Dennis lives in downtown San Pedro.

	Suspects					Professions					Towns				
	Albert	Dennis	Michael	Nicholas	Vincent	Architect	Dentist	Engineer	Lawyer	Tennis pro	Billings	Flagstaff	Midvale	San Pedro	Tulverton
Ages 23															
26															
29															
32															
35															
Towns Billings										
Flagstaff										
Midvale										
San Pedro										
Tulverton										
Professions Architect					
Dentist					
Engineer					
Lawyer					
Tennis pro					

Ages	Suspects	Professions	Towns
23			
26			
29			
32			
35			

HOT PURSUIT

You're in hot pursuit of a suspect, but rain has swept through the entire county, flooding all the bridges indicated by circles. Your job is to travel to each location where the criminal has been seen—A through I, in any order—by restoring only 2 of the bridges.

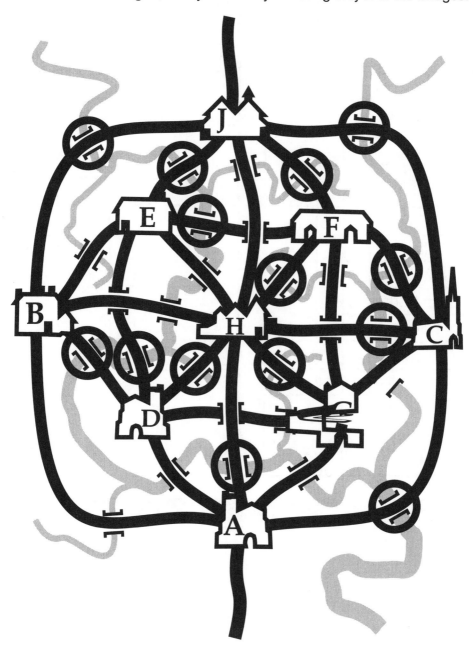

Answers on page 388.

SPY FLY

As an international spy, your mission is to travel from your headquarters at Seth Castle to your safe house at Faro. To disguise your trail, you must stop once—and only once—at each airport. See if you can find the cheapest route for your trip. Less than $290 would make you a Steady Sleuth; less than $280, a Cool Operator; less than $270, a Crafty Agent. If you can make it on $250, then you're a Super Spy!

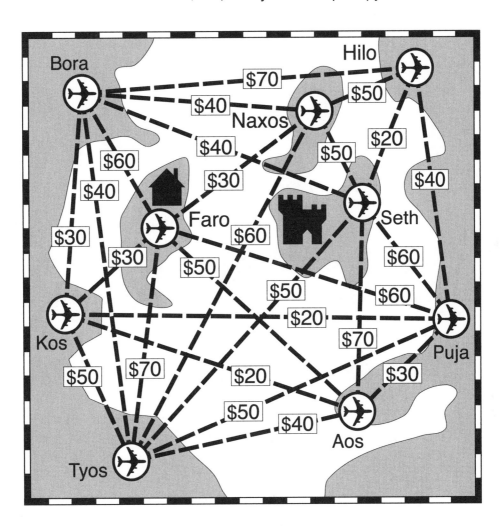

CRYPTO-LOGIC

Each of the numbers in the sequence below represents a letter. Use the mathematical clues to determine which number stands for which letter and reveal the encrypted word.

Hint: Remember that a / indicates divided by, and that all sums in parentheses must be done first.

3 2 1 9

Clues:

X−E=M

3N=E

X=10

X−N=7

2M=A

FIND A CLUE ON A RAID

Change just one letter on each line to go from the top word to the bottom word. Do not change the order of the letters. You must have a common English word at each step.

CLUE

———

———

———

———

———

RAID

Answers on page 389.

BUILDING BLUEPRINTS

Using the building blueprints, can you chart a course to the safe at the marked location before the thief absconds with the loot?

ART FAIR HUNT

Can you determine the order of the booths at the art fair based on the information below?

You are walking past a line of booths at an art fair. You pass the booth with black and white photographs after you pass the place with oil portraits, but before you pass the place with color photographs. The place with quilts is immediately before the place that sells pottery. You pass the place with watercolors before you pass the places with color photography or with pottery. You pass at least 5 booths before you reach the places that sells decorative wind chimes. Immediately after you pass the place with the wind chimes, you pass the place that sells jewelry and the place that sells lamps, in that order. You pass the place with black and white photographs before you pass the place that sells wind chimes. There are exactly three booths between the place that sells the black and white photographs and the place that sells pottery.

Answers on page 389.

ROBBER RIDDLE

Cryptograms are messages in substitution code. Break the code to read the riddle and its answer. For example, THE SMART CAT might become FVO QWGDF JGF if **F** is substituted for **T, V** for **H, O** for **E,** and so on.

AKZ FMF UKG OIDDGO UBNG B DBUK DGHIOG CIMSC UI UKG DBSN?

DGWBXVG KG ABSUGF UI QBNG VXOG KG KBF B WPGBS CGUBABZ.

TASTY CRYPTOGRAM

Cryptograms are messages in substitution code. Break the code to read the message. For example, THE SMART CAT might become FVO QWGDF JGF if **F** is substituted for **T, V** for **H, O** for **E,** and so on.

NLQ KQUIQN IQUJEQ OCI FOU OIJQS ULJUFQA JK IQECINQSDX FQEN JA Y RYPDN KPIICPASQS WX BCNJCA SQNQUNCIK YAS MPYISK.

151

SPY SCRAMBLE

You're tracking down a mole. You know where she meets with her contact to relay information, but you don't know when. However, you've found a list of random words that you think might combine to form an anagram of the day and time. Can you unscramble the letters and find the meetup details?

YAM FUR HOT SAT EVEN NIT HOME RN GIN

SPY SCRAMBLE

You're tracking down a mole. You know where he meets with his contact to relay information, but you don't know when. However, you've found a list of random words that you think might combine to form an anagram of the day and time. Can you unscramble the letters and find the meetup details?

PAR WILTING YET HATE MIGHT DINT

Answers on page 390.

HOT PURSUIT

You're in hot pursuit of a suspect, but rain has swept through the entire county, flooding all the bridges indicated by circles. Your job is to travel to each location where the criminal has been seen—A through I, in any order—by restoring only 2 of the bridges.

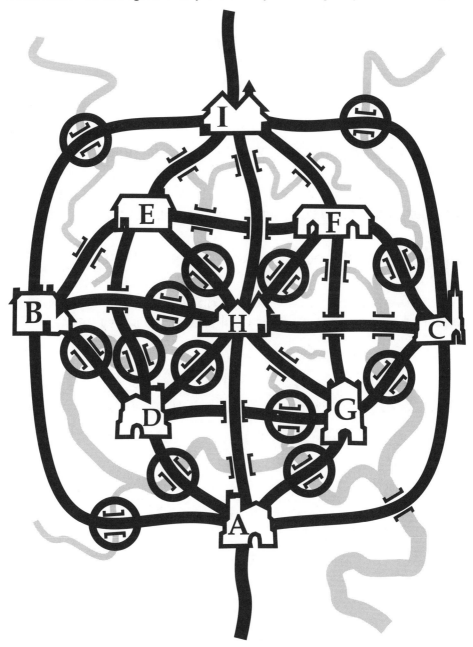

TREASURE HUNT

The treasure hunter found six treasures in a row. At each find, he found a clue for the next treasure. Can you put the list of the six treasures he found in order, using the information below?

1. The diamonds were found either first or last.

2. The antique map led directly to the lost painting, which was not the final find.

3. Exactly two other finds separated the gold bars from the later find of the emeralds.

4. The opals were found sometime after the map, but not immediately after.

5. Neither the emeralds nor the opals were the final find.

6. The emeralds were found before the opals. They may have been found in sequence, or one or more finds could have separated them.

Answers on page 390.

INTERCEPTION

You've intercepted a message that you think contains information about an upcoming meeting. The only problem is, it contains way too many possibilities! Can you figure out the details of the next meeting?

OCTOBER TEN

THE HEATH

ELEVATOR EIGHT

ESCALATOR DURING THE FULL MOON

TANZANIA IN MARCH

OVER AT THE GULF

JANUARY IN NASSAU

NOVEMBER AT THE CAFE

AT A NICE RESTAURANT

NEW MOON IN ORLANDO

OCTOBER AT NOON

ATLANTA IN A TENT

THURSDAY AT THE BEACH

EXPRESSWAY EXIT R

IN TEL-AVIV

EXACTLY MID-DECEMBER

BRIDGE IN VENEZUELA

NEVER AT THE SKATING RINK

Answers on page 390.

IDENTITY PARADE

Mrs. Amnesia was asked to recollect the faces of the 4 suspects who robbed the local bank. Her memory is a bit shaky though. The photos accidentally got put through a shredder, and, currently, only one facial feature in each row is in its correct place. Mrs. Amnesia does know that:

1. B's nose is not next to C's nose.

2. B's hair is one place to the right of B's nose.

3. B's eyes are one place to the right of B's mouth.

4. A's hair is one place to the left of D's mouth.

5. B's eyes are not on the same face as C's nose.

6. C's eyes are one place to the left of C's nose.

Can you find the correct hair, eyes, nose, and mouth for each suspect?

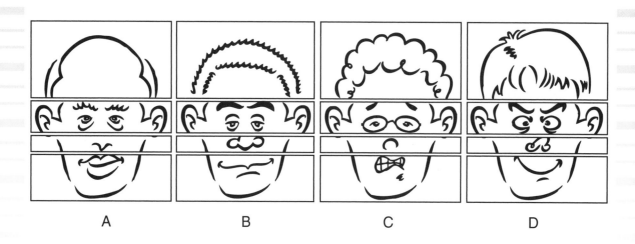

A   B   C   D

Answers on page 390.

MOTEL HIDEOUT

A thief hides out in one of the 45 motel rooms listed in the chart below. The motel's in-house detective received a sheet of four clues, signed "The Logical Thief." Using these clues, the detective found the room number within 15 minutes—but by that time, the thief had fled. Can you find the thief's motel room quicker?

1. Both digits are odd.

2. The second digit is divisible by 3.

3. The first digit is not divisible by 3 or 5.

4. The second digit is not a prime number.

51	52	53	54	55	56	57	58	59
41	42	43	44	45	46	47	48	49
31	32	33	34	35	36	37	38	39
21	22	23	24	25	26	27	28	29
11	12	13	14	15	16	17	18	19

Answers on page 390.

TELEPHONE RECORDS

A local artist named George Wilson has been reported missing. The police have learned that five calls were made from his cell phone on the night he disappeared. None of the five calls were to the same number, and each of them lasted for a different length of time. Using only the clues below, help sort out the information by matching each call to its owner, number, and time, and determine the length of each phone call.

1. Mitchell's phone number doesn't start with "368".

2. The longest phone call was placed five minutes before George dialed 731-9262, and sometime before he called Sarah.

3. Charlie's number is 447-6995.

4. The 48-second phone call was to either Kerry or whoever has the phone number starting with "731".

5. George dialed 592-0021 15 minutes after the 22-second phone call.

6. Whoever received the 3-minute phone call, the person George called at 2:07am, and Vicky are three different people.

7. George called Vicky sometime before 2:10am.

8. Of the two calls placed before 2:00am, one lasted for 3 minutes and the other was to the "239" number.

9. Kerry's home phone number is 239-4827.

10. The 2:07am call didn't last for exactly a minute and a half.

	People					Numbers					Lengths				
	Charlie	Kerry	Mitchell	Sarah	Vicky	239-4827	368-7841	447-6995	592-0021	731-9262	22 seconds	35 seconds	48 seconds	1.5 minutes	3 minutes
Times 1:52am															
1:57am															
2:02am															
2:07am															
2:12am															
Lengths 22 seconds															
35 seconds															
48 seconds															
1.5 minutes															
3 minutes															
Numbers 239-4827															
368-7841															
447-6995															
592-0021															
731-9262															

Times	People	Numbers	Lengths
1:52am			
1:57am			
2:02am			
2:07am			
2:12am			

BLETCHLEY PARK

Every word listed is contained within the group of letters. Words can be found in a straight line horizontally, vertically, or diagonally. They may be read either forward or backward.

ALAN TURING

BANBURISMUS

BOMBE

BUCKINGHAMSHIRE

CLOCK METHOD

CRIB

CRYPTANALYST

DILLY KNOX

ENIGMA

HUT EIGHT

JOAN CLARKE

JOHN HERIVEL

LORENZ

MAVIS BATEY

MILTON KEYNES

MOLE

OFFICIAL SECRETS ACT

PC BRUNO

ULTRA

WRENS

```
E  R  I  H  S  M  A  H  G  N  I  K  C  U  B  A  X
T  A  R  Z  U  L  D  Z  U  D  T  Q  R  B  R  O  P
C  D  L  T  E  T  R  D  V  F  Y  F  I  K  N  T  D
L  L  G  L  D  B  E  G  Q  A  J  R  Q  K  I  C  N
Z  A  O  B  Y  I  L  I  F  U  C  U  Y  L  L  A  A
W  M  I  C  L  F  N  L  G  Z  K  L  J  E  N  S  H
E  G  Q  B  K  F  N  Y  T  H  L  M  Y  V  O  T  T
D  I  M  E  P  M  U  T  J  I  T  A  E  I  A  E  S
L  N  P  B  S  C  E  P  D  X  S  V  A  R  L  R  Y
J  E  S  C  I  Z  B  T  V  K  V  I  W  E  A  C  L
O  Q  N  D  N  T  G  R  H  X  W  S  V  H  N  E  A
A  X  Z  E  K  J  U  U  U  O  K  B  V  N  T  S  N
N  I  R  F  Z  Z  B  Q  U  N  D  A  E  H  U  L  A
C  O  W  U  I  H  E  F  P  B  O  T  V  O  R  A  T
L  M  I  L  T  O  N  K  E  Y  N  E  S  J  I  I  P
A  H  L  V  H  E  Q  I  A  U  B  Y  J  C  N  C  Y
R  W  W  R  E  N  S  N  R  L  J  O  P  R  G  I  R
K  A  Z  S  T  W  Z  T  N  T  I  E  M  J  O  F  C
E  H  Z  T  F  E  M  O  B  R  R  J  T  B  G  F  O
S  U  M  S  I  R  U  B  N  A  B  V  U  E  E  O  E
```

Answers on page 391.

161

CRACK THE CODE

The 6 symbols each represent a different number from 1 to 9. The numbers to the right and below the grid show the totals for the rows and columns. Can you deduce the numerical value of each symbol?

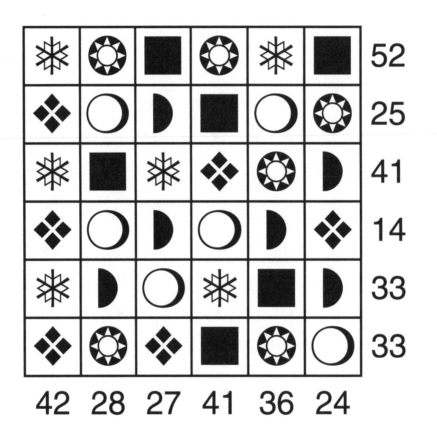

Answers on page 391.

HELP THE DETECTIVE (PART I)

Read the story below, than turn the page and answer the questions.

The detective overheard the jewelry thief tell her accomplice about the different places where she stashed the loot. She said, "The gold bars are in a sack in the treehouse at the farm. The diamonds are taped to a closed vent in the front room of the Chicago two-flat. The ruby choker is in a sack of flour in the pantry at the condo. The emeralds are in the safety deposit box at the bank on Fourth Street."

HELP THE DETECTIVE (PART II)

(Do not read this until you have read the previous page!)

The investigator overheard the information about where the stolen loot was stored, but didn't have anywhere to write it down! Answer the questions below to help the investigator remember.

1. What is found in a treehouse?

A. Gold bars

B. Diamonds

C. Rubies

D. Emeralds

2. What is found in a sack of flour?

A. Ruby bracelet

B. Ruby choker

C. Ruby ring

D. Emeralds

3. The diamonds are found in this building.

A. Farmhouse

B. Two-flat

C. Condo

D. Bank

4. The bank is found here.

A. Fourth Street

B. Fourth Avenue

C. Fourth Drive

D. We are not told.

Answers on page 391.

WHAT DO YOU SEE (PART I)

Study this picture of the crime scene for 1 minute, then turn the page.

WHAT DO YOU SEE? (PART II)

(Do not read this until you have read the previous page!) Which image exactly matches the crime scene?

1

2

3

4

Answers on page 391.

FIND THE WITNESS

On Box Street, there are 5 adjacent houses that are identical to each other. You've been asked to interview Mr. Locke, but without any addresses on the doors you are not sure which house to approach. At the local coffee shop, you ask the waitress for help. She is able to provide the following information:

A. Mr. Locke finds it hard to sleep sometimes with a baby crying on one side of his house, and the heavy metal music playing on the other.

B. Mrs. Franklin is also frequently disrupted by the heavy metal music.

C. House D only listens to classical music.

D. Mrs. Franklin would love to live in a semi-detached property.

E. Mr. Locke hates classical music.

Can you determine which is Mr. Locke's house?

| House A | House B | House C | House D | House E |

POISON! (PART 1)

Long a favorite of mystery-novel writers and opportunistic bad guys, poison has an ancient and infamous reputation. Read some facts about poison below, then turn the page.

Poison Plants

Deadly Nightshade, aka belladonna: Every part of this perennial herb is poisonous, but the berries are especially dangerous. The poison attacks the nervous system instantly, causing a rapid pulse, hallucinations, convulsions, ataxia (lack of muscle coordination) and coma.

Wolfsbane: This deadly plant was used as an arrow poison by the ancient Chinese, and its name comes from the Greek word meaning "dart." Wolfsbane takes a while to work, but when it does, it causes extreme anxiety, chest pain, and death from respiratory arrest.

Meadow Saffron: This tough little plant can be boiled and dried, and it still retains all of its poisonous power. As little as seven milligrams of this stuff could cause colic, paralysis, and heart failure.

Hemlock: This plant is probably the best known of the herbaceous poisons: It was used to knock off the Greek philosopher Socrates. Hemlock is poisonous down to the last leaf and will often send you into a coma before it finishes you for good.

Good Old Arsenic

Arsenic—colorless, tasteless, and odorless—has been called "the poison of kings" and "the king of poisons" because for hundreds of years it was the poison of choice used by members of the ruling class to murder one another.

This close relative of phosphorous exists in a variety of compounds, not all of which are poisonous. Women in Victorian times used to rub a diluted arsenic compound into their skin to improve their complexions, and some modern medications used

to treat cancer actually contain arsenic. When certain arsenic compounds are concentrated, however, they're deadly; arsenic has been blamed for widespread death through groundwater contamination.

Many historians believe that Napoleon died of arsenic poisoning while imprisoned, because significant traces of arsenic were found in his body by forensics experts 200 years after his death. It has been argued, however, that at that time in history, wallpaper and paint often contained arsenic-laced pigments, and that Napoleon was simply exposed to the poison in his everyday surroundings.

Emerald green, a color of paint used by Impressionist painters, contained an arsenic-based pigment. Some historians suggest that Van Gogh's neurological problems had a great deal to do with his use of large quantities of emerald green paint.

Even one of history's best and brightest minds, Leonardo da Vinci, dabbled with chemical weapons. The artist, and sometime inventor of war machines, proposed to "throw poison in the form of powder upon galleys." He stated, "Chalk, fine sulfide of arsenic, and powdered verdigris [toxic copper acetate] may be thrown among enemy ships by means of small mangonels [single-arm catapults], and all those who, as they breathe, inhale the powder into their lungs will become asphyxiated." Ever ahead of his time, the inveterate inventor even sketched out a diagram for a simple gas mask.

Plans of Attack

There are five ways a person can be exposed to poison: ingestion (through the mouth), inhalation (breathed in through the nose or mouth), ocular (in the eyes), dermal (on the skin), and parenteral (from bites or stings).

POISON! (PART II)

(Do not read this until you have read the previous page!)

1. Arsenic is a green powder.

____ True

____ False

2. Parenteral exposure means that poison seeped through the skin.

____ True

____ False

3. The berries of nightshade are poisonous, but not the leaves.

____ True

____ False

4. Socrates was killed by hemlock.

____ True

____ False

5. Wolfsbane does not work immediately.

____ True

____ False

Answers on page 391.

FINGERPRINT MATCH

There are 8 sets of fingerprints. Find each match.

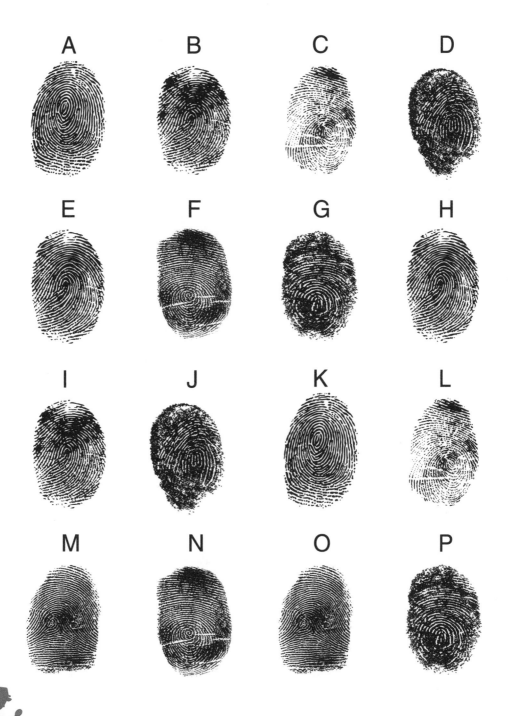

Answers on page 391.

SPY SCRAMBLE

You're tracking down a mole. You know when he's meeting with his contact to relay information, but you don't know where. However, you've found a list of random words that you think might combine to form an anagram of the location. Can you unscramble the letters and find the meetup details?

OF REST REP VERSE LIME MAKER RENT

ROBBER RIDDLE

Cryptograms are messages in substitution code. Break the code to read the riddle and its answer. For example, THE SMART CAT might become FVO QWGDF JGF if **F** is substituted for **T, V** for **H, O** for **E,** and so on.

DSB WRW GSV ILYYVI DVZI DSRGV TOLEVH?

SV WRWM'T DZMG GL YV XZFTSG IVW-SZMWVW.

CRACK THE PASSWORD

A detective has found a memory aid that the criminal left behind, a list of coded passwords. The detective knows that the criminal likes to scramble each password, then remove the same letter from each word. Can you figure out the missing letter and unscramble each word in this set to reveal the passwords?

MENTOR

PIANOS

REPEAL

CRUELLY

CRYPTO-LOGIC

Each of the numbers in the sequence below represents a letter. Use the mathematical clues to determine which number stands for which letter and reveal the encrypted word.

Hint: Remember that a / indicates divided by, and that all sums in parentheses must be done first.

72406

Clues:

S = 5

M + S = 12

2S = U

U - S + 1 = C

C / 2 = E

E + 1 = G

G / 2 = A

C - (A + G) = I

HOT PURSUIT

You're in hot pursuit of a suspect, but rain has swept through the entire county, flooding all the bridges indicated by circles. Your job is to travel to each location where the criminal has been seen—A through I, in any order—by restoring only 2 of the bridges.

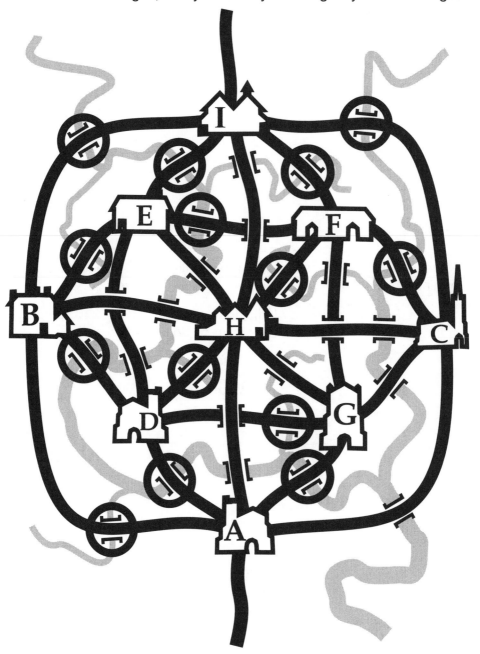

Answers on page 392.

SPY FLY

As an international spy, your mission is to travel from your headquarters at Seth Castle to your safe house at Faro. To disguise your trail, you must stop once—and only once—at each airport. See if you can find the cheapest route for your trip. Less than $290 would make you a Steady Sleuth; less than $280, a Cool Operator; less than $270, a Crafty Agent. If you can make it on $260, then you're a Super Spy!

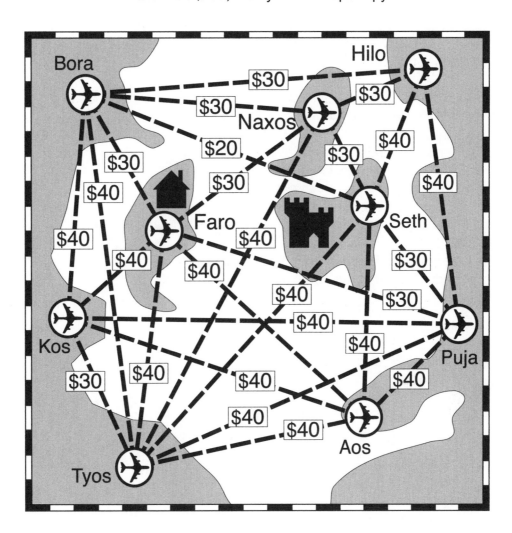

⊕ = Airport
♜ = Start
🏠 = Finish

ILLEGAL PETS

Bremleytown's Animal Control Center has had a busy week! Five different citations were levied by the local authorities against people who were keeping illegal pets in their residences. Using only the clues below, match each law-breaking pet owner to his or her street location, and determine the type of animal they owned and the day on which Animal Control picked it up.

1. The Animal Control team showed up at Edith Estes's door sometime before they picked up the bear cub.

2. Gil Gates had his illegal pet (which wasn't the bear cub) taken away 2 days before the visit to Kirk Lane.

3. The skunk was either the animal picked up on August 7th or the one that was being kept on Walnut Avenue.

4. Animal Control stopped by Walnut Avenue three days before they picked up the wolf on Island Road (which didn't belong to Flora Flynn).

5. Iva Ingram had her pet taken away 3 days before the anaconda was captured. She didn't live on Post Street.

	Owners					Streets					Animals				
	Abe Alvarez	Edith Estes	Flora Flynn	Gil Gates	Iva Ingram	Green Blvd.	Island Rd.	Kirk Ln.	Post St.	Walnut Ave.	Anaconda	Bear cub	Cheetah	Skunk	Wolf
Dates August 4															
August 5															
August 6															
August 7															
August 8															
Animals Anaconda															
Bear cub															
Cheetah															
Skunk															
Wolf															
Streets Green Blvd.															
Island Rd.															
Kirk Ln.															
Post St.															
Walnut Ave.															

Dates	Owners	Streets	Animals
August 4			
August 5			
August 6			
August 7			
August 8			

MOTEL HIDEOUT

A thief hides out in one of the 45 motel rooms listed in the chart below. The motel's in-house detective received a sheet of four clues, signed "The Logical Thief." Using these clues, the detective found the room number within 15 minutes—but by that time, the thief had fled. Can you find the thief's motel room quicker?

1. The number can be divided by 4.

2. The number cannot be divided by 7.

3. The first digit is odd.

4. The second digit is more than twice the first.

51	52	53	54	55	56	57	58	59
41	42	43	44	45	46	47	48	49
31	32	33	34	35	36	37	38	39
21	22	23	24	25	26	27	28	29
11	12	13	14	15	16	17	18	19

Answers on page 392.

TREASURE HUNT

The treasure hunter found six treasures in a row. At each find, she found
a clue for the next treasure. Can you put the list of the six treasures she
found in order, using the information below?

1. The amethysts were one of the first two finds, and were found earlier than
   the diamonds, the rubies, or the sapphires.

2. The diamonds were not the final find.

3. The silver coins were found immediately after the gold bars, and sometime
   before the diamonds, but not immediately before.

4. Exactly two other finds separated the amethysts and the rubies.

Answers on page 392.

LOST IN THE PENTAGON

You need to get to the center of the pentagon to give top secret information to the chief and then dash out the back way. Can you find your way?

Answers on page 393.

CRACK THE CODE

The 7 symbols each represent a different number between 1 and 10. The numbers to the right and below the grid show the totals of that row or column. Can you deduce the numerical value of each symbol?

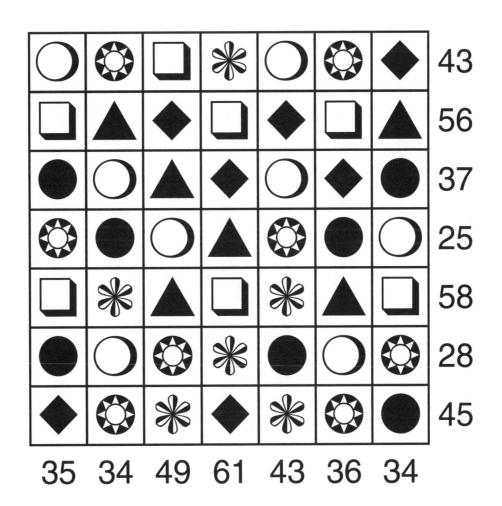

FIND THE WITNESS

On Mitchell Street, there are 5 houses that are identical to each other. You need to gather a witness statement from Michelle and Trevor Banks, but without any address on the doors you are not sure which house to approach. You know that the Banks have two teenaged sons. The staff at the coffee shop around the corner and your own observations give you some clues. From the information given, can you find the right house?

A. There are kids at three of the houses.

B. The single dad lives between the vacant house and the bachelor.

C. The single mom likes the big lot she has at the last corner house.

D. The vacant house is not on the corner.

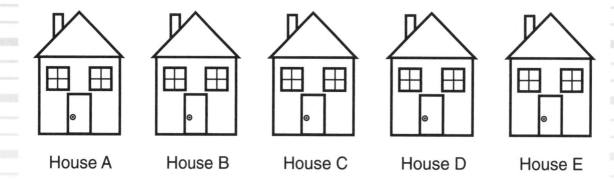

House A   House B   House C   House D   House E

Answers on page 393.

Read the story below, than turn the page and answer the questions.

The detective overheard the jewelry thief tell his accomplice about the different places where he stashed the loot. He said, "The jade figurine is in a box of old magazines in the basement. The ruby is in the pocket of the bathrobe in the closet. The emeralds are in the dining room hutch inside the water pitcher. The opals are underneath the mattress of the bed in the spare room."

HELP THE DETECTIVE (PART II)

(Do not read this until you have read the previous page!)

The investigator overheard the information about where the stolen loot was stored, but didn't have anywhere to write it down! Answer the questions below to help the investigator remember.

1. How many rubies are there?

A. 1

B. 2

C. 3

D. More than 1, but we don't know how many.

2. What is found in a box of old magazines?

A. Jade necklace

B. Jade figurine

C. Emeralds

D. Opals

3. The emeralds are found inside this.

A. Bathrobe pocket

B. Water pitcher

C. Butter dish

D. Carved box

4. The opals are found here.

A. Spare room

B. Dining room

C. Basement

D. Closet

Answers on page 393.

1. If the crime scene technicians did not find a person's fingerprint at the scene of a crime, does that prove they couldn't have been there?

____ Yes

____ No

2. Is "body farm" another word for morgue?

____ Yes

____ No

3. Can a guilty person fool a polygraph test?

____ Yes

____ No

4. Can an innocent person fail a polygraph test?

____ Yes

____ No

5. What does the acronym AFIS stand for?

____ Arson Federal Investigator at the Scene

____ Automated Fingerprint Identification System

____ Automatic Facial Identification System

Answers on page 393.

CRYPTO-LOGIC

Each of the numbers in the sequence below represents a letter. Use the mathematical clues to determine which number stands for which letter and reveal the encrypted word.

Hint: Remember that a / indicates divided by, and that all sums in parentheses must be done first.

15398256

Clues:

R repeats

$R - (R - 1) = T$

$2T = E$

$E \times R = S$

$S + E = L$

$L / 2 = Y$

$3 \times (\frac{1}{2}Y) = C$

$(C-R) \times 2 = K$

$\frac{1}{2}K - T = I$

ROBBER RIDDLE

Cryptograms are messages in substitution code. Break the code to read the riddle and its answer. For example, THE SMART CAT might become FVO QWGDF JGF if **F** is substituted for **T, V** for **H, O** for **E,** and so on.

BWD NXN IWO LJGVQKG TUOS WXH HKMZ BWOS XI
HIKGION IT GKXS?

WO BKH WTUXSV PTG HTRO MWKSVO XS
IWO BOKIWOG.

TREASURE HUNT

The treasure hunter visited eight cities, finding a clue in each one that led her to the treasure in the final city. Can you put the list of the eight cities she visited in order, using the information below?

She went directly from the capital city of one of the smallest countries in Europe to the capital city of the largest country by area in the world.

She went from Tashkent directly to the capital of the United States.

Moscow's clue led her immediately to Oslo.

Montevideo was not one of the first four cities she visited, but she did not find the treasure there.

There were two cities between her visit to Washington, DC, and her visit to Ankara.

There were exactly four cities between her visit to Luxembourg and her visit to New Delhi.

The capital of Norway was one of the first four cities she visited.

Answers on page 393.

A CASE OF ARSON

Change just one letter on each line to go from the top word to the bottom word. Do not change the order of the letters. You must have a common English word at each step.

FIRE

———

———

———

———

CASE

PLANTED EVIDENCE AT THE SCENE

Change just one letter on each line to go from the top word to the bottom word. Do not change the order of the letters. You must have a common English word at each step.

PLANT

———

———

———

SCENE

Answers on page 393.

HOT PURSUIT

You're in hot pursuit of a suspect, but rain has swept through the entire county, flooding all the bridges indicated by circles. Your job is to travel to each location where the criminal has been seen—A through I, in any order—by restoring only 2 of the bridges.

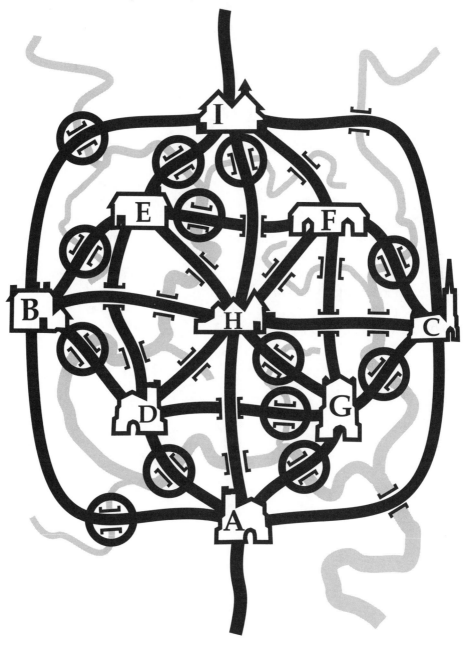

GRAVE ROBBERIES

The state police have been called in to investigate a series of bizarre grave robberies perpetrated in five different cemeteries across Bolton County. Each occurred on a different date and at a different cemetery, none of which were in the same town. Only one grave was robbed in each cemetery. Using only the clues below, help the police solve this mystery by determining the date on which each of the five graves were robbed, as well as the cemetery and town in which each was located.

1. Of the March 20th incident and the one at Dinby Dale Cemetery, one was in Upperdale and the other involved the grave of Ed Lowder.

2. Pat Fowler was interred at Green Lawn Cemetery in Shell City.

3. Holden Bray's grave (which was in either Calvary Cape Cemetery or the cemetery in Verona) was robbed 8 days before the incident in Trenton.

4. Brad Beaudry's grave wasn't robbed on the night of March 20th.

5. Of the two robberies in Upperdale and Shell City, one was at Apple Pine Cemetery and the other was on March 28th.

6. Ed Lowder wasn't buried in Verona.

7. The cemetery in Upperdale was robbed sometime before the one in Wilmette.

	Cemeteries					Graves					Towns				
	Apple Pine	Box Grove	Calvary Cape	Dinby Dale	Green Lawn	Brad Beaudry	Ed Lowder	Holden Bray	Pat Fowler	Ruben Yates	Shell City	Trenton	Upperdale	Verona	Wilmette
Dates March 12th															
March 20th															
March 28th															
April 5th															
April 13th															
Towns Shell City															
Trenton															
Upperdale															
Verona															
Wilmette															
Graves Brad Beaudry															
Ed Lowder															
Holden Bray															
Pat Fowler															
Ruben Yates															

Dates	Cemeteries	Graves	Towns
March 12th			
March 20th			
March 28th			
April 5th			
April 13th			

INTERCEPTION

You've intercepted a message that is meant to reveal a location for an upcoming meeting between two criminal masterminds. The only problem is, the message shows many place names. Can you figure out the right location?

CROATIA

FINLAND

CHILE

GRENADA

GHANA

SAMOA

Answers on page 394.

CRYPTO-LOGIC

Each of the numbers in the sequence below represents a letter. Use the mathematical clues to determine which number stands for which letter and reveal the encrypted word.

Hint: Remember that a / indicates divided by, and that all sums in parentheses must be done first.

5 6 9 4 3 6 1 2

Clues:

I repeats

$I - 1 = S$

$2I = U$

$U / \frac{1}{2} I = P$

$\frac{1}{2} P = Y$

$2 \times Y$ squared $= D$

$\frac{1}{2} Y = F$

$D + F = M$

$P - F = L$

CIPHER TRIVIA

Cryptograms are messages in substitution code. Break the code to read the message. For example, THE SMART CAT might become FVO QWGDF JGF if **F** is substituted for **T, V** for **H, O** for **E,** and so on.

AMXL FSSO GMTLIVW, FSXL WIRHIV ERH VIGIMZIV YWI
XLI WEQI FSSO EW XLI OIC XS XLI GMTLIV. XLI FMFPI
ERH TEVXMGYPEV IHMXMSRW SJ XLI HMGXMSREVC
EVI WSQIXMQIW YWIH FIGEYWI XLIC LEZI QERC ASVHW
EZEMPEFPI. SXLIV TISTPI QMKLX YWI E QSVI SFWGYVI
FSSO JSV ER IBXVE PECIV SJ WIGYVMXC.

Answers on page 394.

MOTEL HIDEOUT

A thief hides out in one of the 45 motel rooms listed in the chart below. The motel's in-house detective received a sheet of four clues, signed "The Logical Thief." Using these clues, the detective found the room number within 15 minutes—but by that time, the thief had fled. Can you find the thief's motel room quicker?

1. Both digits are odd.

2. The first digit is equal to or greater than the second digit.

3. The sum of the digits is 5 or less.

4. The first digit is not divisible by 3.

51	52	53	54	55	56	57	58	59
41	42	43	44	45	46	47	48	49
31	32	33	34	35	36	37	38	39
21	22	23	24	25	26	27	28	29
11	12	13	14	15	16	17	18	19

Answers on page 394.

Study this picture of the crime scene for 1 minute, then turn the page.

WHAT DO YOU SEE? (PART II)

(Do not read this until you have read the previous page!)
Which image exactly matches the crime scene?

1

2

3

4

Answers on page 394.

BUILDING BLUEPRINTS

Using the building blueprints to enter the building, pick up a coded message on the central pathway, and leave the building as quickly as possible.

A

B

TREASURE HUNT

The treasure hunter visited eight cities, finding a clue in each one that led her to the treasure in the final city. Can you put the list of the eight cities she visited in order, using the information below?

The clue in Amsterdam led her immediately to the other city that began with an A.

She visited Skopje immediately before visiting Tokyo.

She did not find the treasure in Lima, Madrid, or Dodoma.

She visited the capital of Peru immediately after visiting the capital of Algeria.

Bangkok was one of the first three cities she visited.

The capital of Spain was the third city she visited.

She visited four other cities between her trips to Dodoma and Skopje.

CRACK THE PASSWORD

A detective has found a memory aid that the criminal left behind, a list of coded passwords. The detective knows that the criminal likes to scramble each password, then remove the same letter from each word. Can you figure out the missing letter and unscramble each word in this set to reveal the passwords?

SINE

PRIMERS

LEARN

MICAS

GEMSTONE MATH

There are 8 types of gems. There is 1 gem of the first type, 2 of the second type, 3 of the third type, 4 of the fourth type, 5 of the fifth type, 6 of the sixth type, 7 of the seventh type, and 8 of the eighth type. From the information given below, can you tell how many gemstones there are of each kind?

There are twice as many garnets as rubies. There are more amethysts than rubies. There are 4 more sapphires than emeralds. There are at least 6 opals. There are fewer diamonds than rubies. There is 1 more pearl than there are garnets. There are twice as many opals as garnets.

Answers on page 395.

FORENSIC CAREERS

Every word listed is contained within the group of letters. Words can be found in a straight line horizontally, vertically, or diagonally. They may be read either forward or backward.

ACCOUNTANT

ANTHROPOLOGIST

BALLISTICS EXPERT

BIOLOGIST

BOTANIST

CHEMIST

COMPUTER ANALYST

DENTIST

DNA ANALYST

DOCUMENTS EXAMINER

ENTOMOLOGIST

INVESTIGATOR

LAB TECHNICIAN

MEDICAL EXAMINER

NURSE

ODONTOLOGY

PATHOLOGIST

PSYCHOLOGIST

SCIENCE TECHNICIAN

TOXICOLOGIST

Y	P	W	Z	B	Z	P	P	R	D	C	H	E	M	I	S	T
G	K	Q	W	P	A	C	C	O	U	N	T	A	N	T	S	V
O	T	J	I	W	U	A	F	F	U	G	T	G	A	I	L	R
L	M	E	D	I	C	A	L	E	X	A	M	I	N	E	R	E
O	L	A	B	T	E	C	H	N	I	C	I	A	N	T	G	N
T	S	I	G	O	L	O	P	O	R	H	T	N	A	U	T	I
N	P	D	G	N	M	Z	V	O	C	O	Y	E	V	V	J	M
O	V	A	U	H	S	O	R	L	B	J	C	U	V	A	K	A
D	T	R	D	E	N	T	O	M	O	L	O	G	I	S	T	X
O	S	I	N	V	E	S	T	I	G	A	T	O	R	P	J	E
E	S	I	G	Q	F	C	E	S	X	M	U	T	Z	A	A	S
P	S	Y	C	H	O	L	O	G	I	S	T	B	F	K	W	T
R	T	S	I	T	N	E	D	Q	D	G	L	N	G	U	S	N
Z	T	H	I	L	P	A	T	H	O	L	O	G	I	S	T	E
P	K	B	N	U	M	D	N	A	A	N	A	L	Y	S	T	M
T	O	X	I	C	O	L	O	G	I	S	T	B	O	D	N	U
T	K	X	R	Q	U	R	R	I	Z	Z	P	H	U	I	W	C
T	S	Y	L	A	N	A	R	E	T	U	P	M	O	C	B	O
T	R	E	P	X	E	S	C	I	T	S	I	L	L	A	B	D
N	A	I	C	I	N	H	C	E	T	E	C	N	E	I	C	S

CRACK THE CODE

The 7 symbols each represent a different number between 1 and 9. The numbers to the right and below the grid show the totals of that row or column. Can you deduce the numerical value of each symbol?

◗	✳	◗	❄	○	✳	■	30
✳	❄	○	◗	✳	◗	✳	26
○	◗	✳	◆	■	✳	◆	39
◗	○	❄	○	❄	◗	✳	16
○	❄	◗	◆	○	✳	✳	27
✳	■	◆	❄	◗	❄	■	39
■	✳	○	◗	◆	■	◆	43
29	29	21	25	26	38	52	

Answers on page 395.

HELP THE DETECTIVE (PART 1)

Read the story below, than turn the page and answer the questions.

The detective overheard the jewelry thief tell her accomplice about the different places where she stashed the loot. She said, "First, the diamond-encrusted watch is in the property on Seventh Street. Second, the ruby bracelet is in the apartment on First Avenue. Third, the emerald tiara is in the shed behind the house on Lake Court. Fourth, the opal necklace is in the townhome on River Street."

HELP THE DETECTIVE (PART II)

(Do not read this until you have read the previous page!)

The investigator overheard the information about where the stolen loot was stored, but didn't have anywhere to write it down! Answer the questions below to help the investigator remember.

1. The diamond-encrusted watch is found at this location.

A. First Street

B. First Avenue

C. Seventh Street

D. Seventh Avenue

2. The emerald tiara is found at this location.

A. Lake Court

B. Lake Street

C. River Court

D. River Street

3. The ruby bracelet is found in this type of building.

A. Apartment

B. Shed

C. House

D. Townhome

4. The opal necklace is found in this type of building.

A. Apartment

B. Shed

C. House

D. Townhome

Answers on page 395.

FIND THE WITNESS

On Baldwin Avenue, there are 5 houses that are identical to each other. You need to follow up with a witness, Joanna Winchell, but without any address on the doors you are not sure which house to approach. You know that Winchell is a single mom and that her daughter Sophie owns a cat. The staff at the ice cream shop around the corner and your own observations give you some clues. From the information given, can you find the right house?

A. Only two children live full-time on the street, and they live next door to each other.

B. The divorced man in house D has custody of his kids ever other weekend.

C. The people in both corner houses have dogs, not cats.

D. Sophie used to come into the ice cream shop with her next door neighbor and babysitter Hannah, but Hannah is off at college now, and her parents are thinking of moving to a smaller place for "empty nesters."

| House A | House B | House C | House D | House E |

WITNESS STATEMENTS

There was a break-in at Sal's jewelry store last night! Police have interviewed five people who claimed to have witnessed the theft, but their stories vary quite a bit. Help the police sort out their statements by matching each witness report to the correct height and weight of the person they saw, and the type of car in which they made their getaway.

1. Of the person Gerald saw and the 190-pound suspect, one was 5'2" and the other drove a Nissan.

2. The man Russell saw was 3 inches shorter than whoever was driving the Toyota, and 6 inches shorter than the 135-pound suspect.

3. Yolanda's suspect was either 5'2" or 5'8" tall.

4. The 190-pound suspect was nine inches shorter than whoever was driving the Mazda.

5. The man driving the Honda appeared to be 5'8" tall.

6. Angela's suspect wasn't 5'5" tall or 160 pounds.

7. The 145-pound suspect wasn't 5'11", and didn't drive the Nissan.

	Witnesses					Weights					Cars				
	Angela S.	Gerald F.	Russell T.	Sarah M.	Yolanda V.	135 lbs	145 lbs	160 lbs	190 lbs	225 lbs	Chevrolet	Honda	Mazda	Nissan	Toyota
Heights 5' 2"															
5' 5"															
5' 8"															
5' 11"															
6' 2"															
Cars Chevrolet															
Honda															
Mazda															
Nissan															
Toyota															
Weights 135 lbs															
145 lbs															
160 lbs															
190 lbs															
225 lbs															

Heights	Witnesses	Weights	Cars
5' 2"			
5' 5"			
5' 8"			
5' 11"			
6' 2"			

Answers on page 396.

MOTEL HIDEOUT

A thief hides out in one of the 45 motel rooms listed in the chart below. The motel's in-house detective received a sheet of four clues, signed "The Logical Thief." Using these clues, the detective found the room number within 15 minutes—but by that time, the thief had fled. Can you find the thief's motel room quicker?

1. Multiply the first digit by 2 to get the second digit.

2. The first digit is a prime number.

3. The second digit is not prime.

4. It is not divisible by 9.

51	52	53	54	55	56	57	58	59
41	42	43	44	45	46	47	48	49
31	32	33	34	35	36	37	38	39
21	22	23	24	25	26	27	28	29
11	12	13	14	15	16	17	18	19

Answers on page 396.

CRIME RHYMES

Each clue leads to a 2-word answer that rhymes, such as BIG PIG or STABLE TABLE. The numbers in parentheses after the clue give the number of letters in each word. For example, "cookware taken from the oven (3, 3)" would be "hot pot."

1. Suspect swore he was getting fast food (3, 5): _____

2. Arsonist who hated musical instruments set this (4, 4): _____

3. Murder at the racetrack (12, 4): _____

4. Cantaloupe thief (5, 5): _____

5. Scoff at idea of using this poison (5, 7): _____

6. Provided poison (8, 7): _____

7. Noisy diamond heist (3, 6): _____

8. When the funeral home thought something might be going on (9, 9):

_____

Answers on page 396.

HOT PURSUIT

You're in hot pursuit of a suspect, but rain has swept through the entire county, flooding all the bridges indicated by circles. Your job is to travel to each location where the criminal has been seen—A through I, in any order—by restoring only 2 of the bridges.

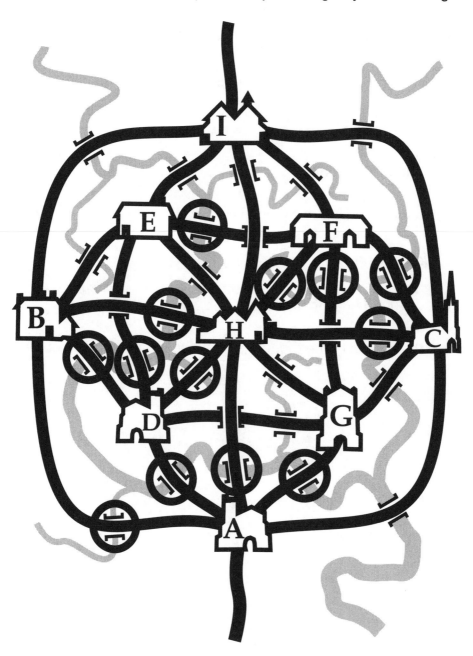

Answers on page 396.

Each of the numbers in the sequence below represents a letter. Use the mathematical clues to determine which number stands for which letter and reveal the encrypted word.

Hint: Remember that a / indicates divided by, and that all sums in parentheses must be done first.

5 9 1 3 7 3 2

Clues:

E repeats

W<R<E

O=H+S

O>H>S

R squared+1=H

O-3=T

T+1=V

Each of the numbers in the sequence below represents a letter. Use the mathematical clues to determine which number stands for which letter and reveal the encrypted word.

Hint: Remember that a / indicates divided by, and that all sums in parentheses must be done first.

7 3 2 1 5

Clues:

D = R – 3

D + I = 7

2G = D

2D = P

10 – P = 2

(R + I) / 2 = T

1/2G = H

THE BODY FARM (PART I)

When will an employee not be reprimanded for laying down on the job? When that worker is a Body Farm recruit. Hundreds of rotting corpses get away with such shenanigans every day at the University of Tennessee's "Body Farm," and they have yet to be written up for it. In fact, they are praised for their profound contributions to science. Read the following information, then turn the page.

Forensic anthropologist William M. Bass had a dream. As an expert in the field of human decomposition, he couldn't fathom why a facility devoted to this under-studied process didn't exist. So, in 1972, working in conjunction with the University of Tennessee, he founded the Body Farm or, more specifically, the University of Tennessee Forensic Anthropology Facility.

If you're going to start a body farm, it doesn't take a forensic anthropologist to realize that there might be a problem in obtaining bodies. One way is to use bodies that have been donated for medical studies. Another focuses on cadavers that rot away each year at medical examiners offices, with nary a soul to claim them. Enter Bass and his associates.

Just outside of Knoxville, the eerie three-acre wooded plot that Bass claimed for his scientific studies—which is surrounded by a razor wire fence (lest the dead bodies try to escape)—is where an unspecified number of cadavers in various states of decomposition are kept. While some hang out completely in the open, others spend their time in shallow graves or entombed in vaults. Others dip their toes and other body parts in ponds. And a few spend eternity inside sealed car trunks.

So why is this done? What can be learned from observing human flesh and bone decay in the hot Tennessee sun? Plenty, according to scientists and members of the media who have studied the Body Farm. "Nearly everything known about the science of human decomposition comes from one place—forensic anthropologist William Bass' Body Farm," declared CNN in high praise of the facility. The bodies are strewn in different positions and under varying circumstances for reasons far from happenstance. Each cadaver will display differing reactions to decomposition, insect and wildlife interference, and the elements. These invaluable indicators can help investigators zero-in on the cause and time of death in current and future criminal cases.

Bass himself claims that knowledge gleaned from Body Farm studies has proven especially helpful to murder investigations. "People will have alibis for certain time periods, and if you can determine death happened at another time, it makes a difference in the court case," said Bass. Even the prestigious FBI uses the Body Farm as a real-world simulator to help train its agents. Every February, representatives visit the site to dig for bodies that farm hands have prepared as simulated crime scenes. "We have five of them down there for them," explains Bass. "They excavate the burials and look for evidence that we put there."

Although many other proposed farms never got off the ground due to community protest, since the inception of Bass's original Body Farm, other facilities have been established, including one at Western Carolina University. Ideally, Bass would like to see body farms all over the nation. Since decaying bodies react differently depending on their climate and surroundings, says Bass, "It's important to gather information from other research facilities across the United States."

Such is life down on the Body Farm.

THE BODY FARM (PART II)

(Do not read this until you have read the previous page!)

1. The Body Farm is the only facility of its kind in the United States.

____ True

____ False

2. One thing studied at the Body Farm is how insects can affect decomposition of cadavers.

____ True

____ False

3. The Body Farm is a training site for investigators.

____ True

____ False

4. Climate can greatly affect decomposition rates.

____ True

____ False

5. The Body Farm was founded in 1942.

____ True

____ False

Answers on page 396.

SPY SCRAMBLE

You're tracking down a mole. You know when he's meeting with his contact to relay information, but you don't know where. However, you've found a list of random words that you think might combine to form an anagram of the location. Can you unscramble the letters and find the meetup details?

DIRT OH ROOF FUSE MUM LINT HEED MORN STAR TIE CON

CRACK THE PASSWORD

A detective has found a memory aid that the criminal left behind, a list of coded passwords. The detective knows that the criminal likes to scramble each password, then remove the same letter from each word. Can you figure out the missing letter and unscramble each word in this set to reveal the passwords?

AROMA

TRANCE

FOAMING

AMICUS

SPY FLY

As an international spy, your mission is to travel from your headquarters at Seth Castle to your safe house at Faro. To disguise your trail, you must stop once—and only once—at each airport. See if you can find the cheapest route for your trip. Less than $260 would make you a Steady Sleuth; less than $250, a Cool Operator; less than $240, a Crafty Agent. If you can make it on $230, then you're a Super Spy!

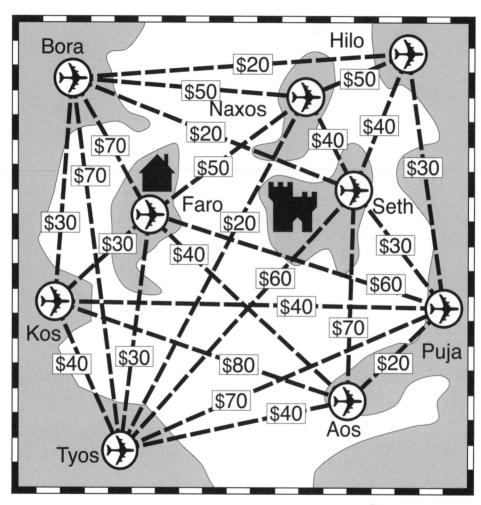

⊕ = Airport
♜ = Start
🏠 = Finish

Answers on page 397.

INTERCEPTION

You've intercepted a message that is meant to reveal a location for an upcoming meeting between two criminal masterminds. The only problem is, the message shows many place names. Can you figure out the right location?

ABUJA

BUDAPEST

ACCRA

DHAKA

JAKARTA

TRIPOLI

SEOUL

ASTANA

ATHENS

Answers on page 397.

CRYPTO-LOGIC

Each of the numbers in the sequence below represents a letter. Use the mathematical clues to determine which number stands for which letter and reveal the encrypted word.

Hint: Remember that a / indicates divided by, and that all sums in parentheses must be done first.

5 4 3 2 1

Clues:

The square root of L is S

S-1=T

TxT=T

2L=U

B+A=U

A+2=B

CRYPTO-LOGIC

Each of the numbers in the sequence below represents a letter. Use the mathematical clues to determine which number stands for which letter and reveal the encrypted word.

Hint: Remember that a / indicates divided by, and that all sums in parentheses must be done first.

8 1 4 4 3

Clues:

R=10

I=(R/2)-3

2I=E

E/E=W

E-W=T

2T=L

L+I=S

Answers on page 397.

Cryptograms are messages in substitution code. Break the code to read the message. For example, THE SMART CAT might become FVO QWGDF JGF if F is substituted for **T, V** for **H, O** for **E,** and so on.

OJP GJKYMP, "HO HM Y KHRRBP UKYGGPR HC Y AXMOPKX UKYGGPR HCMHRP YC PCHLAY" UYM NHKMO MYHR VX MHK UHCMOEC TJQKTJHBB HC Y KYRHE YRRKPMM HC 1939. JP UYM MGPYDHCL EN KQMMHY'M QCGKPRHTOYVHBHOX, MYXHCL, "H TYCCEO NEKPTYMO OE XEQ OJP YTOHEC EN KQMMHY."

Cryptograms are messages in substitution code. Break the code to read the message. For example, THE SMART CAT might become FVO QWGDF JGF if F is substituted for **T, V** for **H, O** for **E,** and so on.

HNVCHGYW IBDEGK CSEWYU KHY CEGK BA IBKH JEV JCEUY, IEJYU BZ UEJHLYSS HEVVYKK'J ALOKLBZES UYKYOKLQY LZ "KHY VESKYJY AESOBZ," EZU CHLSLC VEGSBRY, CGBKEDBZLJK BA GEWVBZU OHEZUSYG'J "KHY ILD JSYYC."

MOTEL HIDEOUT

A thief hides out in one of the 45 motel rooms listed in the chart below. The motel's in-house detective received a sheet of four clues, signed "The Logical Thief." Using these clues, the detective found the room number within 15 minutes—but by that time, the thief had fled. Can you find the thief's motel room quicker?

1. It is a prime number.

2. It is less than 40.

3. The sum of the digits is greater than 8.

4. The second digit is less than nine.

51	52	53	54	55	56	57	58	59
41	42	43	44	45	46	47	48	49
31	32	33	34	35	36	37	38	39
21	22	23	24	25	26	27	28	29
11	12	13	14	15	16	17	18	19

Answers on page 397.

CRACK THE CODE

The 7 symbols each represent a different number between 1 and 9. The numbers to the right and below the grid show the totals of that row or column. Can you deduce the numerical value of each symbol?

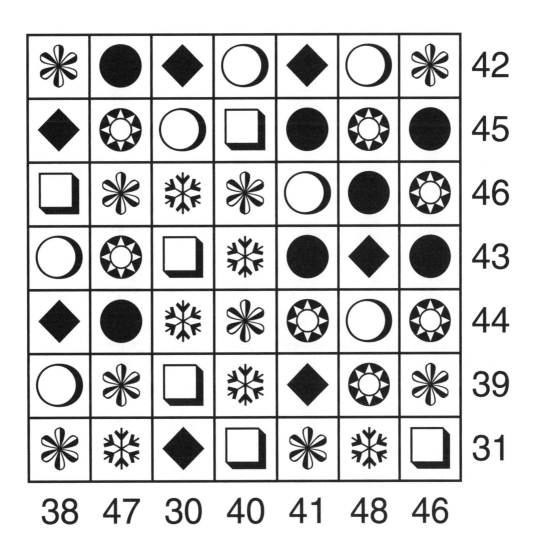

Answers on page 397.

POP QUIZ: FORENSIC SCIENCE

1. A Chinese book from the 13th century, Hsi DuanYu (the Washing Away of Wrongs) described this:

____ how to tell drowning from strangulation

____ how to tell drowning from natural death

____ how to tell heart attack from strangulation

2. The first instance of bullet comparison being used to solve a murder occurred in this century:

____ 1600s

____ 1700s

____ 1800s

____ 1900s

3. In the U.S., the first use of DNA evidence to solve a crime occurred in this decade.

____ 1970s

____ 1980s

____ 1990s

4. Scientist Karl Landsteiner established that there were different blood types in this decade.

____ 1830s

____ 1900s

____ 1970s

5. The FBI was founded in this year.

____ 1888

____ 1908

____ 1932

Answers on page 397.

HELP THE DETECTIVE (PART 1)

Read the story below, than turn the page and answer the questions.

The detective overheard the jewelry thief tell his accomplice about the different places where he stashed the loot. He said, "The diamond is in the canister full of loose tea. The emerald is in the refill bottle of liquid soap in the half bathroom. The ruby is inside the winter boot in the hall closet. The garnet ring is taped to the back of the spice rack."

HELP THE DETECTIVE (PART II)

(Do not read this until you have read the previous page!)

The investigator overheard the information about where the stolen loot was stored, but didn't have anywhere to write it down! Answer the questions below to help the investigator remember.

1. The diamond is found in a canister containing this.

A. Tea

B. Coffee beans

C. Spices

D. Soap

2. What is found taped to the spice rack?

A. Diamond

B. Emerald

C. Ruby

D. Garnet

3. The ruby is found here.

A. A shoe in the bedroom closet.

B. A winter boot in the bedroom closet.

C. A winter boot in the hall closet.

D. A sneaker in the hall closet.

4. The emerald is found here.

A. A bottle of liquid soap.

B. A bottle of liquid shampoo.

C. A bottle of laundry detergent.

D. In the bathroom, but we don't know a more specific location.

Answers on page 398.

FINGERPRINT MATCH

Find one or more fingerprints that match the one in the box.

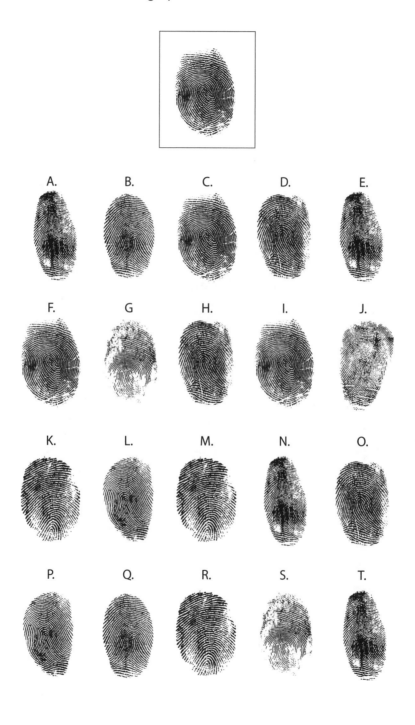

A.   B.   C.   D.   E.

F.   G   H.   I.   J.

K.   L.   M.   N.   O.

P.   Q.   R.   S.   T.

Answers on page 398.

FIND THE WITNESS

On Box Street, there are 5 adjacent houses that are identical to each other. You've been asked to visit Mr. Foreman, but without any addresses on the doors, you are not sure which house to approach. At the local coffee shop, you ask the waitress for help. She is able to provide the following information:

1. Two of the 5 houses contain children and adults.

2. Mr. Foreman lives alone.

3. Both houses with children have 2 neighboring properties and are not adjacent to each other.

4. The children often pass through Mrs. Cato's garden to play with each other.

5. The residents of the house located 2 spots to the right of Mrs. Cato's get along well with everyone on the street.

Which house does Mr. Foreman live in?

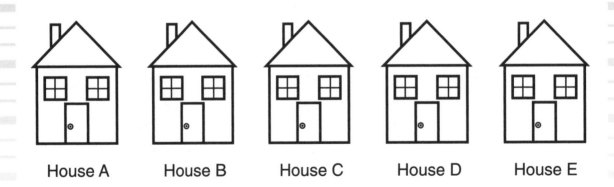

House A   House B   House C   House D   House E

Answers on page 398.

WHAT DO YOU SEE? (PART 1)

Study this picture of the crime scene for 1 minute, then turn the page.

WHAT DO YOU SEE? (PART II)

(Do not read this until you have read the previous page!)
Which image exactly matches the crime scene?

1

2

3

4

Answers on page 398.

IDENTITY PARADE

Oops! Four mug shots were accidentally sent through the shredder, and Officer Barry is trying to straighten them out. Currently, only one facial feature in each row is in its correct place. Officer Barry knows that:

1. C's eyes are one place to the left of his mouth.

2. B's mouth is not next to C's mouth.

3. A's nose is one place to the left of D's hair.

4. B's eyes are on the same face as A's mouth, and are one place to the right of B's hair.

5. B's nose is one place to the right of his mouth.

Can you find the correct hair, eyes, nose, and mouth for each suspect?

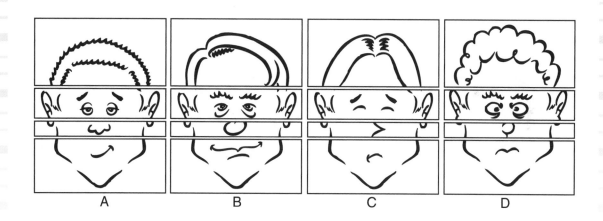

A   B   C   D

INTERNATIONAL FUGITIVES

This was a busy week for Interpol, the international law enforcement agency. Five different criminals from the international "10 Most Wanted" list were apprehended, each in a different country and on a different day. None of the five committed the same crime. Using only the clues below, match each captured fugitive to his crime, and determine the date and location (country) in which he was finally apprehended.

1. Cal Calumnet wasn't apprehended in France.

2. The robbery suspect was captured 3 days before Ben Blackforth.

3. Gil Grendle was wanted for either robbery or arson.

4. Of Ben Blackforth and whoever was captured on October 7th, one was wanted for the arson and the other was tracked down in Sweden.

5. The October 5th capture was of either Cal Calumnet or the man wanted for tax evasion.

6. The forger was captured 2 days before the arrest in Uganda.

7. The arrest in France occurred sometime after that of Dale Dornmer.

8. Neither Dale Dornmer nor Cal Calumnet was captured in Peru.

	Criminals					Crimes					Countries				
	Blackforth	Calumnet	Dornmer	Filcher	Grendle	Arson	Blackmail	Forgery	Robbery	Tax evasion	France	Moldova	Peru	Sweden	Uganda
Dates October 3															
October 4															
October 5															
October 6															
October 7															
Countries France															
Moldova															
Peru															
Sweden															
Uganda															
Crimes Arson															
Blackmail															
Forgery															
Robbery															
Tax evasion															

Dates	Criminals	Crimes	Countries
October 3			
October 4			
October 5			
October 6			
October 7			

Cryptograms are messages in substitution code. Break the code to read the message. For example, THE SMART CAT might become FVO QWGDF JGF if **F** is substituted for **T, V** for **H, O** for **E,** and so on.

RUDUTYSJ QHDEBT KIUT Q REEA SYFXUH JE IUDT CUIIQWUI TKHYDW JXU QCUHYSQD HULEBKJYED. XU KIUT Q REEA SQBBUT SECCUDJQHYUI ED JXU BQMI EV UDWBQDT RO MYBBYQC RBQSAIJEDU.

Cryptograms are messages in substitution code. Break the code to read the message. For example, THE SMART CAT might become FVO QWGDF JGF if **F** is substituted for **T, V** for **H, O** for **E,** and so on.

ONF YNABXWB LJW KN VJMN CX KNURNEN CQJC RC RB WXC ZDRCN JW NJBH CQRWP CX RWENWC J VNCQXM XO BNLANC FARCRWP FQRLQ BQJUU KJOOUN RWENBCRPJCRXW. HNC RC VJH KN AXDWMUH JBBNACNM CQJC QDVJW RWPNWDRCH LJWWXC LXWLXLC J LRYQNA FQRLQ QDVJW RWPNWDRCH LJWWXC ANBXUEN.

—NMPJA JUUJW YXN

Answers on page 398.

HOT PURSUIT

You're in hot pursuit of a suspect, but rain has swept through the entire county, flooding all the bridges indicated by circles. Your job is to travel to each location where the criminal has been seen—A through I, in any order—by restoring only 2 of the bridges.

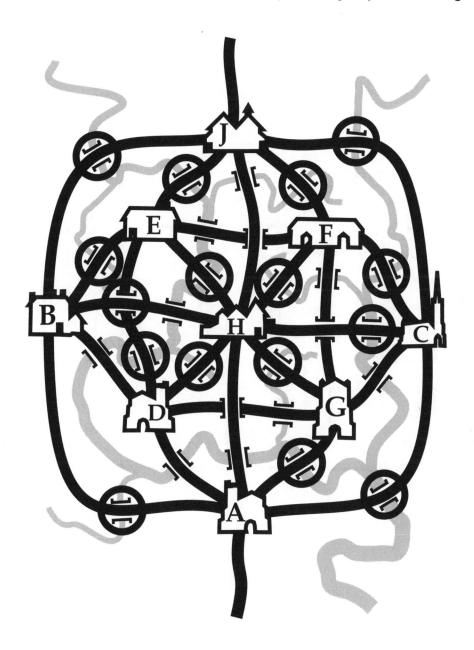

BUILDING BLUEPRINTS

You're following a criminal through a building of twists and turns. Find the most direct route to catch the criminal in time.

START

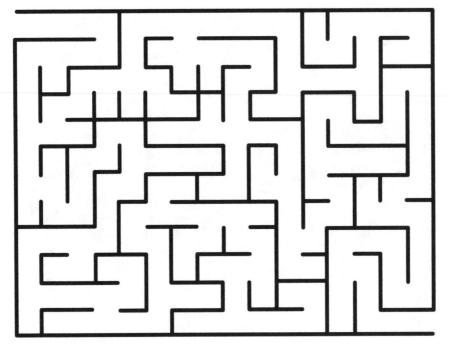

FINISH

Answers on page 399.

SPY FLY

As an international spy, your mission is to travel from your headquarters at Seth Castle to your safe house at Faro. To disguise your trail, you must stop once—and only once—at each airport. See if you can find the cheapest route for your trip. Less than $310 would make you a Steady Sleuth; less than $300, a Cool Operator; less than $290, a Crafty Agent. If you can make it on $280, then you're a Super Spy!

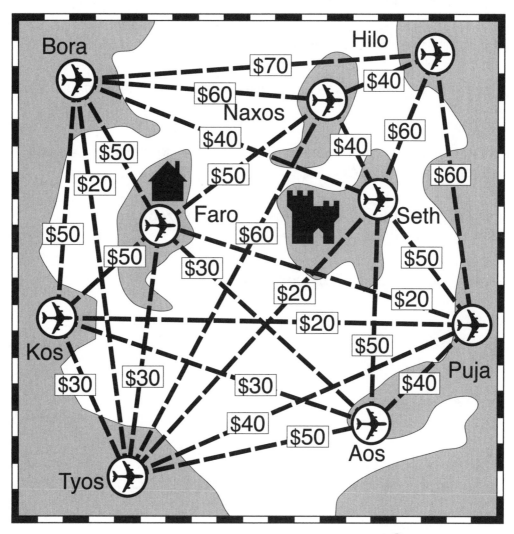

⊕ = Airport
♜ = Start
🏠 = Finish

TREASURE HUNT

The treasure hunter visited eight cities, finding a clue in each one that led her to the treasure in the final city. Can you put the list of the eight cities she visited in order, using the information below?

She began in one of the two cities on the West coast.

The two cities in Texas were not visited sequentially.

Chicago was one of the first three cities visited, and was visited before either Texas city.

After visiting Dallas, she went to one other city before Boston, and neither were the first or final destination.

After going to Los Angeles, the treasure hunter visited two other cities before arriving in St. Louis.

Boston was visited immediately before Tallahassee.

Portland was visited after Austin, but not immediately, and sometime before Tallahassee.

Answers on page 399.

CRYPTO-LOGIC

Each of the numbers in the sequence below represents a letter. Use the mathematical clues to determine which number stands for which letter and reveal the encrypted word.

Hint: Remember that a / indicates divided by, and that all sums in parentheses must be done first.

8 4 9 3 2 1 7

Clues:

O squared = O + O

1/2 O = V

P + V = 10

P − O = E

2R = T

2P / 3 = T

R + (R / 3) = M

2M = I

CRYPTO-LOGIC

Each of the numbers in the sequence below represents a letter. Use the mathematical clues to determine which number stands for which letter and reveal the encrypted word.

4 9 1 4 3 8 5

Clues:

I squared = E

(E + 1) / U = G

2A = U

A = 2

G = R + A

R repeats

N = 2R

CRIME STINKS

Change just one letter on each line to go from the top word to the bottom word. Do not change the order of the letters. You must have a common English word at each step.

CRIME

———

———

———

———

———

———

STINK

HEROES

Cryptograms are messages in substitution code. Break the code to read the message. For example, THE SMART CAT might become FVO QWGDF JGF if **F** is substituted for **T, V** for **H, O** for **E,** and so on.

TKQZJX OFQCT OMQ Z, M XQFKH FR ISFIGMO ZJTZMJY KYDT GSDZQ CMJXKMXD GF IQDMGD IFTDY RFQ GSD KJZGDT YGMGDY AZCZGMQE GSMG IFKCT JFG BD TDIZHSDQDT BE GSD FHHFYZJX YZTD. TKQZJX OFQCT OMQ ZZ, JMLMVF YFCTZDQY, HQZAMQZCE AMQZJDY, MCYF BDIMAD IFTD GMCWDQY ZJ GSD RZXSG MXMZJYG SZGCDQ MJT GSD MPZY HFODQY.

CRACK THE CODE

The 7 symbols each represent a different number between 1 and 9. The numbers to the right and below the grid show the totals of that row or column. Can you deduce the numerical value of each symbol?

❖	✹	◗	○	■	❖	■	25
■	✹	■	✹	◗	○	❖	27
❄	■	❄	❖	✹	✹	❄	37
○	◗	✹	✹	❖	❄	○	26
◗	✹	○	❖	■	◗	✹	26
✹	✹	◗	○	❄	✹	■	31
❖	❄	○	✹	✹	◗	❄	31
30	29	34	16	32	28	34	

Answers on page 399.

MEDICAL EXAMINERS

Every name listed is contained within the group of letters. Names can be found in a straight line horizontally, vertically, or diagonally. They may be read either forward or backward.

AL ROBBINS (CSI: Crime Scene Investigation)

ALEXX WOODS (CSI: Miami)

CAMILLE SAROYAN (Bones)

DAVID PHILLIPS (CSI: Crime Scene Investigation)

ELIZABETH RODGERS (Law and Order franchise)

EVE LOCKHART (Waking the Dead)

FELIX GIBSON (Waking the Dead)

FRANKIE WHARTON (Waking the Dead)

GERALD JACKSON (NCIS)

JIMMY PALMER (NCIS)

JORDAN CAVANAUGH (Crossing Jordan)

JULIANNA COX (Homicide)

KAY SCARPETTA (Patricia Cornwell's book series)

LORETTA WADE (NCIS: New Orleans)

MAURA ISLES (Rizzoli and Isles)

MAX BERGMAN (Hawaii Five-O)

MELINDA WARNER (Law and Order: SVU)

QUINCY (Quincy, M.E.)

ROSE SCHWARTZ (NCIS: Los Angeles)

```
L M K C A M I L L E S A R O Y A N
N O S N K A Y S C A R P E T T A D
O F R E N O S K C A J D L A R E G
T O T E L X O C A N N A I L U J Y
R R A G T S F Y F L E K Z D P C C
A L A L L T I M S Q V J A U G M H
H L W H H Q A A A B G X B F S E G
W N E A K B U W R X K H E E P L U
E P P X B C F I A U B R T L V I A
I N Y E X P O P N D A E H I X N N
K Z U R W W Q L M C E M R X G D A
N A J H I N O T E P Y L O G F A V
A L B O N Y E O Q V S A D I M W A
R R E T O A K N D A E P G B M A C
F O D E E X G C O S H Y E S D R N
J B C S Z X G E G O Y M R O Q N A
S B L P H W E I M V Y M S N D E D
Y I S P I L L I H P D I V A D R R
T N P G J D Q P Q R O J F D X B O
Y S Q R O S E S C H W A R T Z L J
```

MOTEL HIDEOUT

A thief hides out in one of the 45 motel rooms listed in the chart below. The motel's in-house detective received a sheet of four clues, signed "The Logical Thief." Using these clues, the detective found the room number within 15 minutes—but by that time, the thief had fled. Can you find the thief's motel room quicker?

1. It is not divisible by 5.

2. It is divisible by 3.

3. The first digit is larger than the second.

4. The second digit is greater than 2.

51	52	53	54	55	56	57	58	59
41	42	43	44	45	46	47	48	49
31	32	33	34	35	36	37	38	39
21	22	23	24	25	26	27	28	29
11	12	13	14	15	16	17	18	19

Answers on page 400.

SPY SCRAMBLE

You're tracking down a mole, and you've found a list of 5 days or dates and landmarks where the mole will be—but the information for each meetup is scrambled together. The letters are in order but not consecutive. Can you decipher the meeting times and places?

1. EJIFUFNETELTWOEWLVEER

Day/date: _____

Location: _____

2. ISDTEOSNOEFHMEANRGCHE

Day/date: _____

Location: _____

3. TONOPOFVEMMOBERUNTHITRTIFUETHJI

Day/date: _____

Location: _____

4. CHOALOSSLLOWEUMEEN

Day/date: _____

Location: _____

5. NEMXATTCHUUESPDICACHYU

Day/date: _____

Location: _____

MARKED BILLS

The local police have been tracking a series of marked bills that were stolen during a recent string of bank robberies, in an effort to capture the perpetrators. So far, five such bills have been located. Each was used in a different place and on a different day, and each bill was of a different denomination (such as a $10 or a $20). Using only the clues below, match each marked bill to the date and location in which it was spent, and determine the serial number and denomination of each one.

1. C-918303 was used 8 days after the bill that popped up in Midvale.

2. The $100 bill wasn't spent on April 13th.

3. P-101445 was either the $20 bill or the one used on April 5.

4. The $5 bill with the serial number B-492841 was used 4 days after F-667280, but not in Finsberg.

5. The Midvale bill was used 4 days after G-718428 was passed somewhere in Torbin.

6. The marked $20 bill was spent 4 days after the one in Nettleton.

7. Neither the $10 bill nor the $100 bill was used on April 1st.

		Serials					Locations					Denominations				
		B-492841	C-918303	F-667280	G-718428	P-101445	Finsberg	Midvale	Nettleton	Torbin	Uteville	$5	$10	$20	$50	$100
Dates	April 1															
	April 5															
	April 9															
	April 13															
	April 17															
Denominations	$5															
	$10															
	$20															
	$50															
	$100															
Locations	Finsberg																
	Midvale																
	Nettleton																
	Torbin																
	Uteville																

Dates	Serials	Locations	Denominations
April 1			
April 5			
April 9			
April 13			
April 17			

CRYPTO-LOGIC

Each of the numbers in the sequence below represents a letter. Use the mathematical clues to determine which number stands for which letter and reveal the encrypted word.

Hint: Remember that a / indicates divided by, and that all sums in parentheses must be done first.

649157

Clues:

$A = 8$

$A / B = 4$

$A / 2B = 2I$

$4I = E$

$1 \frac{1}{2} E = G$

$G + E = R$

$R / 2 = U$

$R - 1 = N$

$N - 2I = S$

IN PLAIN SIGHT

Cryptograms are messages in substitution code. Break the code to read the message. For example, THE SMART CAT might become FVO QWGDF JGF if **F** is substituted for **T, V** for **H, O** for **E,** and so on.

LSIQ UVY KVQKIDA UVYB FICCDPI WQ DQVJSIB NVBF
VN JIMJ—NVB IMDFRAI, SWGWQP WQNVBFDJWVQ
WQ D PBVKIBU AWCJ VB D KADCCWNWIG DG—WJ WC
KDAAIG CJIPDQVPBDRSU. LBWJWQP D FICCDPI WQ
WQEWCWHAI WQX DQG LBWJWQP D BIPYADB FICCDPI
VEIB WJ WC VQI NVBF VN CJIPDQVPBDRSU.

HOT PURSUIT

You're in hot pursuit of a suspect, but rain has swept through the entire county, flooding all the bridges indicated by circles. Your job is to travel to each location where the criminal has been seen—A through I, in any order—by restoring only 2 of the bridges.

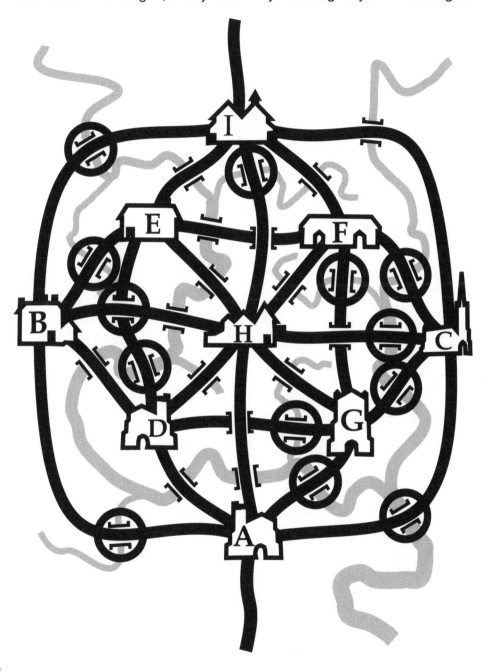

SPY SCRAMBLE

You're tracking down a mole, and you've found a list of 5 cities and times when the mole's flight will arrive in that city—but the information for each meetup is scrambled together. The letters are in order but not consecutive. Can you decipher the cities and times?

1. BLUAESNOTSFALIIRGEHST

Where: _____

When: _____

2. SISNUGNARPIOSREE

Where: _____

When: _____

3. ELSEYVDNEENYAM

Where: _____

When: _____

4. MCHIIDCNAIGGHOT

Where: _____

When: _____

5. FIJFTOHEENAHUNNDNEREDSHBOUURRGS

Where: _____

When: _____

Answers on page 400.

SPY FLY

As an international spy, your mission is to travel from your headquarters at Seth Castle to your safe house at Faro. To disguise your trail, you must stop once—and only once—at each airport. See if you can find the cheapest route for your trip. Less than $300 would make you a Steady Sleuth; less than $290, a Cool Operator; less than $280, a Crafty Agent. If you can make it on $270, then you're a Super Spy!

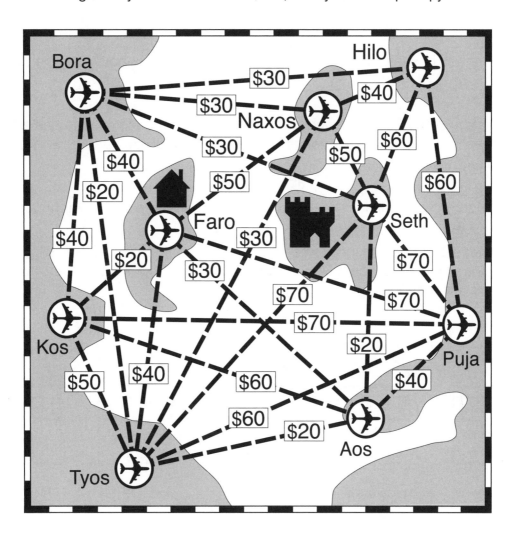

⊕ = Airport
🏰 = Start
🏠 = Finish

Answers on page 401.

FIND THE WITNESS

On Carbon Lane, there are 5 houses that are identical to each other. You need to follow up with a witness to a car accident on his street, Manuel Rodriguez, but without any address on the doors you are not sure which house to approach. You know that from a previous statement that Rodriguez lives with his wife and at least one daughter. The staff at the corner bar and your own observations give you some clues. From the information given, can you find the right house?

A. There are two houses where the only kids are boys. One is house A. The other is either house C or house D.

B. There is a widow who lives by herself somewhere on the block, who has said she loves what her next door neighbors do with their garden and how they get their daughters involved.

C. The couple without children has children living on either side of their house.

D. Mr. Rodriguez said at the initial interview that he didn't think that the neighbors on either side of him were home when the car accident happened, as they would have been at work or school.

House A   House B   House C   House D   House E

Answers on page 401.

TREASURE HUNT

The treasure hunter visited eight cities, finding a clue in each one that led him to the treasure in the final city. Can you put the list of the eight cities he visited in order, using the information below?

1. The treasure hunter proceeded directly from Maryland to Wisconsin.

2. San Diego was one of the final four cities.

3. Oklahoma City was one of the first four cities.

4. The treasure hunter did not begin his search in Topeka, Milwaukee, or Boise.

5. The treasure hunter did not end his search in Charleston, Oklahoma City, or Baltimore.

6. After Milwaukee, he visited exactly two other cities before visiting Atlanta.

7. After Oklahoma City, he visited exactly two other cities before visiting San Diego.

8. South Carolina was visited immediately before Kansas.

9. The city whose name begins with a C was visited before the cities beginning with A or B.

10. The treasure hunter stopped in Idaho sometime after California but before Georgia.

BUILDING BLUEPRINTS

You've found a set of the building blueprints for the criminal's lair. But there are some false ones in the pile, too! Only one of the 3 pieces (labeled A, B, and C) will allow you to go from start to finish without getting stuck. Which one is it?

START →   → END

A

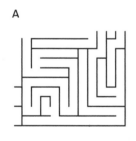

B

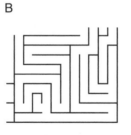

C

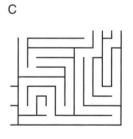

Answers on page 401.

ALL SECRET PLOTS LEAVE CLUES

Change just one letter on each line to go from the top word to the bottom word. Do not change the order of the letters. You must have a common English word at each step.

PLOTS

———————

———————

———————

———————

———————

CLUES

CRYPTO-LOGIC

Each of the numbers in the sequence below represents a letter. Use the mathematical clues to determine which number stands for which letter and reveal the encrypted word.

Hint: Remember that a / indicates divided by, and that all sums in parentheses must be done first.

7 3 5 3 9 6 2 8 3

Clues:

The value equal to the number of times it is present represents E

T squared is 12E

I squared + I = T

P - S = V

V = 2 x I squared

S x P = P

D + C = P + E

D > T

RACE TO A SOLUTION

Cryptograms are messages in substitution code. Break the code to read the message. For example, THE SMART CAT might become FVO QWGDF JGF if **F** is substituted for **T, V** for **H, O** for **E,** and so on.

WDQGN WI GWNFX PWNGGN WO W CJPEGX,
LBPE DNWIPBO SGPWHG W HXOQGNX
IJTGFBOQ. QYG HXOQGNBGO BI YBO KJKRFWN
SGOQOGFFBIA IJTGFO JDQGI YWL W PJIIGPQBJI
QJ QYG SNBQBOY NWPBIA UJNFL.

A LADY OF MYSTERY

Cryptograms are messages in substitution code. Break the code to read the message. For example, THE SMART CAT might become FVO QWGDF JGF if **F** is substituted for **T, V** for **H, O** for **E,** and so on.

Z.P. JDRTF, HWCU ZEVOOGF PWCWIEV JDRTF, QDF
D HCGIGFE LCGRT QCGITC. ETC ZCWIDBWUGFI
QDF ZWOGLT LWRRDUPTC DPDR PDOBOGTFE, QEW
DOFW QCWIT ZWTICV. FET QDF BGNTU IET IGIOT WX
HDCWUTFF ODITC GU OGXT.

HOT PURSUIT

You're in hot pursuit of a suspect, but rain has swept through the entire county, flooding all the bridges indicated by circles. Your job is to travel to each location where the criminal has been seen—A through I, in any order—by restoring only 2 of the bridges.

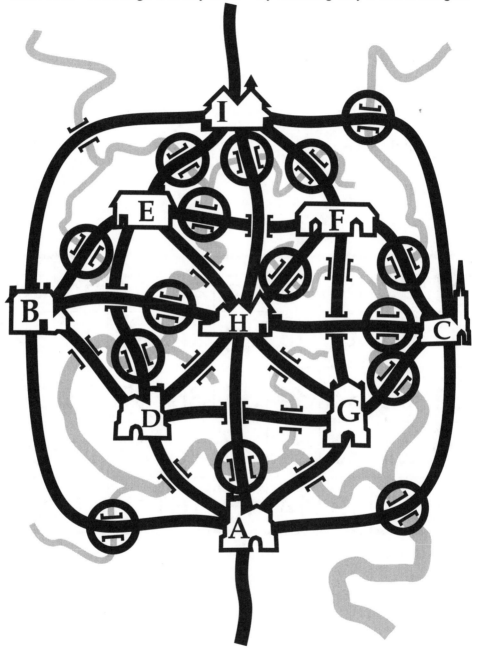

MOTEL HIDEOUT

A thief hides out in one of the 45 motel rooms listed in the chart below. The motel's in-house detective received a sheet of four clues, signed "The Logical Thief." Using these clues, the detective found the room number within 15 minutes—but by that time, the thief had fled. Can you find the thief's motel room quicker?

1. The sum of the digits is less than 6.

2. The first digit is not 4.

3. The second digit is not 2.

4. It is divisible by 2.

51	52	53	54	55	56	57	58	59
41	42	43	44	45	46	47	48	49
31	32	33	34	35	36	37	38	39
21	22	23	24	25	26	27	28	29
11	12	13	14	15	16	17	18	19

Answers on page 402.

Read the story below, than turn the page and answer the questions.

The detective overheard the jewelry thief tell his accomplice about the different places where he stashed the loot. He said, "The rubies are taped underneath the bathroom sink on the first floor. The pearls are in a box in the hall closet on the second floor. The emeralds are underneath the carpet in the den on the third floor. The opals are in a trunk in the attic."

HELP THE DETECTIVE (PART II)

(Do not read this until you have read the previous page!)

The investigator overheard the information about where the stolen loot was stored, but didn't have anywhere to write it down! Answer the questions below to help her remember.

1. On which floor are the pearls found?

_____

2. Which gems are found underneath the bathroom sink?

_____

3. Where will you find the emeralds?

_____

4. Which gems are found in a trunk?

_____

Answers on page 402.

CRACK THE CODE

The 7 symbols each represent a different number between 1 and 9. The numbers to the right and below the grid show the totals of that row or column. Can you deduce the numerical value of each symbol?

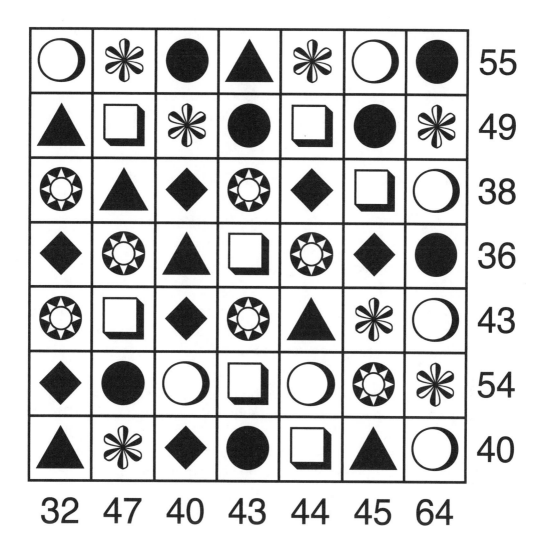

REMEMBERING THE SCENE (PART 1)

You will be grilled on the witness stand for your testimony in the case, and you'll want to answer each question promptly, accurately, and thoroughly. Read over your case notes, then turn the page and see how much you remember.

The burglary and assault took place on Monday morning, March 14. The homeowner, Daniel J. Farsnooth, had been knocked out by burglars when he returned home after his morning run, interrupting the in-progress burglary. They subsequently fled the scene of the crime.

Farsnooth lives alone. He has owned the house for three years. He runs regularly at the same time every morning (leaving his house approximately 6:30 AM, returning 7:15 AM, before leaving again for work at 8 AM).

There was blood (Farsnooth's) in the foyer in three different locations.

An umbrella stand had been knocked over in the struggle.

Three hairs were found that might belong to the robbers.

One partial muddy shoeprint had been left on the entryway rug; it did not match any of the shoes in Farsnooth's closet, but he had had friends over on Sunday for a barbecue and said it could have been left on Sunday.

According to Farsnooth, all missing items in the house had been taken from the living room. He listed the following items as stolen: one DVD player; 3 DVDs (The Martian; Star Wars: The Force Awakens; Captain America: Civil War); stack of mail, including a credit card application and multiple ads; decorative clock, approximate value $75-100; one laptop. The TV had been moved to the edge of its stand.

According to Farsnooth, the front door was closed but probably not locked when he returned to the house after running. He went to unlock it automatically, but he noted that the door did not open when he did so, and he had to try again. This led him to believe later that it had been unlocked and was the point of entry for the thieves. There were no other signs of forced entry at any of the doors.

He had not seen anything out of place when he approached the house. There was no car parked in his driveway. There were multiple cars parked in the street, but he noted none that seemed out of place. He did not remember specifics about any of the cars on the street.

When he entered the house, he heard voices and saw two people wearing black ski masks, dressed in black, rushing at him. After a scuffle, one of them hit him on the head, and he fell down. The robbers ran past him through the open front door and fled on foot. He heard a car start up shortly afterward. He identified their voices as male, no accent. They were both of medium height and slim build.

REMEMBERING THE SCENE (PART II)

(Do not read this until you have read the previous page!)

1. How many DVDs were stolen?

A. 1

B. 2

C. 3

D. 4

2. The TV was stolen as well.

_____ True

_____ False

3. A partial fingerprint was found in the foyer.

_____ True

_____ False

4. Farsnooth's wife was away on vacation when the robbers came.

_____ True

_____ False

5. How many robbers were there?

A. 1

B. 2

C. 3

D. Unknown

6. A clock was stolen. What was its approximate value?

A. $10

B. $50

C. $75

D. $500

Answers on page 402.

WHAT DO YOU SEE? (PART 1)

Study this picture of the crime scene for 1 minute, then turn the page.

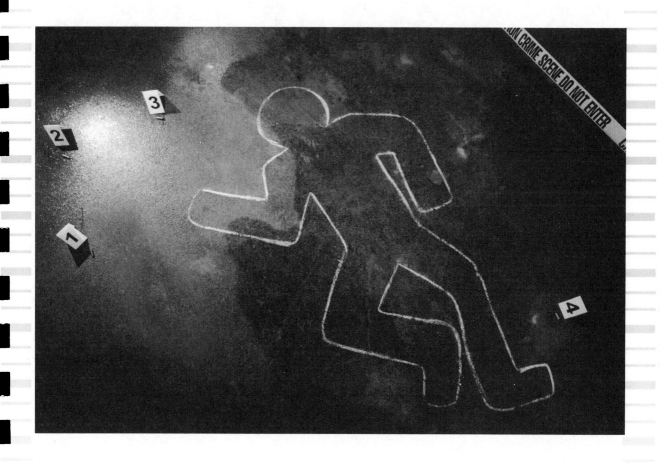

WHAT DO YOU SEE? (PART II)

(Do not read this until you have read the previous page!)
Which image exactly matches the crime scene?

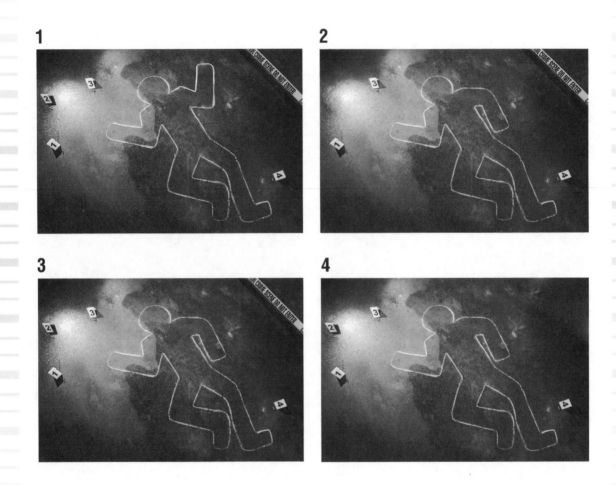

1

2

3

4

Answers on page 402.

FIND THE WITNESS

On Box Street, there are 5 adjacent houses that are identical to each other. You've been asked to visit Mr. Stark, but without any addresses on the doors you are not sure which house to approach. At the local coffee shop, you ask the waitress for help. She is able to provide the following information:

A. There are always decorations in House B's windows and in one of the houses adjacent to it.

B. Mr. Stark hates decorations.

C. The occupants of House E keep to themselves.

D. Mr. Stark's girlfriend lives in House C, but they don't live together.

E. Mr. Stark and his girlfriend think alike in all regards.

House A

House B

House C

House D

House E

PARADE PARKING

Even though signs were posted all over the city warning people not to park on certain streets because of the upcoming parade, the Polksville police department still towed 5 cars as a result of parking violations. Each of the 5 was picked up on a different street and at a different time, and each was a different brand of automobile. Using only the following clues, determine the brand and license plate for each car as well as when and where it was picked up.

1. The car picked up on Park Street was towed sometime after the Subaru.

2. The first car to be towed this morning was the Alfa Romeo.

3. Of the car that was illegally parked in Mitre Square and the one picked up at 6:15 am (which didn't have a license plate ending in P09), one was the Cadillac and the other had the license plate beginning with A14.

4. The car that was picked up on Bolero Court didn't have a Q in its license plate.

5. The car picked up on Racine Boulevard didn't have a J in its license plate.

6. The Subaru was towed sometime after the Cadillac (which didn't have the license plate beginning with BYS).

7. Of the Hyundai and the car with the license plate ending in 01C, one was picked up at Park Street and the other at Bolero Court.

8. Neither the Isuzu, the car picked up on First Street (which was not the Isuzu), nor the car with the A14-S1D license plates were the first to be towed.

9. The last car to be towed did not have the A14-S1D license plates.

		License Plates					Locations					Brands				
		A14-S1D	BYS-81S	JIB-P09	QE2-01C	XR6-192	Bolero Ct.	First St.	Mitre Sq.	Park St.	Racine Blvd.	Alfa Romeo	Cadillac	Hyundai	Isuzu	Subaru
Times	6:10 A.M.															
	6:15 A.M.															
	6:20 A.M.															
	6:25 A.M.															
	6:30 A.M.															
Brands	Alfa Romeo															
	Cadillac															
	Hyundai															
	Isuzu															
	Subaru															
Locations	Bolero Ct.															
	First Sq.															
	Mitre Sq.															
	Park St.															
	Racine Blvd.															

Times	License Plates	Locations	Brands
6:10 A.M.			
6:15 A.M.			
6:20 A.M.			
6:25 A.M.			
6:30 A.M.			

SPY FLY

As an international spy, your mission is to travel from your headquarters at Seth Castle to your safe house at Faro. To disguise your trail, you must stop once—and only once—at each airport. See if you can find the cheapest route for your trip. Less than $290 would make you a Steady Sleuth; less than $280, a Cool Operator; less than $270, a Crafty Agent. If you can make it on $260, then you're a Super Spy!

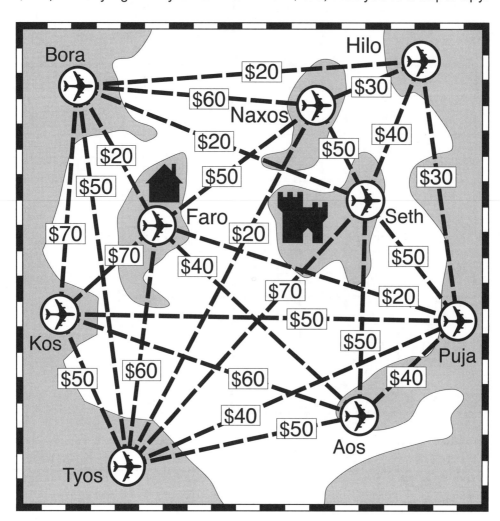

⊕ = Airport

♜ = Start

🏠 = Finish

Answers on page 402.

CRYPTO-LOGIC

Each of the numbers in the sequence below represents a letter. Use the mathematical clues to determine which number stands for which letter and reveal the encrypted word.

Hint: Remember that a / indicates divided by, and that all sums in parentheses must be done first.

5 9 3 5 4 3 9 4 7

Clues:

$(P+1)$squared$=O$

$S=O-P$

$P=2F$

Fsquared$=P$

$U+R=S$

$R+F=U$

Usquared$=N$

$(N+O)/T=T$

A MAKER OF PUZZLES

Cryptograms are messages in substitution code. Break the code to read the message. For example, THE SMART CAT might become FVO QWGDF JGF if **F** is substituted for **T, V** for **H, O** for **E,** and so on.

**BTJOX PSPTJTX VKQ KJ TJAHDQB IKRBTIKRDFDKJ KJP
MSYYHT FOTKRLO VBL FOTKRTP IKJX IKRBTIKRDFKH
KJP HLADF MSYYHTQ. BT SQTP RBT MQTSPLJXI
QMBDJW VBTJ BT ZDOQR MSCHDQBTP.**

FINGERPRINT MATCH

Find the matching fingerprint(s). There may be more than one.

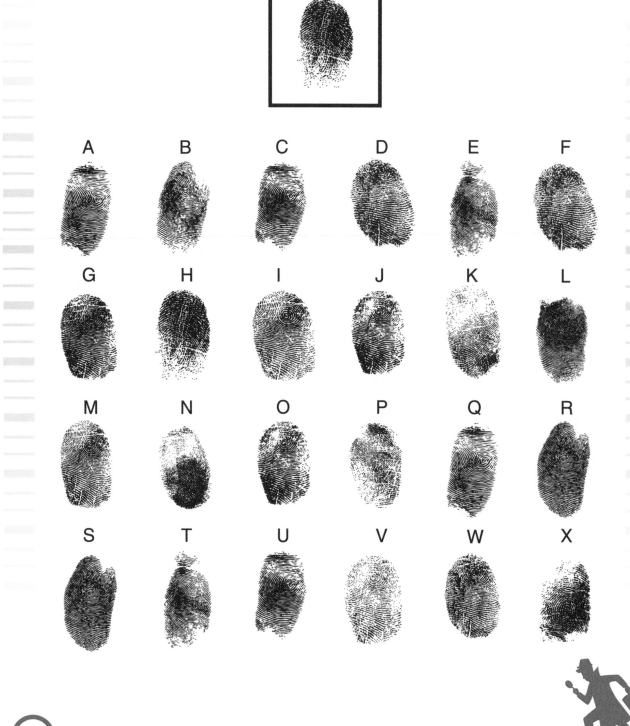

Answers on page 403.

HOT PURSUIT

You're in hot pursuit of a suspect, but rain has swept through the entire county, flooding all the bridges indicated by circles. Your job is to travel to each location where the criminal has been seen—A through I, in any order—by restoring only 2 of the bridges.

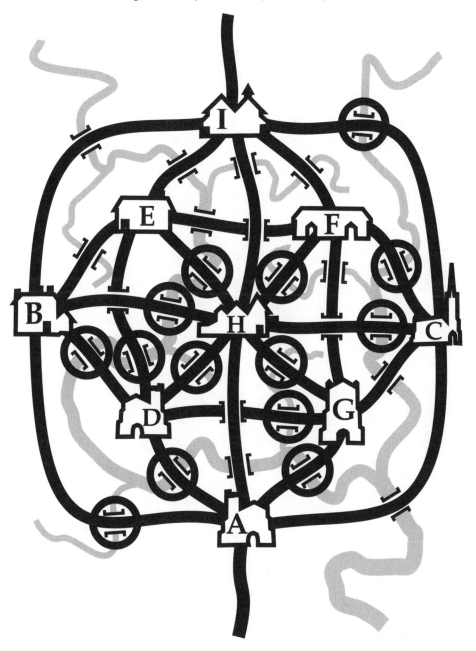

SOLVING CASES

Change just one letter on each line to go from the top word to the bottom word. Do not change the order of the letters. You must have a common English word at each step.

SOLVE

————

————

————

————

————

————

————

————

————

CASES

Answers on page 403.

SETTING A PRECEDENT

Cryptograms are messages in substitution code. Break the code to read the message. For example, THE SMART CAT might become FVO QWGDF JGF if **F** is substituted for **T**, **V** for **H**, **O** for **E**, and so on.

PRLYK YBBYC GEP HM TECMHRPKPR OJP NYOJPK EN
OJP AERPKC RPOPTOHSP MOEKX. JHM GKEOYLECHMO
T. YQLQMOP RQGHC UYM YC YAYOPQK MEBSPK EN
TKHAPM. JP PMOYVBHMJPR AYCX TECSPCOHECM EN
BYOPK RPOPTOHSP NHTOHEC.

A MYSTERY FROM HISTORY

Cryptograms are messages in substitution code. Break the code to read the message. For example, THE SMART CAT might become FVO QWGDF JGF if **F** is substituted for **T**, **V** for **H**, **O** for **E**, and so on.

GSP ITQMWOS NKMHFOCWXG WF K RKNTHF
NKMHFOCWXG GSKG SKF OSKDDPMUPV
OCQXGTUCKXSPCF. GSP NKMHFOCWXG FHXXTFPVDQ
VKGPF BKOE GT GSP PKCDQ RWRGPPM OPMGHCQ.
WG OTMGKWMF VCKJWMUF TR XDKMGF KMV TGSPC
TBZPOGF KOOTNXKMWPV BQ GPLG, BHG MT TMP SKF
BPPM KBDP GT VPOWXSPC GSP GPLG.

INTERCEPTION

You've intercepted a message that is meant to reveal a location for an upcoming meeting between two criminal masterminds. The only problem is, the message doesn't make sense. Can you figure out the right location?

WAUKESHA

SOUTH

ISLINGTON

GAULT

OMAN

DORIC

SPY FLY

As an international spy, your mission is to travel from your headquarters at Seth Castle to your safe house at Faro. To disguise your trail, you must stop once—and only once—at each airport. See if you can find the cheapest route for your trip. Less than $270 would make you a Steady Sleuth; less than $260, a Cool Operator; less than $240, a Crafty Agent. If you can make it on $230, then you're a Super Spy!

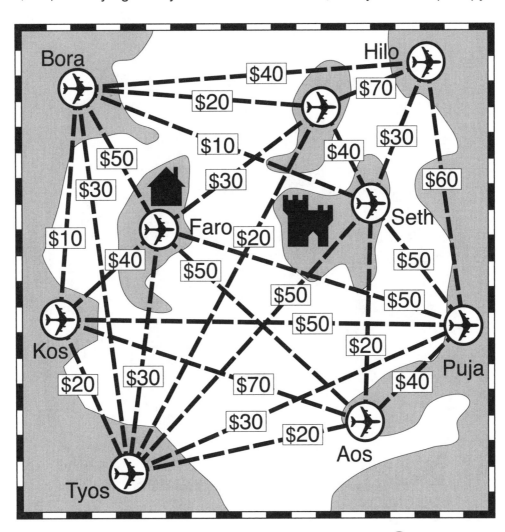

⊕ = Airport

🏰 = Start

🏠 = Finish

HOT PURSUIT

You're in hot pursuit of a suspect, but rain has swept through the entire county, flooding all the bridges indicated by circles. Your job is to travel to each location where the criminal has been seen—A through I, in any order—by restoring only 2 of the bridges.

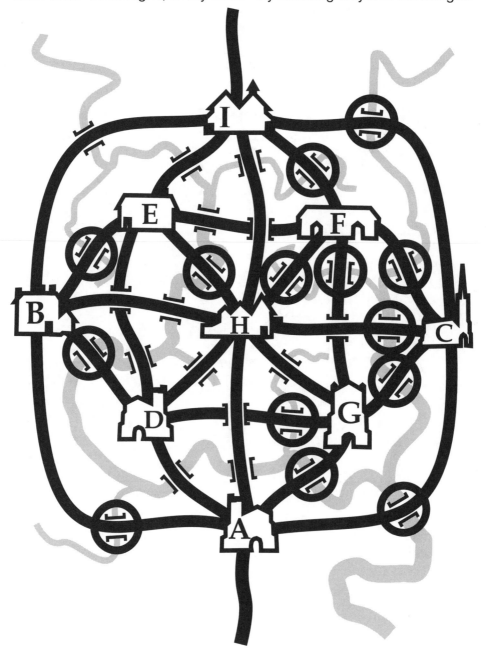

Answers on page 404.

MOTEL HIDEOUT

A thief hides out in one of the 45 motel rooms listed in the chart below. The motel's in-house detective received a sheet of four clues, signed "The Logical Thief." Using these clues, the detective found the room number within 15 minutes—but by that time, the thief had fled. Can you find the thief's motel room quicker?

1. The first digit and the second digit are one digit apart (e.g, 23, 32).

2. The sum of the digits is 5 or greater.

3. It is divisible by 3.

4. It is less than 7 squared.

51	52	53	54	55	56	57	58	59
41	42	43	44	45	46	47	48	49
31	32	33	34	35	36	37	38	39
21	22	23	24	25	26	27	28	29
11	12	13	14	15	16	17	18	19

Answers on page 404.

CRACK THE CODE

The 7 symbols each represent a different number between 1 and 9. The numbers to the right and below the grid show the totals of that row or column. Can you deduce the numerical value of each symbol?

■	✵	❋	◗	❋	✵	■	38
✵	◗	✵	❋	■	✵	◆	40
❋	■	◆	✵	✵	○	◗	43
✵	◆	◗	○	◗	◆	○	56
✵	○	✵	◆	❋	○	◗	48
❋	◆	○	◗	✵	❋	◆	44
■	✵	■	✵	■	✵	○	32
30	49	46	44	35	37	60	

Answers on page 404.

FIND THE WITNESS

On Calendar Court, there are 5 houses that are identical to each other. You need to follow up with a witness, Yvette White, but without any address on the doors you are not sure which house to approach. You know that from a previous statement that White and her husband have two children, a boy and a girl. The staff at the corner coffee shop and your own observations give you some clues. From the information given, can you find the right house?

A. One staff member says she knows that the couple in house A do not have children, but every other house has at least one child.

B. Another staff member isn't sure where White lives, but he says he's heard her say that she's lucky that both her next door neighbors have kids for her kids to play with.

C. There's a house with a newborn baby somewhere on the block, but not next door to White.

D. The house with the newborn is not next to the couple without children.

| House A | House B | House C | House D | House E |

Answers on page 404.

INVESTIGATIVE TOOLS

Every word listed is contained within the group of letters. Words can be found in a straight line horizontally, vertically, or diagonally. They may be read either forward or backward.

AUDIO RECORDER

BARRICADE TAPE

BINDLE PAPER

BIOHAZARD BAGS

BOOTIES

CAMERA

CASTING MATERIALS

CHALK

CONSENT TO SEARCH FORMS

FLARES

FLASHLIGHT

GLOVES

LATENT PRINT KIT

MEASURING TAPE

NOTEBOOK

PAPER BAGS

PLASTIC BAGGIES

RULER

SPRAY PAINT

TWEEZERS

E S S T P F H A P A P E R B A G S
P Y L H S G V Y K M L R M B C S M
A V A G T E C B I O E O S C E G R
T A I I I G R X R E A T V P S A O
G C R L K O L A H K S N U L V B F
N B E H T R O O L I R I B A G D H
I E T S N S N B G F E A A S J R C
R K A A I E L R B P Z P R T I A R
U L M L R I K U P I E Y R I K Z A
S A G F P T E L S Z E A I C B A E
A H N C T O C E B J W R C B I H S
E C I A N O H R N G T P A A N O O
M G T M E B G L O V E S D G D I T
F A S E T G T A T J I Q E G L B T
S G A R A V L R E G P R T I E V N
S X C A L R L Q B A X Z A E P Z E
R T Y V K H F T O T M B P S A J S
A G E B V T I S O U U K E B P W N
G I C M V D H E K G K H U J E E O
R E D R O C E R O I D U A P R A C

Answers on page 404.

RARE WINES

Georgina Guernsey's prized wine cellar was broken into last night, and five of her most rare bottles were stolen! She's absolutely beside herself...especially since she was planning on having her annual Spring garden party this weekend. Help the police figure out what's missing by matching each missing bottle of wine to its type, vintage year, and country of origin.

1. The Friambliss was bottled 8 years before the French wine.

2. The syrah, the Friambliss, and the Spanish wine were bottled in three different years.

3. The Weimerund isn't a merlot, and it wasn't bottled in 1958.

4. Of the Ece Suss and the 1970 bottle, one is from Greece and the other is a merlot.

5. The 1958 bottle is either the pinot gris or the Spanish wine.

6. Ania Branco wasn't ever made in France.

7. The Italian wine was bottled 4 years before the Spanish one, which wasn't the chardonnay.

8. Of the merlot and the pinot gris, one was from France and the other was a 1962 vintage.

9. The 1966 wine wasn't a syrah.

	Wines					Types					Countries				
	Ania Branco	Ece Suss	Friambliss	Vendemmia	Weimerund	Chardonnay	Merlot	Pinot Gris	Pinot Noir	Syrah	France	Greece	Italy	Portugal	Spain
Vintages 1954															
1958															
1962															
1966															
1970															
Countries France															
Greece															
Italy															
Portugal															
Spain															
Types Chardonnay															
Merlot															
Pinot Gris															
Pinot Noir															
Syrah															

Vintages	Wines	Types	Countries
1954			
1958			
1962			
1966			
1970			

Answers on page 405.

SPY SCRAMBLE

You have five secret meetings coming up. The dates have been sent separately. In this missive, you are given a city name, a meeting location, and a time for each meeting—but the information for each meetup is scrambled together. The letters are in order but not consecutive. Can you find all the words?

1. LPNOUAROOISVREN

City name: _____

Meeting location: _____

Time: _____

2. NESTASEWYTVORUEOFENKCLIIBTYERPMTY

City name: _____

Meeting location: _____

Time: _____

3. VHICONTOGKRIATENONGPAMEAK

City name: _____

Meeting location: _____

Time: _____

4. BAPAMRCRCORELGUNIONAELLNG

City name: _____

Meeting location: _____

Time: _____

5. SESPATWATTCENOLEEEDPMLE

City name: _____

Meeting location: _____

Time: _____

Answers on page 405.

BUILDING BLUEPRINTS

Navigate through this busy office as quickly and quietly as possible with the secret message you're carrying!

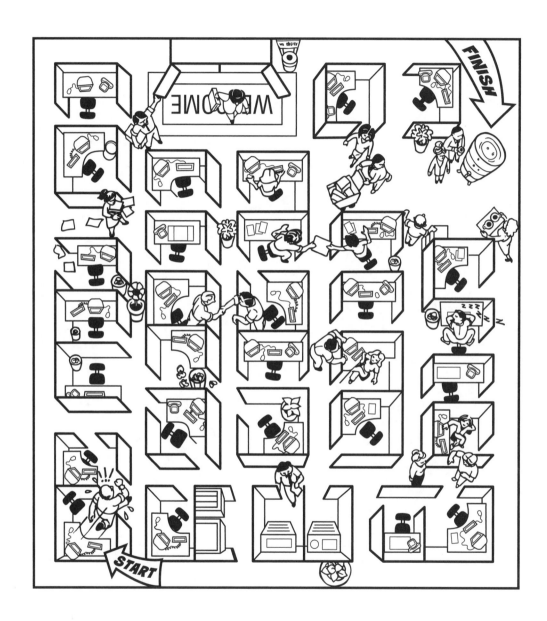

SPY FLY

As an international spy, your mission is to travel from your headquarters at Seth Castle to your safe house at Faro. To disguise your trail, you must stop once—and only once—at each airport. See if you can find the cheapest route for your trip. Less than $280 would make you a Steady Sleuth; less than $270, a Cool Operator; less than $250, a Crafty Agent. If you can make it on $230, then you're a Super Spy!

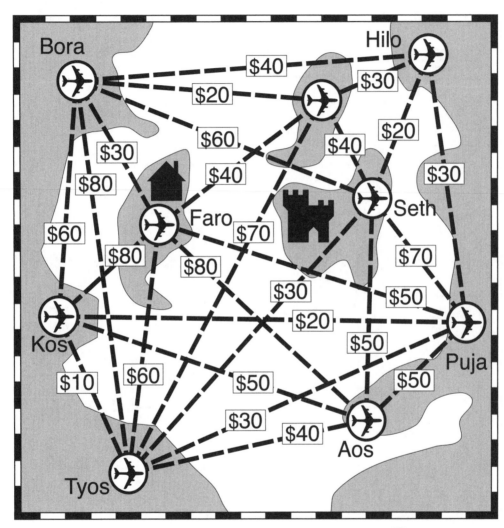

⊕ = Airport
♜ = Start
🏠 = Finish

Answers on page 405.

CRYPTO-LOGIC

Each of the numbers in the sequence below represents a letter. Use the mathematical clues to determine which number stands for which letter and reveal the encrypted word.

Hint: Remember that a / indicates divided by, and that all sums in parentheses must be done first.

5934217

Clues:

Z = 25

Z / C = C

2C = T

T - U = L

2E = L

E + C = N

N + 2 = U

3U = 8M

4U = 10P

M + P + L = O

O - 11 = H

O + 2 = F

O - 2 = X

CRACK THE PASSWORD

A detective has found a memory aid that the criminal left behind, a list of coded passwords. The detective knows that the criminal likes to scramble each password, then remove the same letter from each word. Can you figure out the missing letter and unscramble each word in this set to reveal the passwords?

PARCEL

RESEATED

PILFER

UNIT

WE STILL DON'T KNOW WHO DONE IT

Cryptograms are messages in substitution code. Break the code to read the message. For example, THE SMART CAT might become FVO QWGDF JGF if **F** is substituted for **T, V** for **H, O** for **E,** and so on.

DBQ OYIDPL PBLDARQS UYLQ GBRDARQL NKQONL DO YJNTDJC OJDI NKQ GLYWQAAY LNQTYJN MYJNBQJ IPLQPI. GB 1990, IQB FDLGBM YL FDAGUQ DOOGUQJL LNDAQ 13 TDJCL DO YJN TDJNK KPBSJQSL DO IGAAGDBL DO SDAAYJL. QIFNX OJYIQL YN NKQ IPLQPI LKDT TKQJQ NKQ YJNTDJC TYL.

Answers on page 405.

DON'T LEAVE A PRINT

Change just one letter on each line to go from the top word to the bottom word. Do not change the order of the letters. You must have a common English word at each step.

LEAVE

______

______

______

______

______

______

______

______

______

PRINT

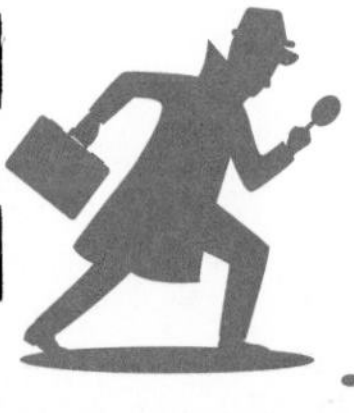

Answers on page 406.

QUOTABLE CRYPTOGRAMS

Cryptograms are messages in substitution code. Break the code to read the message. For example, THE SMART CAT might become FVO QWGDF JGF if **F** is substituted for **T, V** for **H, O** for **E,** and so on. These quotes all use the same substitution cipher and share a common theme.

QPYHY EHY VX NYOHYQN QPEQ QURY TXYN VXQ HYBYEM.
—ZYEV HEOUVY

U NPEMM JY EN NYOHYQ EN QPY KHEBY.
—RUKWYM TY OYHBEVQYN

E GXVTYHFWM FEOQ QX HYFMYOQ WAXV, QPEQ YBYHL
PWREV OHYEQWHY UN OXVNQUQWQYT QX JY QPEQ
AHXFXWVT NYOHYQ EVT RLNQYHL QX YBYHL XQPYH.
—OPEHMYN TUOCYVN

VX XVY YBYH CYYAN E NYOHYQ NX GYMM EN E OPUMT.
—BUOQXH PWKX

QPHYY REL CYYA E NYOHYQ, UF QGX XF QPYR EHY TYET.
—JYVZERUV FHEVCMUV

Answers on page 406.

TREASURE HUNT

The treasure hunter visited eight cities, finding a clue in each one that led him to the treasure in the final city. Can you put the list of the eight cities he visited in order, using the information below?

1. The treasure hunter flew from Seattle, Washington to Washington D.C.

2. Albuquerque was neither one of the first two nor the final two cities.

3. After visiting Michigan, the treasure hunter went to two other cities before going to Richmond.

4. Philadelphia was visited immediately after Virginia.

5. Cleveland was visited sometime after Albuquerque, but not immediately after.

6. Des Moines was visited sometime before Pennsylvania, but not immediately before.

7. Detroit was one of the first four cities visited, but not the third.

8. Cleveland was one of the last four cities visited, but not the sixth.

9. The nation's capital was visited before Iowa or Michigan.

10. Ohio was visited before Pennsylvania.

HOT PURSUIT

You're in hot pursuit of a suspect, but rain has swept through the entire county, flooding all the bridges indicated by circles. Your job is to travel to each location where the criminal has been seen—A through I, in any order—by restoring only 2 of the bridges.

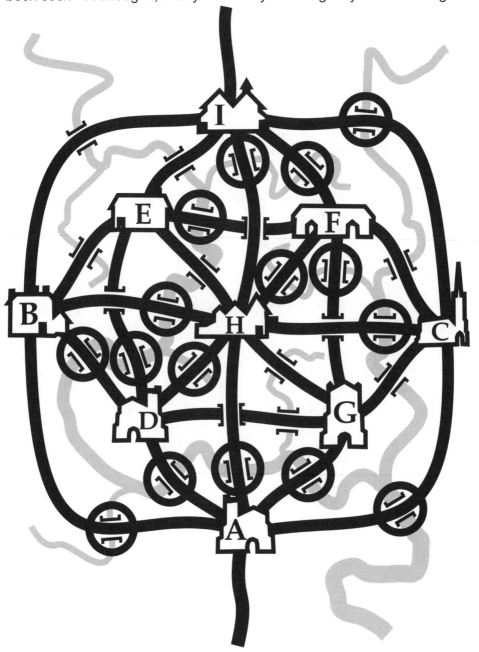

Answers on page 406.

SPY FLY

As an international spy, your mission is to travel from your headquarters at Seth Castle to your safe house at Faro. To disguise your trail, you must stop once—and only once—at each airport. See if you can find the cheapest route for your trip. Less than $280 would make you a Steady Sleuth; less than $260, a Cool Operator; less than $240, a Crafty Agent. If you can make it on $220, then you're a Super Spy!

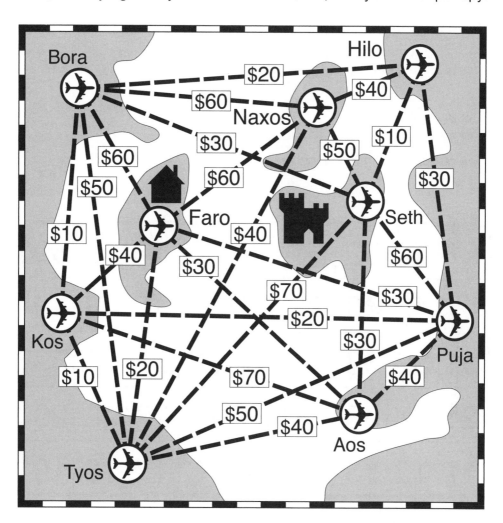

⊕ = Airport

🏰 = Start

🏠 = Finish

MOTEL HIDEOUT

A thief hides out in one of the 45 motel rooms listed in the chart below. The motel's in-house detective received a sheet of four clues, signed "The Logical Thief." Using these clues, the detective found the room number within 15 minutes—but by that time, the thief had fled. Can you find the thief's motel room quicker?

1. It is not a prime number.

2. The first digit is odd, and the second even.

3. It is divisible by 6.

4. The sum of its digits is less than 9.

51	52	53	54	55	56	57	58	59
41	42	43	44	45	46	47	48	49
31	32	33	34	35	36	37	38	39
21	22	23	24	25	26	27	28	29
11	12	13	14	15	16	17	18	19

Answers on page 406.

Study this picture of the crime scene for 1 minute, then turn the page.

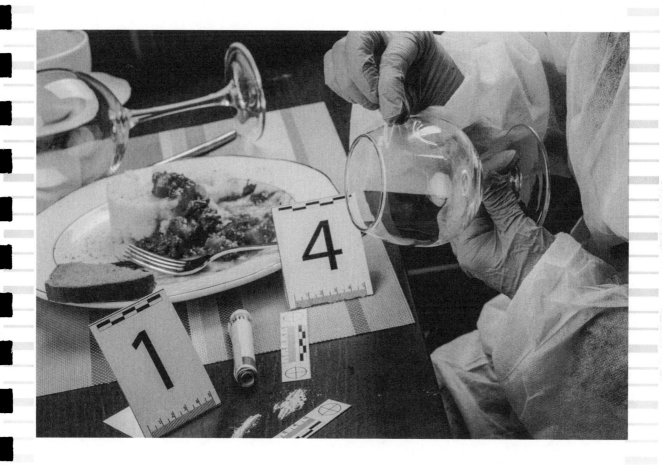

WHAT DO YOU SEE? (PART II)

(Do not read this until you have read the previous page!)

1. How many numbered placards are found on the table?

____ One, numbered 1

____ Two, numbered 1 and 2

____ Two, numbered 1 and 4

2. The crime scene investigator is holding this object to examine it.

____ Wineglass

____ Teacup

____ Fork

3. This utensil is resting on the plate.

____ Spoon

____ Fork

____ Butter knife

4. The food on the plate includes a slice of bread.

____ True

____ False

5. A wineglass had been knocked over.

____ True

____ False

Answers on page 407.

CRACK THE CODE

The 8 symbols each represent a different number between 1 and 10. The numbers to the right and below the grid show the totals of that row or column. Can you deduce the numerical value of each symbol?

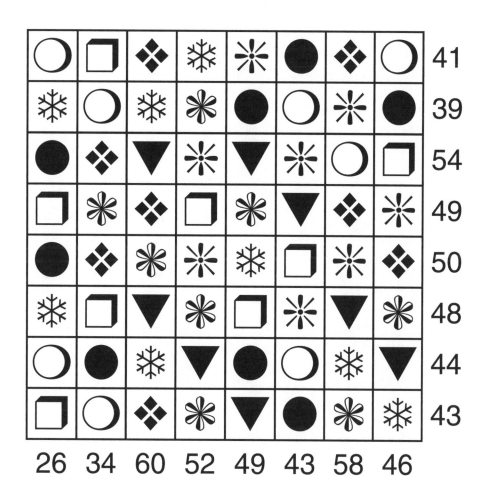

○	☐	❖	❄	✳	●	❖	○	41
❄	○	❄	✾	●	○	✳	●	39
●	❖	▼	✾	▼	✳	○	☐	54
☐	✾	❖	☐	✾	▼	❖	✳	49
●	❖	✾	✳	❄	☐	✳	❖	50
❄	☐	▼	✾	☐	✳	▼	✾	48
○	●	❄	▼	●	○	❄	▼	44
☐	○	❖	✾	▼	●	✾	❄	43
26	34	60	52	49	43	58	46	

Answers on page 407.

SMUGGLED ELECTRONICS

The F.B.I. has received a tip-off that a notorious criminal gang is planning to smuggle counterfeit electronics out of Amity Airport this morning. The informant indicated that 5 different shipments (each containing a different type of consumer electronic device) would go out, each on a different flight. Help the agents bust this smuggling ring by matching each illegal shipment to its flight number, departure time, and gate number.

1. The cell phones are going out of either gate 6 or gate 11.

2. The flight at gate 18 will leave 7 minutes before the one out of gate 3.

3. The earliest departure isn't at gate 7.

4. Flight 92 is either the one with the laptops or the one leaving at 8:17am.

5. Flight 233 will depart sometime after 8:05am.

6. The plane that departs at 8:24am, the one with the counterfeit tablets, and the one leaving from gate 11 are three different flights.

7. Of the tablet and the laptop shipments, one will leave at 8:31am and the other is stored on flight 356.

8. Of the plane at gate 3 and Flight 233, one has a shipment of flat-screen televisions and the other will depart at 8:17am.

9. The watch shipment is scheduled to depart sometime before the plane with the illegal cell phones (which isn't flight 108).

10. Flight 356 will leave 7 minutes after the plane at gate 18.

	Flights					Gates					Items				
	92	108	233	356	510	3	6	7	11	18	Cell phones	Laptops	Tablets	Televisions	Watches
Departures 8:03am															
8:10am															
8:17am															
8:24am															
8:31am															
Items Cell phones															
Laptops															
Tablets															
Televisions															
Watches															
Gates 3															
6															
7															
11															
18															

Departures	Flights	Gates	Items
8:03am			
8:10am			
8:17am			
8:24am			
8:31am			

Answers on page 407.

FINGERPRINT MATCH

Find the matching fingerprint(s). There may be more than one.

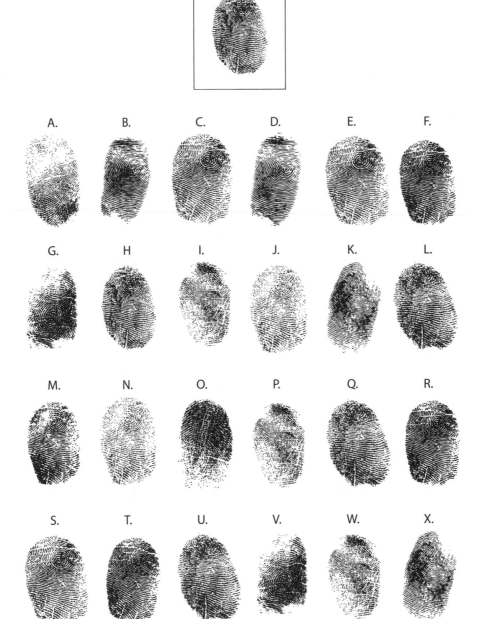

A.   B.   C.   D.   E.   F.

G.   H.   I.   J.   K.   L.

M.   N.   O.   P.   Q.   R.

S.   T.   U.   V.   W.   X.

Answers on page 407.

FIND THE WITNESS

On Chicago Avenue, there are 5 houses that are identical to each other. You need to follow up with a witness, Jimmy Perez, but without any address on the doors you are not sure which house to approach. You know that from a previous statement that Perez lives with his husband and has no children. The staff at the corner coffee shop and your own observations give you some clues. From the information given, can you find the right house?

A. One staff member says that Perez drives a compact and his husband has an SUV.

B. They do not have a motorcycle but are interested in buying one, and have said they'll get advice from their next door neighbor.

C. Houses A and E have motorcycles in front of them.

D. House B has a minivan parked in front of it and children's toys in the yard.

House A   House B   House C   House D   House E

Answers on page 407.

GEMSTONE MATH

There are 7 types of gems. There is 1 gem of the first type, 2 of the second type, 3 of the third type, 4 of the fourth type, 5 of the fifth type, 6 of the sixth type, and 7 of the seventh type. From the information given below, can you tell how many gemstones there are of each kind?

There are at least 5 garnets. There are fewer than 4 rubies. There are 2 more amethysts than rubies. There are even numbers of zircons and sapphires, but a greater number of sapphires. There are fewer agates than rubies. There are 3 more garnets than pearls.

CRYPTO-LOGIC

Each of the numbers in the sequence below represents a letter. Use the mathematical clues to determine which number stands for which letter and reveal the encrypted word.

5 3 2 5 9 6 1

Clues:

$2A+2U=X$

$X=3A+U+D$

$C+D=X$

$2N=X$

$E=U+A+D$

$E=6$

Answers on page 407.

INTERCEPTION

You've intercepted a message between two spies. At first glance it doesn't seem to make sense, but can you decipher the true message to reveal the date and location of a meeting?

PET ASP PUT POT AHA SET OFT PAD ESP

ICE FED ODE

ATE USE ORE TIN AFT

AMP APE MEN INT YON

A SAD STATISTIC

Cryptograms are messages in substitution code. Break the code to read the message. For example, THE SMART CAT might become FVO QWGDF JGF if **F** is substituted for **T, V** for **H, O** for **E,** and so on.

RDA MAOZAJRKCA LB QRLHAJ KOR RDKR EQ OAZLTAOAP EQ JLR TAOX DECD. LJHX BETA RL RAJ MAOZAJR IECDR WA OAZLTAOAP.

A MYSTERIOUS EVENT

Cryptograms are messages in substitution code. Break the code to read the message. For example, THE SMART CAT might become FVO QWGDF JGF if **F** is substituted for **T, V** for **H, O** for **E,** and so on.

SCI YITO 1911 DKVLGVIJ T KLSTPGI RTQI LA TOS SCIAS—SCI HLKT GDQT WTQ QSLGIK AOLH SCI GLUVOI PY TK IHMGLYII. CI WTQ RTUBCS SWL YITOQ GTSIO TKJ SCI MTDKSDKB WTQ OISUOKIJ SL DSQ CLHI.

CRYPTO-LOGIC

Each of the numbers in the sequence below represents a letter. Use the mathematical clues to determine which number stands for which letter and reveal the encrypted word.

Hint: Remember that a / indicates divided by, and that all sums in parentheses must be done first.

86513294

Clues:

$F = 10$

$F - T - U - I = 4$

T, U and I are all letters in the encrypted word

$U < I$

$T > I$

$Y + C = F$

$3Y = 4T$

$S = 1 \frac{1}{3} C$

$S - T = R$

$9R = P = 5N$

THE CON ARTIST

The F.B.I. has been on the hunt for a con artist accused of swindling thousands of dollars from his victims. His real name is Barney Green, but he routinely jumps from place to place using a new assumed name whenever he moves to a new location. Barney always creates a new fake "career" for each of his identities, and he never kept the same identity for more than a month. Help the F.B.I. track Mr. Green's latest movements by matching each name he used to its correct location and month, and determine the "career" he invented for each fake identity.

1. Of the "Fred Flores" identity and whichever name Barney used in Trippany, one was supposedly a doctor and the other was used in July.

2. Mr. Green didn't pass himself off as a lawyer while he was using the name "Pat Perry."

3. Barney pretended to be an accountant one month and a bank manager during another. One of those two identities was "Abe Avery". The other was the one he used in June.

4. He pretended to be "Sean Starr" sometime after he passed himself off as an accountant.

5. The F.B.I. know two of Barney's fake names were "Abe Avery" and "Matt Mintz," and that of those two, he used one in the city of Valero and he used the other in May.

6. Barney was in the town of Hoople either in August or in whichever month he pretended to be a dentist (but not both).

7. Mr. Green claimed to be a reporter one month before he was in Beaverton. Sometime after he left Beaverton he used the name "Pat Perry".

8. We know for a fact that Barney was pretending to be a doctor during his time in Opalville, and that he was in Nanaimo in May.

9. He never used the name "Lou Lemon" during his time in Beaverton, and he didn't pass himself off as an accountant in April.

		Names						Towns						Careers					
		Abe Avery	Fred Flores	Lou Lemon	Matt Mintz	Pat Perry	Sean Starr	Beaverton	Hoople	Nanaimo	Opalville	Trippany	Valero	Accountant	Bank mgr.	Dentist	Doctor	Lawyer	Reporter
Months	March																		
	April																		
	May																		
	June																		
	July																		
	August																		
Careers	Accountant																		
	Bank mgr.																		
	Dentist																		
	Doctor																		
	Lawyer																		
	Reporter																		
Towns	Beaverton																		
	Hoople																		
	Nanaimo																		
	Opalville																		
	Trippany																		
	Valero																		

Months	Names	Towns	Careers
March			
April			
May			
June			
July			
August			

SPY FLY

As an international spy, your mission is to travel from your headquarters at Seth Castle to your safe house at Faro. To disguise your trail, you must stop once—and only once—at each airport. See if you can find the cheapest route for your trip. Less than $310 would make you a Steady Sleuth; less than $300, a Cool Operator; less than $290, a Crafty Agent. If you can make it on $280, then you're a Super Spy!

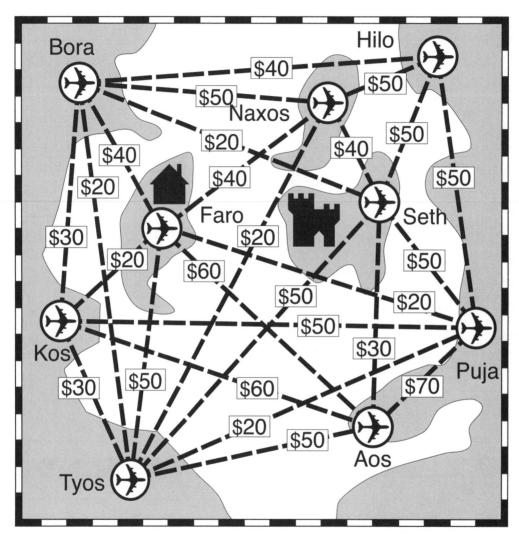

⊕ = Airport
♜ = Start
🏠 = Finish

Answers on page 408.

BUILDING BLUEPRINTS

Can you use the building blueprints to find the fastest way through the building in order to intercept the criminal before he can find the exit?

START

FINISH

Answers on page 408.

MOTEL HIDEOUT

A thief hides out in one of the 45 motel rooms listed in the chart below. The motel's in-house detective received a sheet of four clues, signed "The Logical Thief." Using these clues, the detective found the room number within 15 minutes—but by that time, the thief had fled. Can you find the thief's motel room quicker?

1. The first digit is larger than the second.

2. The second digit is not 3 or 4.

3. It is not divisible by 3 but is divisible by 4.

4. The sum of the digits is less than 7.

51	52	53	54	55	56	57	58	59
41	42	43	44	45	46	47	48	49
31	32	33	34	35	36	37	38	39
21	22	23	24	25	26	27	28	29
11	12	13	14	15	16	17	18	19

Answers on page 408.

HOT PURSUIT

You're in hot pursuit of a suspect, but rain has swept through the entire county, flooding all the bridges indicated by circles. Your job is to travel to each location where the criminal has been seen—A through I, in any order—by restoring only 2 of the bridges.

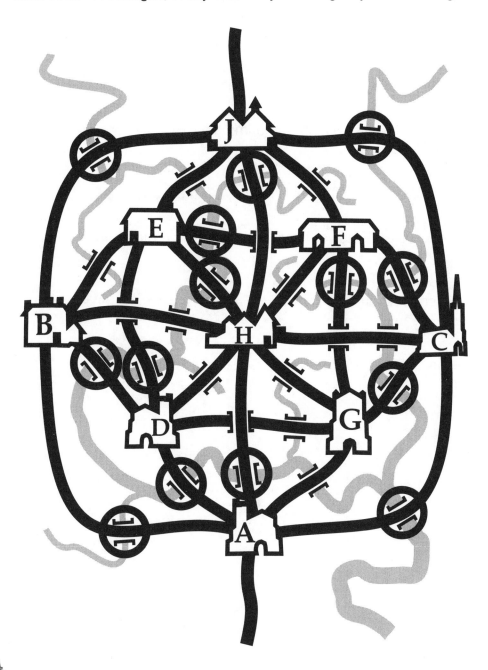

TREASURE HUNT

The treasure hunter visited eight cities in North America, finding a clue in each one that led him to the treasure in the final city. Can you put the list of the eight cities he visited in order, using the information below?

1. Both Canadian cities were visited before either city in Mexico.

2. A tip in New Orleans sent him immediately to Nevada.

3. Salt Lake City was visited sometime after Houston but sometime before Reno.

4. Mexico City was visited immediately before Guadalajara.

5. After he visited Ottawa, he visited exactly two other cities before going to Toronto.

6. At least three cities separated his trip to Houston with his later trip to New Orleans.

7. The final city was in the United States.

Answers on page 408.

CRACK THE CLUES

Change just one letter on each line to go from the top word to the bottom word. Do not change the order of the letters. You must have a common English word at each step.

CRACK

—————

—————

—————

—————

—————

—————

—————

—————

—————

—————

CLUES

LOST LIBRARY BOOKS

Middleworth Library considers books that have been overdue for more than 6 months to be officially "lost" and sends a library detective out to try to retrieve them from the last person to have borrowed them. This week five such books have been reported as lost. Help the library detective find them by matching each book to its author and publication date, and determine the name of the last person to have borrowed each book from the library.

1. Midge Mintz didn't publish any books in the 1940s.

2. *In or Out*, the book Edith borrowed, and the one published in 1970 are three different books.

3. Heddy Heath's book came out 13 years after Keith Koch's.

4. The book last borrowed by Danica was either *Grey Skies* or the one written by Midge Mintz.

5. *High Tide* was published 26 years after Just Friends.

6. Of Nick Norris's book and High Tide, one was borrowed by Charles and the other by Bailey.

7. Keith Koch's book came out 13 years before *In or Out*.

8. The book Bailey borrowed was published 26 years after the one Angelica took out.

9. Charles borrowed a book that was published in 1970.

	Borrowers					Authors					Titles				
	Angelica	Bailey	Charles	Danica	Edith	Heddy Heath	Jim Joyner	Keith Koch	Midge Mintz	Nick Norris	Fine Days	Grey Skies	High Tide	In or Out	Just Friends
Years 1918															
1931															
1944															
1957															
1970															
Titles Fine Days															
Grey Skies															
High Tide															
In or Out															
Just Friends															
Authors Heddy Heath															
Jim Joyner															
Keith Koch															
Midge Mintz															
Nick Norris															

Years	Borrowers	Authors	Titles
1918			
1931			
1944			
1957			
1970			

CRACK THE CODE

The 8 symbols each represent a different number between 1 and 10. The numbers to the right and below the grid show the totals of that row or column. Can you deduce the numerical value of each symbol?

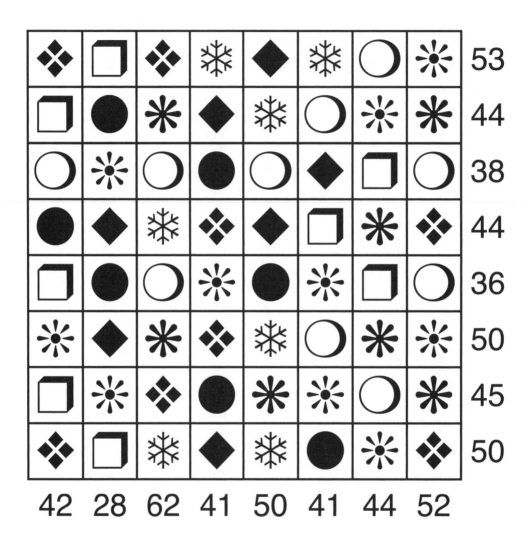

Answers on page 409.

HELP THE DETECTIVE (PART 1)

Read the story below, than turn the page and answer the questions.

The detective overheard the jewelry thief tell her accomplice about the different places where she stashed the loot. She said, "The emeralds are underneath the loose floorboard in the house in Paris. The diamonds are behind the false brick wall in the basement of the house in Prague. The rubies are stored in a safe in the spare bedroom of the apartment in Budapest. The opals are hidden in a trunk in the attic of the chalet in Switzerland. The strings of pearls are taped to the underside of the desk drawer in the den of the house in Luxembourg."

HELP THE DETECTIVE (PART II)

(Do not read this until you have read the previous page!)

The investigator overheard the information about where the stolen loot was stored, but didn't have anywhere to write it down! Answer the questions below to help him remember.

1. The rubies can be found in a house in Prague.

A. True

B. False

2. The strings of pearls are taped to the underside of the desk drawer in the den of the apartment in Luxembourg.

A. True

B. False

3. The emeralds are found underneath a floorboard in Paris.

A. True

B. False

4. The diamonds are found behind a false brick wall.

A. True

B. False

5. The opals are found in Budapest.

A. True

B. False

Answers on page 409.

IDENTITY PARADE

Oops! Four mugshots accidentally got sent through the shredder, and Officer Wallers is trying to straighten them out. Currently, only one facial feature in each row is in its correct place. Officer Wallers knows that:

1. C's nose is 1 place to the right of her mouth and 2 places to the right of D's hair.

2. C's eyes are 2 places to the left of her hair.

3. A's eyes are 1 place to the right of B's nose and 1 place to the right of D's mouth.

Can you find the correct hair, eyes, nose, and mouth for each person?

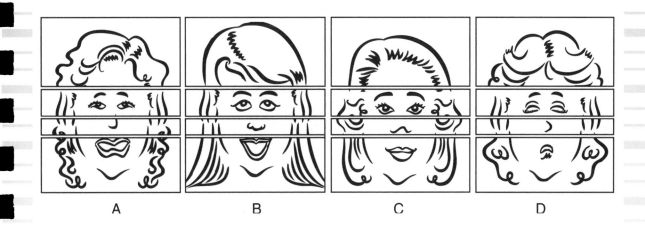

A   B   C   D

Answers on page 409.

ESPIONAGE

Every word listed is contained within the group of letters. Words can be found in a straight line horizontally, vertically, or diagonally. They may be read either forward or backward.

AGENT	EYES ONLY
ASSET	HANDLER
BLACK OPERATIONS	HONEY TRAP
BLOWN	INFILTRATION
BRUSH PASS	LEGEND
BURNED	MOLE
CHICKEN FEED	NUGGET
CLANDESTINE	NURSEMAID
COMPROMISED	PROVOCATEUR
COVER	SLEEPER
DEAD DROP	SPYMASTER
DOUBLE AGENT	TIMED DROP
EXFILTRATION	TRADECRAFT

```
T R A D E C R A F T Y T L Z E R M
I S K I L H O L L A B E U X L N A
M Q D N S A N W E N J G F O O W G
E K E F S N R I X G G G G D M Y E
D W E I A D U E K Q E U C E T H N
D E F L P L R R T F X N H A T O T
R E N T H E T U S S G F D D R N A
O N E R S R A N E E A B N D E E E
P I K A U R Q G E T M M S R V Y Y
S T C T R B U E O G A A Y O O T E
R S I I B Q R M F S A C I P C R S
N E H O Y E W J S Z X E O D S A O
W D C N P Q B E P C F Z L V Z P N
O N M E J S T I A U S A W B O Z L
L A E X F I L T R A T I O N U R Y
B L A C K O P E R A T I O N S O P
S C R B L W C O M P R O M I S E D
```

KNOWNS AND UNKNOWNS (PART I)

Study the synopsis of the crime, then turn to the next page to test your knowledge.

Victim: Priscilla A. Hrupington

Cause of death: Stabbed by a set of gardening shears.

Approximate time of death: between 10 PM on Friday evening and 1 AM on Saturday morning.

Location: Found dead in hotel room 218 by housekeeping at ~8:30 AM, Saturday, May 21. The hotel was in California; the victim lived in Ohio. The hotel was hosting a convention at the time, the annual convention for the organization Growers of Roses & Orchids in Extreme Environments (GOREE). Hrupington was a registered member of the convention, and her program, name badge, and materials were found in her room. The program showed that on Friday afternoon during the 2 PM-2:50 time slot, she was scheduled to be part of a panel on mulch, and her fellow panelists, when interviewed, said that it had gone smoothly and without incident.

Details:

Dolores Simonova, the hotel housekeeper, knocked on the door and did not receive a response. The placard on the door read, "Housekeeping please." Simonova opened the door using her master key card. The chain was not on, nor was the deadbolt in place. Simonova entered the room and immediately saw Hrupington. She says that she gave "a short scream" but no one came in response. She backed out of the room and blocked the entryway with her cart, then immediately alerted the hotel's manager through walkie-talkie. The hotel's manager called 911 (call logged 8:42 AM). Simonova did not remember seeing Hrupington at any point previously. She had cleaned the room the previous day and not encountered her then.

The victim was lying face up on the bed, on top of the bedspread. She was dressed in blouse, pants, underwear, and socks. A blazer had been left on a nearby chair. A watch, brooch, and bracelet were found on the end table by the bed. There were no signs of struggle.

Hrupington's purse had been left at the scene. Inside were a driver's license and credit cards. There was an ATM receipt from Wednesday the 18th indicating that Hrupington had withdrawn $80, but no cash was found. A smartphone was found in the purse.

No laptop was found, although Hrupington's roommate (Patricia E. Flugelflugh) stated that she had one. Flugelflugh said that it was not at the apartment she shared with the victim (search of shared apartment confirms). She stated that Hrupington sometimes brought it with her on travel and sometimes did not. Flugelflugh also said the victim might have left it at her boyfriend's residence, as she often spent the time there, did work when she did so, and left the laptop there for several days.

The victim's boyfriend of 6 months (Kenneth E. Fogletrutt) also attested that the victim had owned a laptop. He said that the victim had been wavering about whether to bring it and may have decided against it, but it was not at his apartment. He also implied that the reason Hrupington often left it at his apartment was that the victim's roommate was untrustworthy and that Hrupington was planning on moving out when the lease was up. Flugelflugh denied this, saying that Fogletrutt was "shady in small ways," that he took advantage of Hrupington's trusting nature by often borrowing money from her, and that if Hrupington was planning on moving out it was "news to her."

Both agreed that the gardening shears were not the victim's, as they did not recognize in. In addition, the victim flew and would not have been able to take anything of the sort through airport security.

(Do not read this until you have read the previous page!)

    1. The murderer stole Hrupington's laptop.

_____ True

_____ Possibly true

_____ False

    2. A local thief broke in to Hrupington's room to steal valuables and was interrupted, leading to the murder.

_____ Seems likely

_____ Seems unlikely

    3. The murderer stole $80 cash from the scene of the crime.

_____ True

_____ Possibly true

_____ False

    4. The murderer brought the gardening shears to the scene of the crime.

_____ Seems likely

_____ Seems unlikely

    5. The victim was found on Saturday morning but was killed on Friday morning.

_____ True

_____ Possibly true

_____ False

Answers on page 409.

QUICK CRIME QUIZ

1. Long before they were used to identify criminals, fingerprints were sometimes used to "sign" documents in lieu of a signature.

____ True

____ False

2. In Mark Twain's books "Life on the Mississippi" and "Pudd'n Head Wilson," these were used to identify perpetrators of crimes.

____ Hair

____ Fingerprints

____ Footprints

3. The Bertillion method, named after the French police officer who invented it, used body measurements to establish identity.

____ True

____ False

4. Bertillion was also the first person to standardize the use of:

____ DNA testing

____ Mug shots

5. America's first detective agency, the Pinkertons, was created in this year.

____ 1850

____ 1912

Answers on page 410.

Other convention participants and hotel dwellers were interviewed to trace Hrupington's movements during the GOREE conference (see pages 322-323). They are presented below in the order collected. Read and then turn the page.

Rebecca Thrush (front desk clerk at hotel): Processed Hrupington's check-in on Thursday evening as part of a rush of travelers who came in around 8 PM from an airport shuttle that runs every half-hour. Computer records show Hrupington's reservation as being processed at 8:13 PM. Thrush's interaction with Hrupington was neutral and standard. Thrush did not remember if Hrupington had been interacting with other people in the check-in line. As per hotel policy, she did not announce Hrupington's room number aloud, but wrote in on the keycard slip that she handed over to Hrupington.

Kenneth Smith (business traveler, room 216): Smith checked in on Friday at approximately 11 AM (hotel records confirm). He was not attending the convention, but traveling for business. Smith did not remember seeing Hrupington at any point. On Friday evening, Smith returned to his room after a business dinner at approximately 9 PM. At some point later than that, he heard people walking down the hall outside his room and a female voice said, "Bye, Prissy!" before hearing sounds like someone entering the room next to his. Shortly thereafter, the television turned on. He did not hear voices but didn't rule out a guest. Could have been anytime between 9:30 and 11 PM, when Smith went to bed. He did not hear any unusual sounds during the night, but wears earplugs while on business trips.

Freesia Jones (convention goer, room 220): Knew the victim. She and Hrupington had met at previous yearly conventions and maintained an occasional e-mail correspondence between times, focused on plant care. She saw Hrupington leave her hotel room on Friday morning around 9 AM as they both headed to the morning panels. They made plans to attend a 2 PM panel on Saturday together and go for a coffee afterwards to catch up. (Hrupington's phone confirms the appointment.) Jones did not attend the victim's mulch panel at 2 PM as she was manning a flower booth from 1-3 Friday. She knocked on Hrupington's hotel door at 7 PM to see if she wanted to go to dinner with Freesia and two other convention attendees, but there was no response. Jones returned to her hotel room at about 11:30 PM. She did not hear remember hearing a TV in the other room at that time. She went to bed around

midnight, and thought she might have heard someone walk down the hallway and enter the victim's room, or another room nearby, not long afterward, rousing her briefly from a light sleep. She woke up at 7 AM and did not hear any noises from the victim's room.

Wendall Waxman (convention goer, moderator of Friday's mulch panel, room 201): Had corresponded with Hrupington via e-mail after the panel assignments were announced in January and had "seen her in passing before," but had first spoken to her in person at the panel itself. Described her as "polite, knowledgeable, calm," did not speak much of her personal life. Said the panel was successful and that there were no conflicts between panelists. Nothing inflammatory/controversial was said and the response from the audience was good. Had not seen Hrupington afterwards, but thought it possible that they could have attended some of the same larger panels. Had not seen Hrupington on their shared floor.

Rebecca Podunski (convention goer, panelist alongside Hrupington, room 308): Had met Hrupington before at previous conventions; did not correspond between times. Described her as doing "solid but not groundbreaking work." Said the panel was for her taste a bit staid, but Waxman, Hrupington, and most of the audience seemed to want it that way. Said victim was at 4 PM panel on rose hybrids that was "deathly boring" and spent much of her time on her smartphone but then asked question at the end.

Heather White (waitstaff, hotel restaurant and bar): White was on duty both Thursday night 6-11 PM and Friday night 6-midnight. Victim came to hotel bar on Thursday night at 10 PM, alone, and sat in 2-seat table. Had a drink or two, a few small tapas plates (hotel credit card receipts confirm). Chatted briefly with other people who would stop at her table (White identified one of them as Waxman.) On Friday, came to restaurant with group ~6:30 PM. Group of four, two women, two men. Paid in pooled cash. White said conversation seemed friendly, conversational. Group closed out tab, paying in cash, and left together around 8:00.

WITNESS STATEMENTS (PART II)

(Do not read this until you have read the previous page!)

Put together a timeline of the victim's final days by matching
a time on the left to an event on the right:

Thursday, 8 PM   Freesia Jones sees Hrupington outside their rooms

Thursday, 10 PM   Hrupington attends dinner at hotel restaurant

Friday, 9 AM   Hrupington moderates mulch panel

Friday, 2 PM   Hrupington checks into hotel

Friday, 4 PM   Hrupington visits hotel bar

Friday, 6:30 PM   Hrupington leaves restaurant

Friday, 8 PM   Hrupington attends rose panel

Friday, post-9 PM   Smith hears movement in room next to his (Hrupington's)

Bonus: Do you spot a discrepancy in any of the witness statements?

Answers on page 410.

Study this picture of the crime scene for 1 minute, then turn the page.

WHAT DO YOU SEE? (PART II)

(Do not read this until you have read the previous page!)

1. The victim's purse was:

___ Open

___ Closed

2. One of the victim's shoes had fallen off.

___ True

___ False

3. This piece of furniture was at the left side of the scene.

___ Chest of drawers

___ Dressing table

4. The victim's phone was found near this hand:

___ Left hand

___ Right hand

5. Was there a set of keys anywhere in the scene?

___ Yes

___ No

Answers on page 410.

CRYPTO-LOGIC

Each of the numbers in the sequence below represents a letter. Use the mathematical clues to determine which number stands for which letter and reveal the encrypted word.

Hint: Remember that a / indicates divided by, and that all sums in parentheses must be done first.

7 3 4 2 9 4 7 1 3 6

Clues:

The numerals (1-9) not included in this encryption represent B and S

$B = A + G$

$A - 1 = G$

$A + T = E + I$

$E = A$ squared

T and I are adjacent values

$L \times P = 60$

$60 / N = 15$

P is not featured

ADDING INSULT TO INJURY

Cryptograms are messages in substitution code. Break the code to read the message. For example, THE SMART CAT might become FVO QWGDF JGF if **F** is substituted for **T, V** for **H, O** for **E,** and so on.

1994 RVW SBF SBFAS LA V UFPRCLI LA FKUVPK HTINB'R MVCISCIJ SBF RNPFVH APLH V JVGGFPY CI LRGL. SBF SBCFUFR GFAS QFBCIK V ILSF SBVIECIJ SBF HTRFTH ALP MLLP RFNTPCSY. SBF GVRS GVTJB WVR LI SBF HTRFTH, SBLTJB, VR MLGCNF PFNLUFPFK SBF MVCISCIJ VIK NVTJBS SBF SBCFUFR.

ANNA'S ALIBIS

Anna is in a real pickle. The police are convinced she was involved in a break-in last week, even though she swears she was nowhere near the scene of the crime when it took place! Help her sort out her defense by matching each of her corroborating alibis for the night in question with their correct time and location, and determining the relationship with each (friend, cousin, etc.).

1. Anna's Ewing Avenue alibi was either her co-worker or the person who was with her at 10:00pm.

2. Penny Pugh isn't Anna's cousin.

3. Lina Lopez was with Anna sometime after she was on Delancey Road, and thirty minutes before Anna was with her co-worker.

4. Of Anna's 8:00pm and 10:00pm alibis, one was her neighbor and the other was with her on Border Lane.

5. Norma Neet was with Anna one hour after she was on Delancey Road.

6. Penny Pugh, the bartender, and Anna's two alibis on First Street and Ewing Avenue were four different people.

7. Anna's friend was with her on First Street that night, but not at 9:30pm.

8. Anna spent some time with her bartender (who isn't Oda Osborn) that night at her favorite bar on Capitol Street.

	Alibis					Relations					Locations				
	Lina Lopez	Maddy Meyer	Norma Neet	Oda Osborn	Penny Pugh	Bartender	Cousin	Co-worker	Friend	Neighbor	Border Ln.	Capitol St.	Delancey Rd.	Ewing Ave.	First St.
Times 8:00pm															
8:30pm															
9:00pm															
9:30pm															
10:00pm															
Locations Border Ln.															
Capitol St.															
Delancey Rd.															
Ewing Ave.															
First St.															
Relations Bartender															
Cousin															
Co-worker															
Friend															
Neighbor															

Times	Alibis	Relations	Locations
8:00pm			
8:30pm			
9:00pm			
9:30pm			
10:00pm			

Answers on page 410.

333

CRIME RHYMES

Each clue leads to a 2-word answer that rhymes, such as BIG PIG or STABLE TABLE. The numbers in parentheses after the clue give the number of letters in each word. For example, "cookware taken from the oven (3, 3)" would be "hot pot."

1. The case of the theft of the animal intestines was also called the case of the (6, 5): _____

2. A murder in December (8, 8): _____

3. The lawbreaker who sent hidden messages was the (10, 8): _____

4. To accuse a British "Sir" with a fancy title (6, 6): _____

5. A police inspector changes around assignments for the police under him (5, 4): _____

6. To take someone else's breakfast food (5, 7): _____

7. The smuggled dog was also called the (7, 6): _____

8. The incident of theft among the troupe of silent performers was called the (4, 5): _____

Answers on page 410.

CRACK THE CODE

The 8 symbols each represent a different number between 1 and 10. The numbers to the right and below the grid show the totals of that row or column. Can you deduce the numerical value of each symbol?

✳	●	✳	●	✳	●	▼	❋	21
●	▼	◻	✳	◆	✳	❄	✳	35
◻	◆	❄	◐	❄	◆	◯	◻	60
▼	◻	❋	▼	◯	❋	◆	●	36
❋	●	◯	✳	❄	◻	◯	❋	46
◆	◯	❄	❋	◻	●	❄	▼	46
❄	◆	◻	▼	✳	◯	●	❋	41
◆	▼	◆	◯	❄	❋	▼	◻	43
40	**34**	**55**	**29**	**52**	**39**	**40**	**39**	

FINGERPRINT MATCH

There are 12 sets of fingerprints. Find each match.

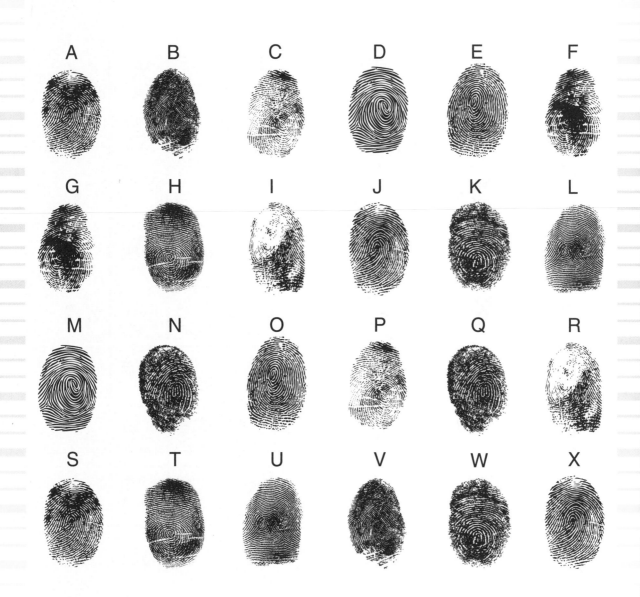

A   B   C   D   E   F

G   H   I   J   K   L

M   N   O   P   Q   R

S   T   U   V   W   X

Answers on page 411.

MOTEL HIDEOUT

A thief hides out in one of the 45 motel rooms listed in the chart below. The motel's in-house detective received a sheet of four clues, signed "The Logical Thief." Using these clues, the detective found the room number within 15 minutes—but by that time, the thief had fled. Can you find the thief's motel room quicker?

1. The sum of the digits is greater than 7.

2. The second digit is more than double the first digit.

3. The first digit is divisible by 2.

4. The second digit is divisible by 4.

51	52	53	54	55	56	57	58	59
41	42	43	44	45	46	47	48	49
31	32	33	34	35	36	37	38	39
21	22	23	24	25	26	27	28	29
11	12	13	14	15	16	17	18	19

Answers on page 411.

POLICE DISPATCHER

Trevor was on-call today as the Libertyville Police Department's primary dispatcher. He received six calls during the morning shift, each from a different part of town, and each for a different reason (such as a stolen car or a bank robbery). He dispatched a different officer for each of these six calls. Using only the clues below, help him sort out his dispatch log by matching each call to its time, location, and assigned officer.

1. Of Brenda and whoever was dispatched to deal with the alarm, one went Downtown and the other was sent to the North End.

2. Harry didn't leave at 11:45am.

3. One officer was dispatched to the scene of a truck accident 3 hours after the call to go Downtown.

4. Jeffrey was sent out sometime after the Midtown call.

5. Of Neville and whoever went to investigate the stolen car, one was dispatched at 10:15am and the other went to Midtown.

6. One officer (who wasn't Linda) was sent to check on a cat stuck in a tree 45 minutes before another was sent to the North End.

7. The 10:15am call, Harry's call, the one for the South End, and the one for the bank robbery involved four different officers.

8. Brenda headed out sometime after whoever went Uptown. The Uptown dispatch didn't happen at either 8:45am or 10:15am.

9. The officer that went to the South End left 2 hours and 15 minutes after whoever went to the scene of the bank robbery.

10. Neither Dale nor Linda was dispatched to investigate the trespassing call.

		Officers					Calls						Locations					
		Brenda	Dale	Harry	Jeffrey	Linda	Neville	Accident	Alarm	Bank robbery	Cat in tree	Stolen car	Trespassing	Bus. District	Downtown	Midtown	North End	South End	Uptown
Times	8:45am																		
	9:30am																		
	10:15am																		
	11:00am																		
	11:45am																		
	12:30pm																		
Locations	Bus. District																		
	Downtown																		
	Midtown																		
	North End																		
	South End																		
	Uptown																		
Calls	Accident																		
	Alarm																		
	Bank robbery																		
	Cat in tree																		
	Stolen car																		
	Trespassing																		

Times	Officers	Calls	Locations
8:45am			
9:30am			
10:15am			
11:00am			
11:45am			
12:30pm			

Answers on page 411.

TREASURE HUNT

The treasure hunter visited eight cities around the world, finding a clue in each one that led him to the treasure in the final city. Can you put the list of the eight cities he visited in order, using the information below?

1. He went immediately from a city in Morocco to the capital city of an island country off Africa's southeastern coast.

2. Krakow was one of the first three cities.

3. Quito was one of the last three cities.

4. Kuala Lumpur was visited sometime after Prague and immediately before Singapore.

5. After visiting Antananarivo, he visited exactly two other cities before going to Barcelona.

6. Rabat was visited sometime after the city in the Czech Republic.

7. Singapore was visited sometime before the city in Ecuador, but not immediately before.

8. Poland was visited sometime before Prague.

9. Singapore was visited sometime before Spain.

Answers on page 411.

HOT PURSUIT

You're at the top of the building, and the criminal is about to drive away. This professional building is a maze of corridors and cubicles. Elevators are local or express only; there are no stairs. Time to get moving!

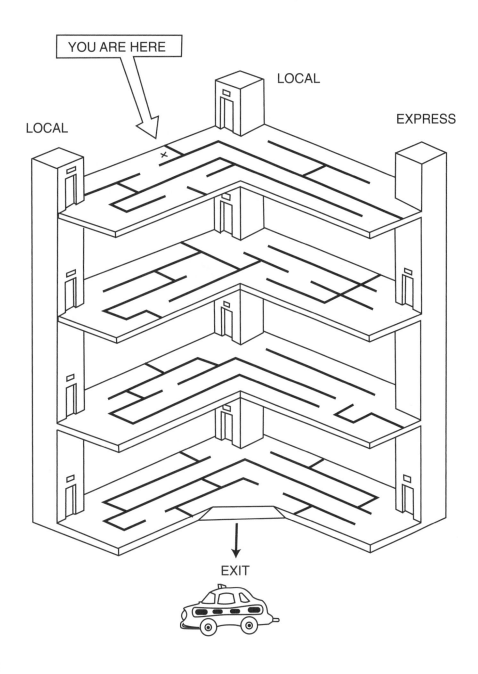

YOU ARE HERE

LOCAL

LOCAL

EXPRESS

EXIT

Answers on page 411.

SPY FLY

As an international spy, your mission is to travel from your headquarters at Seth Castle to your safe house at Faro. To disguise your trail, you must stop once—and only once—at each airport. See if you can find the cheapest route for your trip. Less than $290 would make you a Steady Sleuth; less than $280, a Cool Operator; less than $270, a Crafty Agent. If you can make it on $250, then you're a Super Spy!

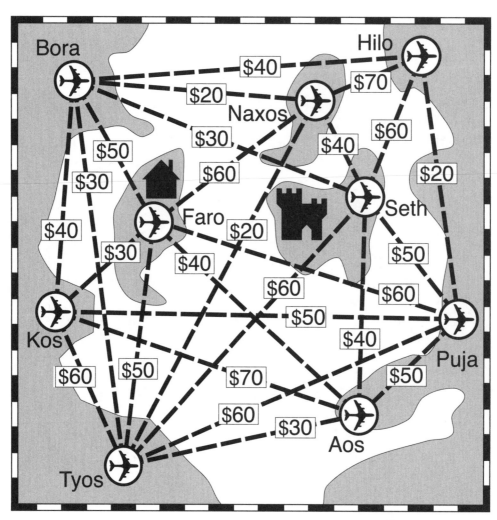

⊕ = Airport
🏰 = Start
🏠 = Finish

Answers on page 412.

Cryptograms are messages in substitution code. Break the code to read the message.
For example, THE SMART CAT might become FVO QWGDF JGF if **F** is substituted for
T, V for **H, O** for **E,** and so on. These four cryptograms share a common theme.

ZN JXL MUGKZNRIRQL, T JUAGUM JRPGAU ZJ ATIIUV
TN TJJUM.

TNRMWUG ERGV DRG T JXL ZJ T YZGVETMAWUG.

EWUN TN PNVUGARSUG TQUNM'J ZVUNMZML ZJ
GUSUTIUV, WZJ RG WUG ARSUG ZJ JTZV MR YU YIREN.

EWUN TN PNVUGARSUG TQUNM QZSUJ GUTI YPM
ZNARNJUCPUNMZTI ZNDRGKTMZRN MR MWU UNUKL
ZN RGVUG MR XGRSU WZKJUID RG WUGJUID, MWTM
ZNDRGKTMZRN ZJ ATIIUV AWZAFUN DUUV.

STOLEN STREET SIGNS

Someone's been stealing street signs in Starrington! Every week (always on a Saturday night) a new sign has gone missing. Each time it's a different type of sign (stop sign, yield sign, etc.) in a different part of town. Help the police track down the thief by matching each sign to the date it went missing and its original location at the intersection of two streets.

1. Of the speed limit sign and the one that was at Barnacle Road, one went missing on July 25th and the other was at the corner of Tarragon Lane.

2. Quinella Street doesn't intersect with Falstaff St.

3. The speed limit sign was stolen sometime after the one from Ralston Avenue.

4. The Amble Lane sign didn't go missing on August 1st.

5. The Dwight Street sign went missing one week before the one from Tarragon Lane.

6. The one-way sign was stolen 1 week before the Casper Boulevard sign, and 3 weeks before the one on Selby Street.

7. The dead end sign, the stop sign, the one from Selby Street, and the two stolen before July 14th were five different signs.

8. One of the missing signs stood at the corner of Selby Street and Barnacle Road. Selby Street doesn't have any "No Parking" signs.

9. Peabody Lane, which has no "Dead End" signs anywhere near it, intersects with either Dwight Street or Everett Avenue (but not both).

10. The stop sign went missing sometime before the sign at Peabody Lane (but not on July 18th).

		Signs						Streets						Streets					
		Dead End	No Parking	One Way	Speed Limit	Stop	Yield	Amble Ln.	Barnacle Rd.	Casper Blvd.	Dwight St.	Everett Ave.	Falstaff St.	Oracle Rd.	Peabody Ln.	Quinella St.	Ralston Ave.	Selby St.	Tarragon Ln.
Dates	July 4th																		
	July 11th																		
	July 18th																		
	July 25th																		
	August 1st																		
	August 8th																		
Streets	Oracle Rd.																		
	Peabody Ln.																		
	Quinella St.																		
	Ralston Ave.																		
	Selby St.																		
	Tarragon Ln.																		
Streets	Amble Ln.																		
	Barnacle Rd.																		
	Casper Blvd.																		
	Dwight St.																		
	Everett Ave.																		
	Falstaff St.																		

Dates	Signs	Streets	Streets
July 4th			
July 11th			
July 18th			
July 25th			
August 1st			
August 8th			

Answers on page 412.

HOT PURSUIT

You're in hot pursuit of a suspect, but rain has swept through the entire county, flooding all the bridges indicated by circles. Your job is to travel to each location where the criminal has been seen—A through I, in any order—by restoring only 2 of the bridges.

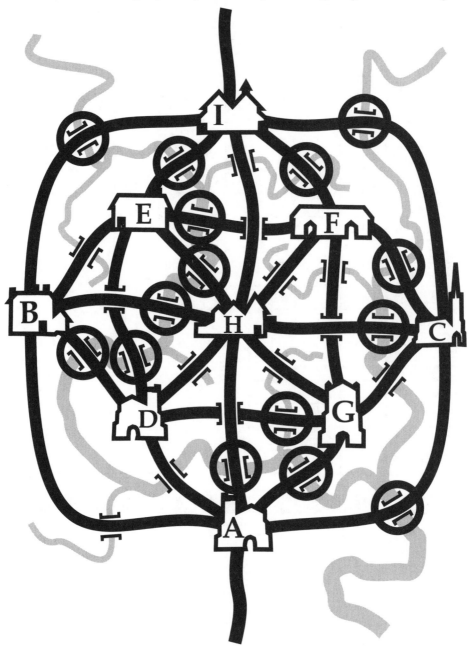

Answers on page 412.

CRYPTO-LOGIC

Each of the numbers in the sequence below represents a letter. Use the mathematical clues to determine which number stands for which letter and reveal the encrypted word.

6 9 8 3 4 2 5 1 7

Clues:

A value which divides perfectly into both its neighbours represents E

A – R = E

R – 2 = V

V + 1 = D

D – V + 1 = S

(S squared) + E = H

V – 6 = P

P + 3 = N

The remaining value signifies I

A PROLIFIC ROBBER

Cryptograms are messages in substitution code. Break the code to read the message. For example, THE SMART CAT might become FVO QWGDF JGF if F is substituted for **T**, **V** for **H**, **O** for **E**, and so on.

BHXG OAEEFRGG, R ZRGRCARG RLO OXAKP, MOHEK FHLK OXRG 10,000 HNBKZOM HP RLO, AGZEQCAGW IRAGOAGW, MZQEIOQLKM, RGC LRLK NHHDM. XK TRM RLLKMOKC AG 2013.

FIND THE WITNESS

On Washington Street, there are 5 houses. You need to follow up with a witness, Jennifer Brown, but without any address on the doors you are not sure which house to approach. You know that from a previous statement that Brown lives with her husband and stepdaughter. The staff at the corner coffee shop and your own observations give you some clues. From the information given, can you find the right house?

A. The Browns recently repainted their house white, like two other homes on their street.

B. There are two houses with kids living in them, and they are not adjacent.

C. House D is green and house C is blue.

D. House A has two kids living in it.

| House A | House B | House C | House D | House E |

Answers on page 413.

SPY FLY

As an international spy, your mission is to travel from your headquarters at Seth Castle to your safe house at Faro. To disguise your trail, you must stop once—and only once—at each airport. See if you can find the cheapest route for your trip. Less than $290 would make you a Steady Sleuth; less than $280, a Cool Operator; less than $270, a Crafty Agent. If you can make it on $260, then you're a Super Spy!

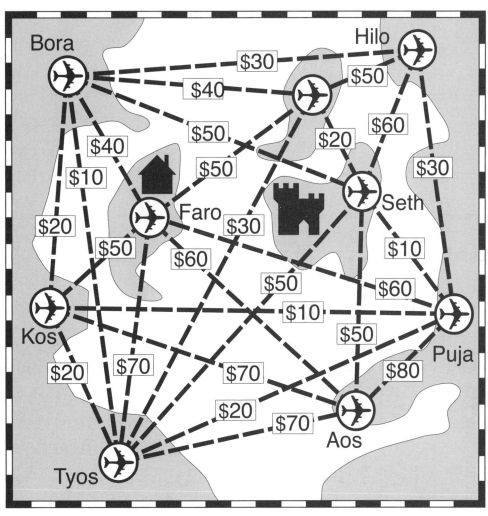

⊕ = Airport
♜ = Start
🏠 = Finish

MOTEL HIDEOUT

A thief hides out in one of the 45 motel rooms listed in the chart below. The motel's in-house detective received a sheet of four clues, signed "The Holiday Thief." Using these clues, the detective found the room number within 15 minutes—but by that time, the thief had fled. Can you find the thief's motel room quicker?

1. The number is not divisible by 4.

2. The first digit is as large or larger than the second digit.

3. The digits add up to 6.

4. The number is divisible by 6.

51	52	53	54	55	56	57	58	59
41	42	43	44	45	46	47	48	49
31	32	33	34	35	36	37	38	39
21	22	23	24	25	26	27	28	29
11	12	13	14	15	16	17	18	19

Answers on page 413.

CRACK THE CODE

The 8 symbols each represent a different number between 1 and 10. The numbers to the right and below the grid show the totals of that row or column. Can you deduce the numerical value of each symbol?

✸	◆	✳	●	❄	✳	●	❄	21
▢	✸	❄	✳	▼	✸	✳	●	33
○	✸	○	◆	✳	▢	✸	❄	40
❄	◆	✸	○	▼	❄	●	▼	37
▼	●	○	●	○	◆	✸	◆	44
●	▢	▼	✸	▢	○	◆	▢	52
◆	○	◆	▢	▼	▢	▼	○	56
✸	▢	✸	❄	●	▼	❄	✸	29

39 43 39 35 44 44 30 38

Answers on page 413.

IN OTHER WORDS

Cryptograms are messages in substitution code. Break the code to read the message. For example, THE SMART CAT might become FVO QWGDF JGF if **F** is substituted for **T, V** for **H, O** for **E,** and so on.

KWDGDWCK RGJ CWKLZJVGOK VDPAOFZ
KZPJZL, ZDVMCYLVP, ROJLVQZ, KTYFGSW,
PJWHLVP, YDF PAYDFZKLVDZ.

NOTHING TO DO WITH DOYLE

Cryptograms are messages in substitution code. Break the code to read the message. For example, THE SMART CAT might become FVO QWGDF JGF if **F** is substituted for **T, V** for **H, O** for **E,** and so on.

C.C. CLHIBR VGRK'S G JDYSDLKGH NBSBYSDUB—
CB VGR G RBQDGH FDHHBQ, LJSBK YLKRDNBQBN
SCB JDQRS DK GIBQDYG. PLQK CBQIGK VBPRSBQ
ITNABSS DK 1861, CB YLKJBRRBN SL 27 ITQNBQR
PTS IGX CGUB PBBK QBRMLKRDPHB JLQ ILQB.
CB VGR GHRL G PDAGIDRS, IGQQDBN SL SCQBB
VLIBK GS SCB SDIB LJ CDR NBGSC.

Answers on page 413.

Cryptograms are messages in substitution code. Break the code to read the message. For example, THE SMART CAT might become FVO QWGDF JGF if F is substituted for **T,** **V** for **H,** **O** for **E,** and so on.

BXOOX QGZ FLQGC BQEXO BHAGXZ PNX KRQGPLADD LQAZXLO JQGJ AG PNXAL PXXG VXQLO QGZ WXJQG PNXAL DAFXOPVDX HF WQGC QGZ PLQAG LHWWXLV. BXOOX'O EHPNXL YXLXDZQ TLHPX Q WHHC QFPXL NAO ZXQPN TAPN PNX ZXZAMQPAHG: "AG DHSAGJ EXEHLV HF EV WXDHSXZ OHG, ERLZXLXZ WV Q PLQAPHL QGZ MHTQLZ TNHOX GQEX AO GHP THLPNV PH QIIXQL NXLX."

THE MASTER FORGER

The art world is agog! Six recently-sold paintings, each supposed to be by the hand of a different world-famous artist, have now been conclusively shown to be forgeries. Authorities believe the same "master forger" is behind all of this but they're still not sure who he or she actually is. Using only the clues available below, match each forged painting to the artist it was claimed to have been painted by, the country it was sold in, and the price it fetched at auction.

1. The Hal Garrison piece sold for four times as much money as "Cold Hills."

2. "Forever Blue" sold for twice as much as the painting sold in Portugal.

3. Of the piece that sold for $8,000,000 and the Inga Howell painting, one was "Cold Hills" and the other was sold in France.

4. The Inga Howell forgery wasn't sold in Spain.

5. "Baby Jane" (which wasn't passed off as a Margot Lane painting) fetched less money at auction than the piece that was sold in Portugal.

6. Of the painting sold in Germany and "Eighteen," one sold for 32 million dollars and the other was alleged to have been an early work by Greta Frank.

7. The Lyle Kramer painting fetched more money at auction than "Forever Blue," which was said to have been a Hal Garrison piece.

8. "Day of Night," the piece that sold for $2,000,000, and the painting that was sold in Norway were three different forgeries.

9. "Awestruck" didn't sell for either $2 million or $4 million.

10. The Freda Estes painting sold for $16,000,000, but not in Norway.

		Paintings						Countries						Artists					
		Awestruck	Baby Jane	Cold Hills	Day of Night	Eighteen	Forever Blue	Canada	France	Germany	Norway	Portugal	Spain	Freda Estes	Greta Frank	Hal Garrison	Inga Howell	Lyle Kramer	Margot Lane
Prices	$1,000,000																		
	$2,000,000																		
	$4,000,000																		
	$8,000,000																		
	$16,000,000																		
	$32,000,000																		
Artists	Freda Estes																		
	Greta Frank																		
	Hal Garrison																		
	Inga Howell																		
	Lyle Kramer																		
	Margot Lane																		
Countries	Canada																		
	France																		
	Germany																		
	Norway																		
	Portugal																		
	Spain																		

Prices	Paintings	Countries	Artists
$1,000,000			
$2,000,000			
$4,000,000			
$8,000,000			
$16,000,000			
$32,000,000			

HOT PURSUIT

You're in hot pursuit of a suspect, but rain has swept through the entire county, flooding all the bridges indicated by circles. Your job is to travel to each location where the criminal has been seen—A through I, in any order—by restoring only 2 of the bridges.

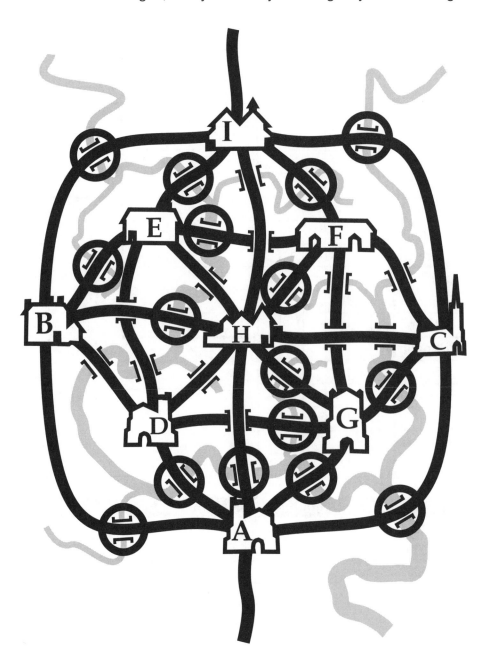

Answers on page 414.

SPY FLY

As an international spy, your mission is to travel from your headquarters at Seth Castle to your safe house at Faro. To disguise your trail, you must stop once—and only once—at each airport. See if you can find the cheapest route for your trip. Less than $320 would make you a Steady Sleuth; less than $310, a Cool Operator; less than $300, a Crafty Agent. If you can make it on $260, then you're a Super Spy!

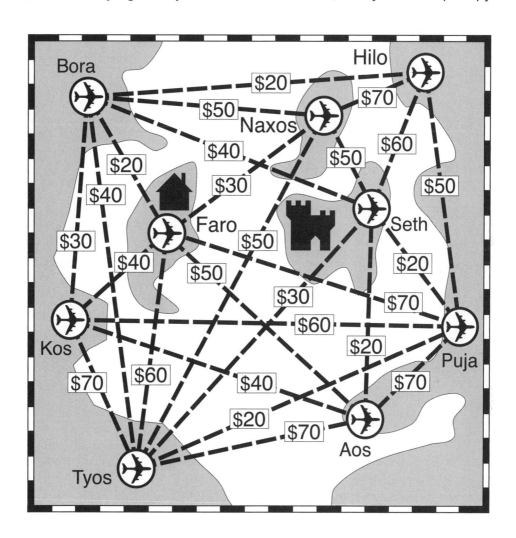

You've intercepted a message. You think it might be the date and location of a meeting, but it doesn't seem to make sense. Can you decipher the true message?

AGREED

HOP ROUND SKI LIFT AT HIGHEST ZUCCHINI

RUN AND NEVER GO ON THIN POSTS

VIA ROAD WALK MORE

BANDANNA IN TAN SIDEWAYS CART

READ THE EXCELLENT PAMPHLET

Answers on page 415.

TREASURE HUNT

The treasure hunter visited nine cities, finding a clue in each one that led her to the treasure in the final city. Can you put the list of the nine cities she visited in order, using the information below?

There were exactly three other cities visited between Paris and Jakarta.

There was at least one city visited between London and Pretoria.

Paris was not the first city visited, and Jakarta was not the last.

Singapore was visited sometime after London and sometime before Cairo and Sydney.

Cairo was visited after London, but not immediately afterward.

The city in Indonesia was visited immediately before the city in Australia, which was visited before either South American city.

There were four cities visited between Pretoria and Buenos Aires.

The treasure was found in Rio de Janeiro.

BANK ROBBERIES

Bledsoe County has been beset by a gang of bank robbers! Five different banks, each in a different town, have been robbed by the same gang in just the past 10 days. The total amount stolen from each bank was never the same, and the gang never robbed more than one bank on any given day. Using only the clues below, help track down the gang by matching each bank to the town it is in, and determine the date each was robbed as well as how much was stolen.

1. The most expensive robbery happened 2 days after Bell Largo was hit.

2. The gang got away with $4,800 2 days before they robbed another bank of $2,500.

3. Of Apex Bank and Wellspring, one was robbed on June 11th and the other lost $4,800.

4. The bank in Grumley was either Wellspring or the one robbed on June 9th.

5. Bell Largo was robbed 2 days before the bank in Cold Spring.

6. The $1,000 robbery took place 2 days before Moneycorp was hit, but not in Yountville.

7. The gang robbed a bank (which wasn't Apex) in Tahoe on June 7th.

8. Cold Spring's bank was robbed on June 11th.

	Banks					Towns					Amounts				
	Apex	Bell Largo	First Trust	Moneycorp	Wellspring	Cold Spring	Grumley	Longwood	Tahoe	Yountville	$1,000	$1,600	$2,500	$4,800	$10,200
Dates June 3															
June 5															
June 7															
June 9															
June 11															
Amounts $1,000															
$1,600															
$2,500															
$4,800															
$10,200															
Towns Cold Spring															
Grumley															
Longwood															
Tahoe															
Yountville															

Dates	Banks	Towns	Amounts
June 3			
June 5			
June 7			
June 9			
June 11			

SPY SCRAMBLE

You need to pick up materials from a series of 5 dead letter drops. For each, you've been given a location in your town and a spot inside that location— but the information for each location is scrambled together. The letters are in order but not consecutive. Can you find all the words?

1. PUUBNDLICERLSEIBCORNDATARYBLE

Place: _____

Details: _____

2. UNPDEARLRARKGGEASZETBPLAONTER

Place: _____

Details: _____

3. TRBEAHININDSLATRAGETGRIEEOSNNIGN

Place: _____

Details: _____

4. STHWIRIDMLOCMIKERNFRGOMPLOEOFLT

Place: _____

Details: _____

5. OUUTNDSERIDEREMDBUSEEUNMCH

Place: _____

Details: _____

Answers on page 415.

HOT PURSUIT

You're at the top of the building, and the criminal is about to drive away. This professional building is a maze of corridors and cubicles. Elevators are local or express only; there are no stairs. Time to get moving!

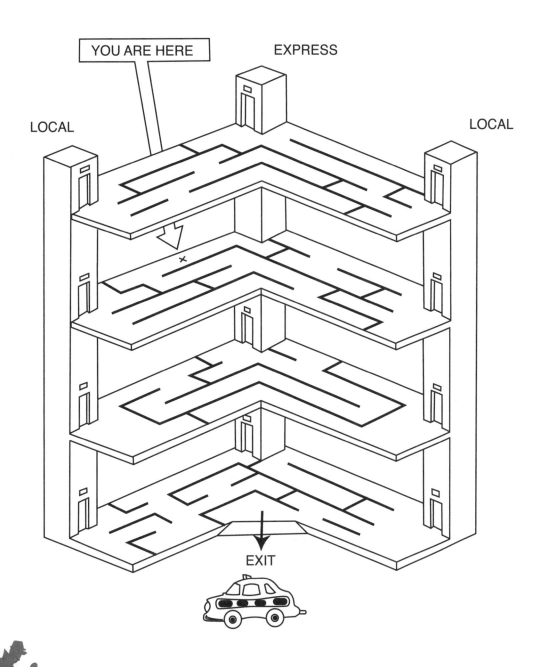

YOU ARE HERE

EXPRESS

LOCAL

LOCAL

EXIT

THE CAT BURGLAR

Maurice St. Clair is considered by many to be the most successful cat burglar of the 20th century. As a local crime reporter, you've been given an assignment to write a story about six of his most daring heists spanning more than 30 years. Using only the clues below, match each of these thefts to the correct month, year, and location, and determine what was stolen in each.

1. The 1991 theft (which wasn't in Seattle) was either the one that happened on July 4th or the one involving the collection of rare blue diamonds.

2. The cash heist, the one in 1998, and the one that took place on April 13th were three different events.

3. Maurice's infamous "Halloween heist" (so-called because it happened on October 31st) didn't involve either diamonds or rubies.

4. Of the cash theft and the Vancouver heist, one happened in July and the other occurred in 1984.

5. The Berlin burglary happened 7 years after the Halloween heist.

6. Of Maurice's 1991 burglary and the one that happened in Paris, one involved blue diamonds and the other occurred on June 15th.

7. The September theft happened sometime after Maurice's infamous London heist.

8. The Seattle heist (which didn't happen in the 1980s) didn't take place in July.

9. The Halloween heist happened 7 years before Maurice's September 10th theft (which involved a large number of pure gold bars).

10. The emerald theft happened sometime before the June 15th heist.

11. The July 4th heist occurred 14 years after the sapphire burglary.

		Cities						Items						Months					
		Antwerp	Berlin	London	Paris	Seattle	Vancouver	Cash	Diamonds	Emeralds	Gold bars	Rubies	Sapphires	April	May	June	July	October	September
Years	1963																		
	1970																		
	1977																		
	1984																		
	1991																		
	1998																		
Months	April																		
	May																		
	June																		
	July																		
	October																		
	September																		
Items	Cash																		
	Diamonds																		
	Emeralds																		
	Gold bars																		
	Rubies																		
	Sapphires																		

Years	Cities	Items	Months
1963			
1970			
1977			
1984			
1991			
1998			

Answers on page 415.

MOTEL HIDEOUT

A thief hides out in one of the 45 motel rooms listed in the chart below. The motel's in-house detective received a sheet of four clues, signed "The Holiday Thief." Using these clues, the detective found the room number within 15 minutes—but by that time, the thief had fled. Can you find the thief's motel room quicker?

1. It is a prime number larger than 20.

2. The second digit is larger than the first.

3. The second digit is divisible by 3.

4. The first digit is not divisible by 2.

51	52	53	54	55	56	57	58	59
41	42	43	44	45	46	47	48	49
31	32	33	34	35	36	37	38	39
21	22	23	24	25	26	27	28	29
11	12	13	14	15	16	17	18	19

Answers on page 415.

WHAT DO YOU SEE? (PART I)

Study this picture of the crime scene for 1 minute, then turn the page.

WHAT DO YOU SEE? (PART II)

(Do not read this until you have read the previous page!)

1. The knickknacks on the fireplace had been knocked over.

____ True

____ False

2. Each small placard around the body indicates a bullet. How many were there?

A. 1

B. 2

C. 3

D. 4

3. A splotch of blood was found on the cushion of the window seat.

____ True

____ False

4. A lamp was knocked over.

____ True

____ False

5. Both chairs in the scene were knocked over.

____ True

____ False

Answers on page 416.

FIND THE WITNESS

On Washington Street, there are 5 houses that are identical to each other. You need to follow up with a witness, Kathy King, but without any address on the doors you are not sure which house to approach. You know that from a previous statement that King is a widow who lives alone. The staff at the corner ice cream shop and your own observations give you some clues. From the information given, can you find the right house?

A. King sometimes brings in the kids who live next door to her to the ice cream shop for a treat.

B. The couple in house B are planning on moving now that their kids are grown up and moved out of the house.

C. The teenaged boy in house E plays music very loudly.

D. King gets along well with the newlyweds with the new baby who lives two doors down.

 House A    House B    House C    House D    House E

Answers on page 416.

FINGERPRINT MATCH

Find the matching fingerprint(s). There may be more than one.

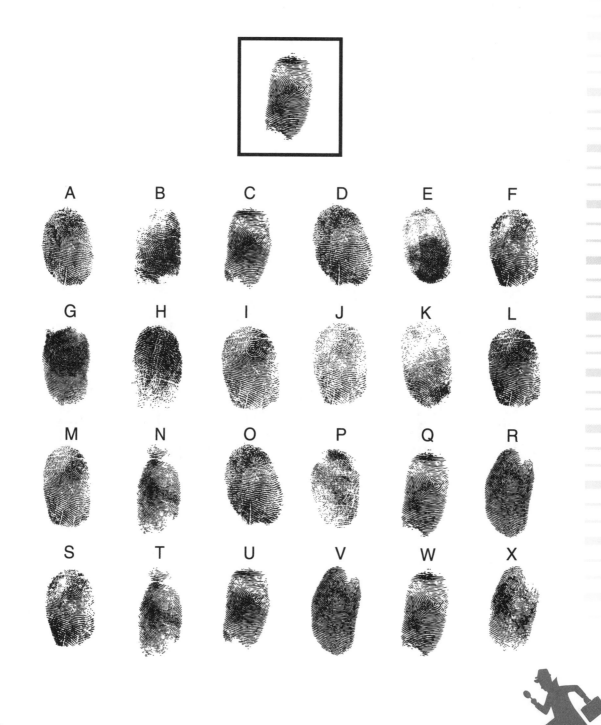

Answers on page 416.

CRACK THE CODE

The 8 symbols each represent a different number between 1 and 9. The numbers to the right and below the grid show the totals of that row or column. Can you deduce the numerical value of each symbol?

✽	●	▢	✳	◆	▢	●	✽	56
✳	◐	❄	◐	❄	◐	✳	◯	18
◆	●	✳	✽	◐	✽	❄	●	45
◆	✳	❄	◐	✳	◐	❄	◆	22
●	◈	✽	●	✽	✳	◈	✳	56
✽	▢	✽	◈	●	◈	●	▢	60
▢	●	▢	❄	◆	●	◐	✳	43
✳	◈	✽	▢	✽	▢	✳	◈	52

48 52 47 39 39 44 39 44

Answers on page 416.

Something has gone drastically wrong in this barbershop.
We count 7 wrong things. Can you find them all?

Answers on page 416.

CODE-DOKU

Solve this puzzle just as you would a sudoku. Use deductive logic to complete the grid so that each row, column, and 3 by 3 box contains the letters from the word POLICEMAN.

	N		I				L
O		N		L			A
					M		
	A		N		M	L	
		M		I			
	E	L	P		C		
M							
P			C		N		E
I			E		O		

FINGERPRINT MATCH (PAGE 4)

The matching pairs are: A and G; B and H; C and E; D and F

QUICK CRIME QUIZ (PAGE 5)

1. Juan Vucetich of Argentina created the first fingerprint classification system for police.
2. No. 3. Yes. It is rare, but it does happen.
4. Yes. Wear, certain chemicals, and certain chemotherapy drugs can erode fingerprints, but it is difficult to do. 5. Researchers have been developing techniques to lift fingerprints off fabric, but it is more difficult than lifting them from other materials.

CODES AND CIPHERS (PAGE 6)

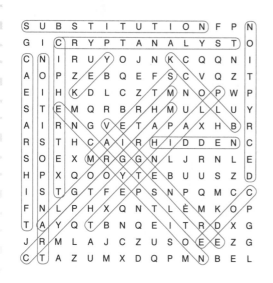

CRACK THE CODE (PAGE 8)

◗ = 2   ▼ = 3
● = 7   ■ = 8

IT'S IN THE BLOOD (PART II) (PAGE IO)

1. A+; 2. O-; 3. AB+; 4. AB-; 5. True

WHAT DO YOU SEE? (PART II) (PAGE I2)

Picture 1 is a match.

BURIED DIAMONDS (PAGE I3)

	Tree	Location	No. Diamonds
1	beech	river	15
2	cedar	garden	10
3	dogwood	lake	8
4	elm	fence	7
5	ash	park	5
6	fir	wood	12

FIND THE WITNESS (PAGE I4)

Mr. Jones lives in House D.

MOTEL HIDEOUT (PAGE 15)

The thief is in room 33.

CRIMINAL WORDS (PAGE 16)

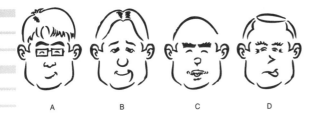

S U S P E C T E D

E X A M I N E R S

B A L L I S T I C

IDENTITY PARADE (PAGE 17)

A   B   C   D

INTERCEPTION (PAGE 18)

A. Ulan Bator. The pattern is that the first vowel in the gem's name is the first letter in the city's name.

SCIENCE WINS! (PAGE 18)

forensic evidence

BUILDING BLUEPRINTS (PAGE 19)

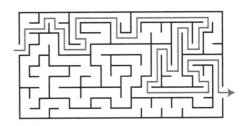

ART THEFTS (PAGE 20)

Months	Titles	Artists	Museums
April	City Dreams	De Lorenzo	Givernelle
May	Apple Cart	Strauss	Tendrille
June	Elba at Dawn	Pocalini	Beaufort
July	Madame V.	Lafayette	Millefoi

CAN A CLUE SET YOU FREE? (PAGE 22)

Answer may vary. CLUE, glue, glee, flee, FREE

TELL A TALE, GO TO JAIL (PAGE 22)

Answers may vary. TALE, tall, pall, pail, JAIL

ROBBER RIDDLE (PAGE 23)

Why was the thief all wet?
He tried to rob a riverbank.

NUMBER NOGGIN-SCRATCHER (PART II) (PAGE 24)

D. 3456

UNSCRAMBLE THE DETECTIVE (PAGE 24)

Solve; evidence; fingerprints; footprints; fibers

HELP THE DETECTIVE (PART II) (PAGE 26)

1. D; 2. B; 3. A; 4.

CRACK THE CODE (PAGE 27)

$$✤ = 3 \qquad ♣ = 4$$
$$✴ = 6 \qquad ◆ = 9$$

FINGERPRINT MATCH (PAGE 28)

J is the matching fingerprint.

ACRONYM QUIZ (PART II) (PAGE 30)

1. B; 2. C; 3. A; 4. B; 5. A

HOT PURSUIT (PAGE 31)

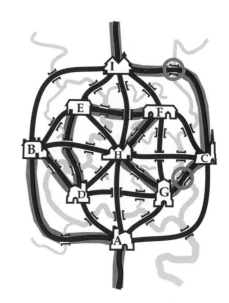

SPY FLY (PAGE 32)

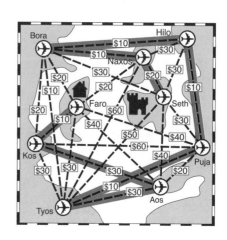

INTERCEPTION (PAGE 33)

Take the central letter of each word and you reveal LONDON.

MOTEL HIDEOUT (PAGE 34)

The thief is in room 15.

FIND THE WITNESS (PAGE 35)

Mr. Linus lives in House E.

PASSING BAD CHECKS (PAGE 36)

Dates	Stores	Towns	Amounts
October 2	Carpet City	Rio Pondo	$125.12
October 6	Well Mart	Georgetown	$85.50
October 10	Quick-Stop	Appleton	$52.89
October 14	David's Deli	Lincoln	$35.15

ELEVATOR WORDS (PAGE 38)

1. CRIME wave; 2. waveform; 3. form letter;
4. letterhead; 5. headband; 6. band music;
7. music SCENE

AUTHORS AND DETECTIVES (PAGE 39)

1. Sherlock Holmes, E. Arthur Conan Doyle; 2. Miss Marple, C., Agatha Christie; 3. C. Auguste Dupin, D. Edgar Allan Poe; 4. Nero Wolfe, A. Rex Stout; 5. Kinsey Millhone, B. Sue Grafton

DETECT THE WORDS (PAGE 39)

The missing letter is I.
Forensic, thief, examine, investigate

DETECTIVES (PAGE 40)

The leftover letters spell: "Sherlock Holmes and Doctor Watson (Doyle)."

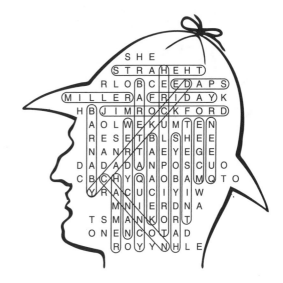

MOTEL HIDEOUT (PAGE 42)

The thief is in room 56.

HELP THE DETECTIVE (PART II) (PAGE 44)

1. B; 2. D; 3. A; D. 4. C

SPY FLY (PAGE 45)

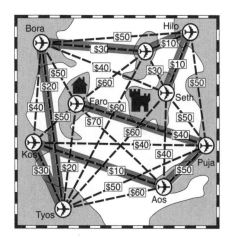

CRACK THE CODE (PAGE 46)

☆ = 1   ♣ = 4   ♦ = 7   ✳ = 9

WHAT DO YOU SEE (PART II) (PAGE 48)

Picture 3 is a match.

HOT PURSUIT (PAGE 49)

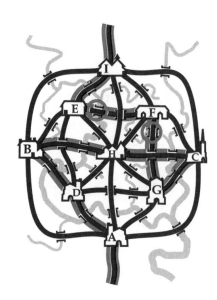

THE MISSING MILLIONAIRE (PAGE 50)

Days	Witnesses	Cities	States
Tuesday	Edna Eddel	Ballingford	Nevada
Wednesday	Hilda Hayes	Tetley	California
Thursday	Susie Seuss	Ventura	Washington
Friday	Walt Wolsen	Pescadero	Oregon

CRIME RHYMES (PAGE 52)

1. prehistory mystery; 2. prospective detective; 3. skater investigator; 4. tooth sleuth; 5. gumshoe queue; 6. peppermint print; 7. birder murder; 8. fluoride homicide

COLD CASE (PAGE 53)

Answers may vary. COLD, hold, hole, home, come, came, CASE

NUMBER NOGGIN-SCRATCHER (PART II) (PAGE 54)

D. 554

CRIME CRYPTOGRAM (PAGE 54)

The actor's costar accused him of a dastardly crime, but the police refused to investigate. What did he do?

He stole the scene!

MOTEL HIDEOUT (PAGE 55)

The thief is in room 51.

DON'T FORGET TO COUNT THE DONUTS (PAGE 56)

19 officers

TUT'S TOMB (PAGE 57)

HOT PURSUIT (PAGE 58)

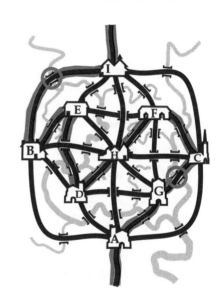

HELP THE DETECTIVE (PART II) (PAGE 60)

1. B; 2. C; 3. D; 4. C

POP QUIZ: TERMINOLOGY (PAGE 61)

1. B; 2. A describes theft, B describes robbery and C describes burglary. 3. B; 4. Accelerant

A CASE OF ARSON (PART II) (PAGE 64)

1. Unlikely. Turpentine was used as an accelerant, and it was not stored in the office. 2. False. 3. Unconfirmed. Greene had returned the keycard issued by the company, but he could have duplicated it prior to leaving. 4. True, his girlfriend. 5. Unconfirmed, as the only word for this was his own.

CRACK THE CODE (PAGE 65)

✿ = 2   ◆ = 4   ✪ = 5

✳ = 7   ▲ = 9

THE KINGS OF KHAFAR (PAGE 66)

Years	Kings	Killers	Poisons
1904	Veri'ma	son	arsenic
1921	Kaponi	uncle	hemlock
1938	Taton-on	cousin	oleander
1955	Lilamaku	brother	cyanide
1972	Anjiwat	wife	strychnine

FIND THE WITNESS (PAGE 68)

Patel is in house B.

MOTEL HIDEOUT (PAGE 69)

The thief is in room 48.

INTERCEPTION (PAGE 70)

Take the last letter of each place name to reveal: CHICAGO

SPY FLY (PAGE 71)

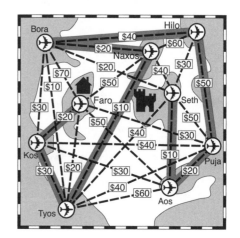

CATCH THE THIEF (PAGE 72)

The missing letter is I.
Diamonds, tiara, diadem, figurine

CRYPTO-LOGIC (PAGE 72)

The word is NEAT. If S is 5, I is 10. If I is 10, T is 1. Therefore N is 4. 4 - A = 1, so A is 3. Therefore E is 9.

WHAT DO YOU SEE?
(PART II) (PAGE 74)

1. D; 2. B; 3. No; 4. Yes

HELP THE DETECTIVE
(PART II) (PAGE 76)

1. A; 2. B; 3. C; 4. D

FINGERPRINT MATCH (PAGE 77)

The matching pairs are: A and K; B and E; C and F; D and I; G and L; H and J.

LOST LUGGAGE (PAGE 78)

Weights	Owners	Colors	Destinations
14 lbs	Felicia	orange	Emeryville
17 lbs	Wendell	blue	Albuquerque
20 lbs	Sierra	green	Boston
23 lbs	Charlie	yellow	Denver
26 lbs	Yolanda	pink	Calgary

SHE'S A COP! (PAGE 80)

Cold Case; CSI; In Plain Sight; Law and Order: SVU; Missing; Police Woman; Saving Grace; T.J. Hooker; The Closer; The Mod Squad; Without a Trace

MOTEL HIDEOUT (PAGE 82)

The thief is in room 41.

IDENTITY PARADE (PAGE 83)

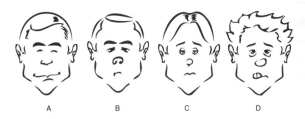

A   B   C   D

TREASURE HUNT (PAGE 84)

The order is: rubies, sapphires, pearls, gold coins, silver necklace, bronze tiara.

CRACK THE CODE (PAGE 85)

✳ = 1   ▲ = 3   ☸ = 4

❀ = 7   ❖ = 9

HOT PURSUIT (PAGE 86)

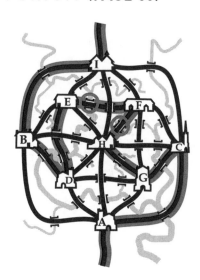

SPY FLY (PAGE 87)

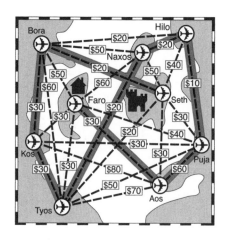

BUILDING BLUEPRINTS (PAGE 88)

B.

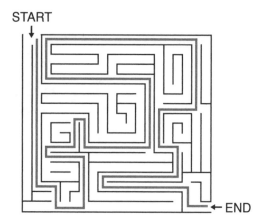

TREASURE HUNT (PAGE 89)

The order is: sapphires, gold coins, pearls, bronze tiara, silver necklace, rubies.

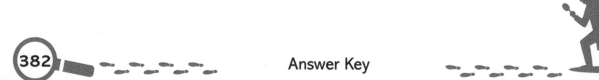

CATCH THE THIEF (PAGE 90)

The missing letter is A.
Departure, Paris, Wednesday, airplane

CRYPTO-LOGIC (PAGE 90)

SIMPLE. If T is 12 then P-1=4. So P is 5.
Therefore O is 10, S is 8. 10-S=M, so M is 2.
So I is 1. E is 3, and L is 6.

ROBBER RIDDLE (PAGE 91)

Why did the thief only say "meow" to the police?
Because he was a cat burglar.

GEMSTONE MATH (PAGE 91)

The count is: 1 aquamarine, 2 zircons,
3 diamonds, 4 garnets, 5 sapphires, and 6 pearls.

CAN'T BUY ME LUNCH (PAGE 92)

Denny had 1 one, 2 fives, and 1 ten for a total of
$21. Michelle had 2 ones, 1 five, and 1 ten for a
total of $17. John had 1 one, 3 fives, and no tens
for a total of $16. Cass had no ones, 2 fives, and
2 tens for a total of $30.

INTERCEPTION (PAGE 93)

Take the first two letters of each place name:
The meet will take place in "The city of Austin
in a big hotel."

WAYWARD HIKERS (PAGE 94)

Times	Hikers	Latitudes	Latitudes
4:20pm	Victoria	64.73	-110.22
5:05pm	Edna	64.19	-109.99
5:50pm	Kari	64.61	-110.01
6:35pm	Randall	64.38	-110.29
7:20pm	Luke	64.08	-110.42

FIND THE WITNESS (PAGE 96)

Riggins lives in house C.

HELP THE DETECTIVE (PART II) (PAGE 98)

1. A; 2. C; 3. B; 4. D

MOTEL HIDEOUT (PAGE 99)

The thief is in room 39.

HOT PURSUIT (PAGE 100)

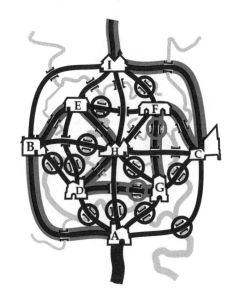

SPY FLY (PAGE 101)

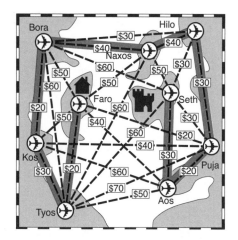

SPY SCRAMBLE (PAGE 102)

corner of Main and First

CRYPTO-LOGIC (PAGE 102)

PACE

CRYPTO-LOGIC (PAGE 103)

GREAT

MEALTIME CRIME (PAGE 103)

What did the headline read for the bakery theft that took place during the solstice in June? The summertime key lime crime.

CRACK THE CODE (PAGE 104)

☆ = 1   ✳ = 2   ✛ = 6

◆ = 8   ✪ = 9

WHAT DO YOU SEE? (PART II) (PAGE 106)

Picture 2 is a match.

A SET OF 13 CRYPTOGRAMS (PAGE 107)

1. The fear of the number thirteen is called triskaidekaphobia. 2. The thirteenth president was Millard Fillmore. 3. A baker's dozen contains thirteen loaves. 4. Thirteen is a prime number. 5. Musician Taylor Swift was born on December thirteenth. 6. The PG-thirteen rating debuted in 1984. 7. Red Dawn was the first movie released with that rating. 8. There are thirteen stripes on the American flag. 9. The Apollo thirteen mission happened in 1970. 10. The movie Friday the Thirteenth debuted in 1980. 11. There are twelve films in the franchise as of 2016. 12. The thirteenth amendment abolished slavery. 13. All these are encrypted with a method called ROT-thirteen.

CRIME RHYMES (PAGE 108)

1. eel steal; 2. bleu clue; 3. beef thief; 4. lime crime; 5. aperitif thief; 6. yacht plot; 7. reflective detective; 8. mint print

Answer Key

MOTEL HIDEOUT (PAGE 109)

The thief is in room 34.

TYPES OF EVIDENCE
(PART II) (PAGE 112)

1. True; 2. False. Palynology is the science that studies plant spores, insects, seeds, and other microorganisms. 3. False. 4. True. 5. True.

FINGERPRINT MATCH (PAGE 113)

The matching pairs are: A and M; B and G; C and P; D and K; E and J; F and O; H and I; L and N

THE ESCAPE ARTIST (PAGE 114)

Years	Prisons	States	Methods
2001	Middle Fork	Alabama	wire cutters
2005	Tulveride	Idaho	uniform
2009	Pennington	Montana	tunnel
2013	Lexington	Virginia	ladder
2017	Calahatchee	Colorado	rope

CRYPTOGRAM (PAGE 116)

Benjamin Franklin was a man of many pursuits. He served on the Committee of Secret Correspondence for the Second Continental Congress. It tried to sway foreign countries to the American cause.

QUOTABLE CRYPTOGRAMS
(PAGE 116)

Those who would give up essential Liberty, to purchase a little temporary Safety, deserve neither Liberty nor Safety.

Love your Enemies, for they tell you your Faults. I wish the Bald Eagle had not been chosen as the representative of our country; he is a bird of bad moral character; like those among men who live by sharping and robbing, he is generally poor, and often very lousy. The turkey is a much more respectable bird. —Benjamin Franklin

HELP THE DETECTIVE
(PART II) (PAGE 118)

1. A; 2. B; 3. D; 4. D

FIND THE WITNESS (PAGE 119)

Jenkins lives in house E.

HOMICIDE: LIFE ON THE STREETS (PAGE 120)

MOTEL HIDEOUT (PAGE 122)

The thief is in room 35.

TREASURE HUNT (PAGE 123)

The order is: Copenhagen (Denmark); Caracas (Venezuela); Canberra (Australia); Dakar (Senegal); Budapest (Hungary); Vientiane (Laos); Kingston (Jamaica); Nairobi (Kenya)

CRACK THE CODE (PAGE 124)

❋ = 3   ◯ = 5   ▲ = 6

❄ = 7   ◗ = 9   ❑ = 10

FIND THE MOLE (PAGE 125)

Answers may vary. FIND, fine, mine, mile, MOLE

FROM CLUES TO TRIAL (PAGE 125)

Answers may vary. CLUES, flues, flies, fries, tries, tried, triad, TRIAL

HOT PURSUIT (PAGE 126)

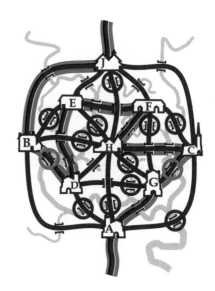

Answer Key

SPY FLY (PAGE 127)

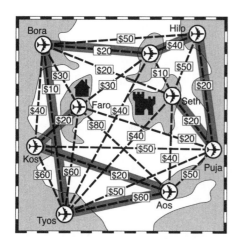

SPY SCRAMBLE (PAGE 128)

woman with a rose brooch will comment on the sunset

CRYPTO-LOGIC (PAGE 128)

DONE

SPY SCRAMBLE (PAGE 129)

third Tuesday of the month at two in the afternoon

A HEATED CRIME (PAGE 129)

What did the arsonist say to his sweetheart? C'mon, baby, light my fire.

PARKING TICKETS (PAGE 130)

Times	Models	Colors	Locations
10:00am	Nissan	black	Sandy St.
11:00am	Chevrolet	silver	Apple Ave.
12:00pm	Mazda	brown	Tawny Terr.
1:00pm	Honda	green	Raffle Rd.
2:00pm	Toyota	blue	Lantern Ln.

MOTEL HIDEOUT (PAGE 132)

The thief is in room 27.

INTERCEPTION (PAGE 133)

Take the central letter of each word: East and Fourth at Eight PM

HELP THE DETECTIVE (PAGE 134)

The order is: notepad, magnifying glass, pencil, fingerprint kit, flashlight, measuring tape

WHAT DO YOU SEE? (PART II) (PAGE 136)

Picture 3 is a match.

HELP THE DETECTIVE (PART II) (PAGE 138)

1. B; 2. A; 3. B; 4. C

INVESTIGATE THE ANAGRAM (PAGE 139)

The missing letter is V.
Solve, evidence, investigate, detective, thieves

NUMBER NOGGIN-SCRATCHER (PART II) (PAGE 140)

C. 672

A FAMOUS MYSTERY WRITER (PAGE 140)

Dame Agatha Christie's fictional detectives included Miss Jane Marple and Hercule Poirot.

BUILDING BLUEPRINTS (PAGE 141)

MOTEL HIDEOUT (PAGE 142)

The thief is in room 22.

CRACK THE CODE (PAGE 143)

❄ = 1   ● = 2   ✳ = 3

❖ = 7   ❑ = 8   ✺ = 9

THE SUSPECT LIST (PAGE 144)

Ages	Suspects	Professions	Towns
23	Vincent	lawyer	Midvale
26	Michael	engineer	Flagstaff
29	Nicholas	tennis pro	Billings
32	Albert	architect	Tulverton
35	Dennis	dentist	San Pedro

HOT PURSUIT (PAGE 146)

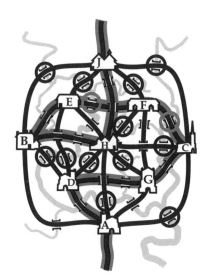

SPY FLY (PAGE 147)

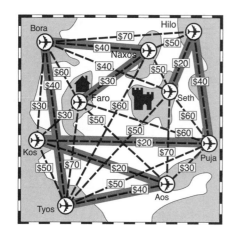

CRYPTO-LOGIC (PAGE 148)

NAME

FIND A CLUE ON A RAID (PAGE 148)

Answers may vary. CLUE, glue, glum, slum, slim, slid, said, RAID

BUILDING BLUEPRINTS (PAGE 149)

ART FAIR HUNT (PAGE 150)

The order is: oil portraits, black and white photographs, watercolor, color photographs, quilt, pottery, windchimes, jewelry, lamps.

ROBBER RIDDLE (PAGE 151)

Why did the robber take a bath before going to the bank?

Because he wanted to make sure he had a clean getaway.

TASTY CRYPTOGRAM (PAGE 151)

The secret recipe for KFC fried chicken is reportedly kept in a vault surrounded by motion detectors and guards.

SPY SCRAMBLE (PAGE 152)

May fourth at seven in the morning

SPY SCRAMBLE (PAGE 152)

April twenty eight at midnight

HOT PURSUIT (PAGE 153)

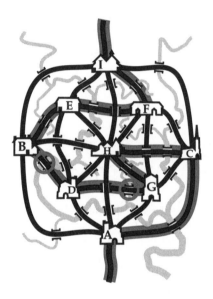

TREASURE HUNT (PAGE 154)

The order is: gold bars, antique map, lost painting, emeralds, opals, diamonds.

INTERCEPTION (PAGE 155)

Take the first and last letter of each phrase. The meeting will take place "On the tenth of June at noon at the riverbank."

IDENTITY PARADE (PAGE 156)

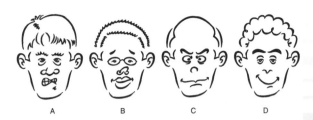

MOTEL HIDEOUT (PAGE 157)

The thief is in room 19.

TELEPHONE RECORDS (PAGE 158)

Times	People	Numbers	Lengths
1:52am	Kerry	239-4827	22 seconds
1:57am	Charlie	447-6995	3 minutes
2:02am	Vicky	731-9262	48 seconds
2:07am	Mitchell	592-0021	35 seconds
2:12am	Sarah	368-7841	1.5 minutes

BLETCHLEY PARK (PAGE 160)

CRACK THE CODE (PAGE 162)

◗ = 1   ◯ = 2   ❖ = 4

✪ = 7   ■ = 9   ❄ = 10

HELP THE DETECTIVE
(PART II) (PAGE 164)

1. A; 2. B; 3. B; 4. A

WHAT DO YOU SEE?
(PART II) (PAGE 166)

Picture 4 is a match.

FIND THE WITNESS (PAGE 167)

Mr. Locke lives in House B.

POISON! (PART II) (PAGE 170)

1. False. 2. False. 3. False. 4. True. 5. True

FINGERPRINT MATCH (PAGE 171)

The matching pairs are: A and K; B and I; C and L; D and J; E and H; F and N; G and P; M and O

SPY SCRAMBLE (PAGE 172)

forest preserve mile marker ten

ROBBER RIDDLE (PAGE 172)

Why did the robber wear white gloves? He didn't want to be caught red-handed.

CRACK THE PASSWORD (PAGE 173)

The missing letter is S.
monster, passion, relapse, scullery

CRYPTO-LOGIC (PAGE 173)

MAGIC. If S is 5 then M is 7, and U is 10.
Therefore C is 6, and E is 3. So G is thereby 4,
and A is 2. A plus G is 6, and 6 - 6 = I which is
therefore zero.

HOT PURSUIT (PAGE 174)

Answers may vary.

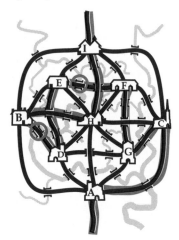

SPY FLY (PAGE 175)

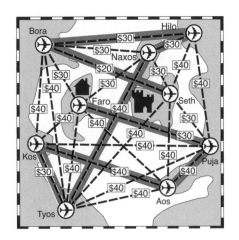

ILLEGAL PETS (PAGE 176)

Dates	Owners	Streets	Animals
August 4	Edith Estes	Walnut Ave.	skunk
August 5	Iva Ingram	Green Blvd.	bear cub
August 6	Gil Gates	Post St.	cheetah
August 7	Abe Alvarez	Island Rd.	wolf
August 8	Flora Flynn	Kirk Ln.	anaconda

MOTEL HIDEOUT (PAGE 178)

The thief is in room 16.

TREASURE HUNT (PAGE 179)

The order is: amethysts, gold bars, silver coins,
rubies, diamonds, sapphires.

Answer Key

LOST IN THE PENTAGON (PAGE 180)

CRACK THE CODE (PAGE 181)

● = 1   ✦ = 3   ○ = 5   ▲ = 7

▢ = 8   ◆ = 9   ✳ = 10

FIND THE WITNESS (PAGE 182)

The Banks live in house A.

HELP THE DETECTIVE (PART II) (PAGE 184)

1. A; 2. B; 3. B; 4. A

POP QUIZ: FORENSIC SCIENCE (PAGE 185)

1. No. They may have been there but worn gloves, for example. 2. No. A body farm describes a place where forensic investigators test to see what happens to corpses under different conditions. 3. Yes. 4. Yes. Many courts do not admit polygraph evidence, because they can show both false negatives and false positives. 5. Automated Fingerprint Identification System

CRYPTO-LOGIC (PAGE 186)

TRICKERY

ROBBER RIDDLE (PAGE 186)

Why did the burglar open his sack when it started to rain?

He was hoping for some change in the weather.

TREASURE HUNT (PAGE 187)

The order is: Luxembourg (Luxembourg); Moscow (Russia); Oslo (Norway); Tashkent (Uzbekistan); Washington DC (United States); New Delhi (India); Montevideo (Uruguay); Ankara (Turkey)

A CASE OF ARSON (PAGE 188)

Answers may vary. FIRE, dire, dirt, dart, cart, cast, CASE

PLANTED EVIDENCE AT THE SCENE (PAGE 188)

Answers may vary. PLANT, slant, scant, scent, SCENE

HOT PURSUIT (PAGE 189)

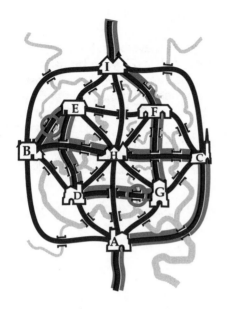

CIPHER TRIVIA (PAGE 193)

With book ciphers, both sender and receiver use the same book as the key to the cipher. The Bible and particular editions of the dictionary are sometimes used because they have many words available. Other people might use a more obscure book for an extra layer of security.

MOTEL HIDEOUT (PAGE 194)

The thief is in room 11.

WHAT DO YOU SEE? (PART II) (PAGE 196)

Picture 4 is a match.

GRAVE ROBBERIES (PAGE 190)

Dates	Cemeteries	Graves	Towns
March 12th	Box Grove	Brad Beaudry	Verona
March 20th	Apple Pine	Ruben Yates	Upperdale
March 28th	Green Lawn	Pat Fowler	Shell City
April 5th	Calvary Cape	Holden Bray	Wilmette
April 13th	Dinby Dale	Ed Lowder	Trenton

BUILDING BLUEPRINTS (PAGE 197)

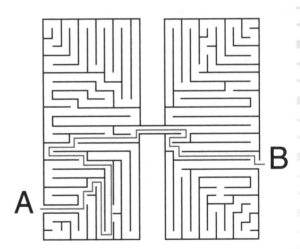

INTERCEPTION (PAGE 192)

Take the central letter of each word and you get ALINAM. Flip this, and it becomes MANILA

CRYPTO-LOGIC (PAGE 193)

SIMPLIFY

TREASURE HUNT (PAGE 198)

The order is: Bangkok (Thailand); Dodoma (Tanzania); Madrid (Spain); Amsterdam (Netherlands); Algiers (Algeria); Lima (Peru); Skopje (Macedonia), and Tokyo (Japan).

CRACK THE PASSWORD (PAGE 199)

The missing letter is O.
noise, primrose, loaner, mosaic

GEMSTONE MATH (PAGE 199)

There are: 1 diamond, 2 rubies, 3 emeralds, 4 garnets, 5 pearls, 6 amethysts, 7 sapphires, 8 opals.

FORENSIC CAREERS (PAGE 200)

```
Y  P  W  Z  B  Z  P  P  R  D  C  H  E  M  I  S  T  T
G  K  Q  W  P  A  C  C  O  U  N  T  A  N  T  S  V
O  T  J  I  W  U  A  F  F  U  G  T  G  A  I  L  R
L  M  E  D  I  C  A  L  E  X  A  M  I  N  E  R  E
O  L  A  B  T  E  C  H  N  I  C  I  A  N  T  G  N
T  S  I  G  O  L  O  P  O  R  H  T  N  A  U  T  I
N  P  D  G  N  M  Z  V  O  C  O  Y  E  V  V  J  M
O  V  A  U  H  S  O  R  L  B  J  C  U  V  A  K  A
D  T  R  D  E  N  T  O  M  O  L  O  G  I  S  T  X
O  S  I  N  V  E  S  T  I  G  A  T  O  R  P  J  E
E  S  I  G  Q  F  C  E  S  X  M  U  T  Z  A  A  S
P  S  Y  C  H  O  L  O  G  I  S  T  B  F  K  W  T
R  T  S  I  T  N  E  D  Q  D  G  L  N  G  U  S  N
Z  T  H  I  L  P  A  T  H  O  L  O  G  I  S  T  E
P  K  B  N  U  M  D  N  A  A  N  A  L  Y  S  T  M
T  O  X  I  C  O  L  O  G  I  S  T  B  O  D  N  U
T  K  X  R  Q  U  R  R  I  Z  Z  P  H  U  I  W  C
T  S  Y  L  A  N  A  R  E  T  U  P  M  O  C  B  O
T  R  E  P  X  E  S  C  I  T  S  I  L  L  A  B  D
N  A  I  C  I  N  H  C  E  T  E  C  N  E  I  C  S
```

CRACK THE CODE (PAGE 202)

◯ = 1   ❄ = 2   ◗ = 3   ✳ = 4
❖ = 7   ■ = 8   ✴ = 9

HELP THE DETECTIVE (PART II) (PAGE 204)

1. C; 2. A; 3. A; 4. D

FIND THE WITNESS (PAGE 205)

The Winchells live in house B.

WITNESS STATEMENTS (PAGE 206)

Heights	Witnesses	Weights	Cars
5' 2"	Russell T.	190 lbs	Chevrolet
5' 5"	Sarah M.	145 lbs	Toyota
5' 8"	Yolanda V.	135 lbs	Honda
5' 11"	Angela S.	225 lbs	Mazda
6' 2"	Gerald F.	160 lbs	Nissan

MOTEL HIDEOUT (PAGE 208)

The thief is in room 24.

CRIME RHYMES (PAGE 209)

1. fry alibi; 2. lyre fire; 3. steeplechase case;
4. melon felon; 5. knock hemlock; 6. supplied
cyanide; 7. gem mayhem; 8. mortician suspicion

HOT PURSUIT (PAGE 210)

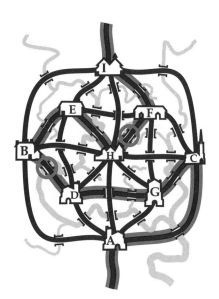

CRYPTO-LOGIC (PAGE 211)

HOWEVER

CRYPTO-LOGIC (PAGE 211)

RIGHT

THE BODY FARM (PART II) (PAGE 214)

1. False. 2. True. 3. True. 4. True. 5. False

SPY SCRAMBLE (PAGE 215)

third floor of museum in the modern art section

CRACK THE PASSWORD (PAGE 215)

The missing letter is L.
amoral, central, flamingo, musical

SPY FLY (PAGE 216)

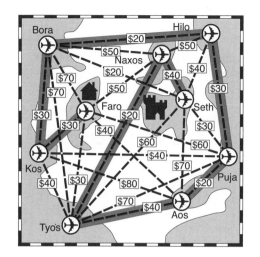

INTERCEPTION (PAGE 217)

Take the second letter of each word and you reveal: BUCHAREST

CRYPTO-LOGIC (PAGE 218)

BLAST

CRYPTO-LOGIC (PAGE 218)

SWEET

WORDS ABOUT A CONUNDRUM (PAGE 219)

The phrase, "It is a riddle wrapped in a mystery wrapped inside an enigma" was first said by Sir Winston Churchill in a radio address in 1939. He was speaking of Russia's unpredictability, saying, "I cannot forecast to you the action of Russia."

WHICH SLEUTH WAS HE AGAIN? (PAGE 219)

Humphrey Bogart played the part of both Sam Spade, based on Dashiell Hammett's fictional detective in "The Maltese Falcon," and Philip Marlowe, protagonist of Raymond Chandler's "The Big Sleep."

MOTEL HIDEOUT (PAGE 220)

The thief is in room 37.

CRACK THE CODE (PAGE 221)

◆ = 1   ▢ = 4   ❄ = 5   ✳ = 6

◉ = 7   ● = 8   ○ = 10

POP QUIZ: FORENSIC SCIENCE (PAGE 222)

1. How to tell drowning from strangulation. 2. 1800s. 3. 1980s. 4. 1900s. 5. 1908.

Answer Key

HELP THE DETECTIVE (PART II) (PAGE 224)

1. A; 2. D; 3. C; 4. A

FINGERPRINT MATCH (PAGE 225)

C, F, and I are matches.

FIND THE WITNESS (PAGE 226)

Mr. Foreman lives in House A.

WHAT DO YOU SEE? (PART II) (PAGE 228)

Picture 1 is a match.

IDENTITY PARADE (PAGE 229)

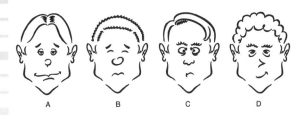

INTERNATIONAL FUGITIVES (PAGE 230)

Dates	Criminals	Crimes	Countries
October 3	Grendle	robbery	Peru
October 4	Dornmer	forgery	Moldova
October 5	Filcher	tax evasion	France
October 6	Blackforth	arson	Uganda
October 7	Calumnet	blackmail	Sweden

HISTORICAL CRYPTOGRAM (PAGE 232)

Benedict Arnold used a book cipher to send messages during the American Revolution. He used a book called Commentaries on the Laws of England by William Blackstone.

QUOTABLE CRYPTOGRAM (PAGE 232)

Few persons can be made to believe that it is not quite an easy thing to invent a method of secret writing which shall baffle investigation. Yet it may be roundly asserted that human ingenuity cannot concoct a cipher which human ingenuity cannot resolve. —Edgar Allan Poe

HOT PURSUIT (PAGE 233)

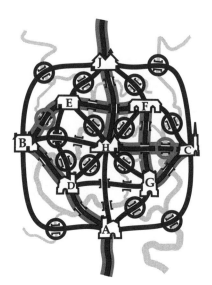

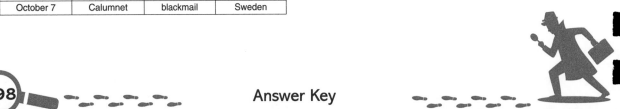

BUILDING BLUEPRINTS (PAGE 234)

SPY FLY (PAGE 235)

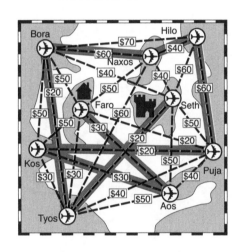

TREASURE HUNT (PAGE 236)

The order is: Los Angeles, California; Chicago, Illinois; Austin, Texas; St. Louis, Missouri; Dallas, Texas; Portland, Oregon; Boston, Massachusetts; Tallahassee, Florida.

CRYPTO-LOGIC (PAGE 237)

IMPROVE

CRYPTO-LOGIC (PAGE 237)

REARING

CRIME STINKS (PAGE 238)

Answers may vary. CRIME, prime, pride, bride, brine, brink, blink, slink, STINK

HEROES (PAGE 238)

During World War I, a group of Choctaw Indians used their language to create codes for the United States military that could not be deciphered by the opposing side. During World War II, Navajo soldiers, primarily marines, also became code talkers in the fight against Hitler and the Axis powers.

CRACK THE CODE (PAGE 239)

❄ = 1   ◆ = 2   ◯ = 3   ✳ = 4
◗ = 5   ■ = 6   ❅ = 8

MEDICAL EXAMINERS (PAGE 240)

```
L M K C A M I L L E S A R O Y A N
N O S N K A Y S C A R P E T T A D
O F R E N O S K C A J D L A R E G
T O T E L X O C A N N A I L U J Y
R R A G T S F Y F L E K Z D P C C
A L A L L T I M S Q V J A U G M H
H L W H H Q A A A B G X B F S E G
W N E A K B U W R X K H E E P L U
E P P X B C F I A U B R T L V I A
I N Y E X P O P N D A E H I X N A
K Z U R W W Q L M C E M R X G D A
N A J H I N O T E P Y L O G F A V
A L B O N Y E O Q V S A D I M W A
R R E T O A K N D A E P G B M A C
F O D E E X G C O S H Y E S D R N
J B C S Z X G E G O Y M R O Q N A
S B L P H W E I M V Y M S N D E D
Y I S P I L L I H P D I V A D R R
T N P G J D Q P Q R O J F D X B O
Y S Q R O S E S C H W A R T Z L J
```

MOTEL HIDEOUT (PAGE 242)

The thief is in room 54.

SPY SCRAMBLE (PAGE 243)

1. June twelve, Eiffel Tower; 2. Ides of March, Stonehenge; 3. November thirtieth, top of Mount Fuji; 4. Halloween, Colosseum; 5. Next Tuesday, Machu Picchu

MARKED BILLS (PAGE 244)

Dates	Serials	Locations	Denominations
April 1	G-718428	Torbin	$50
April 5	F-667280	Midvale	$100
April 9	B-492841	Uteville	$5
April 13	C-918303	Nettleton	$10
April 17	P-101445	Finsberg	$20

CRYPTO-LOGIC (PAGE 246)

GENIUS. If A is 8 then B is 2, and 2I is therefore 2, making I value 1. E is thus 4, and so G is 6. R is hence 10, and so U is 5, and N is 9. 9 - 2 = S which is therefore 7.

IN PLAIN SIGHT (PAGE 246)

When you conceal your message in another form of text—for example, hiding information in a grocery list or a classified ad—it is called steganography. Writing a message in invisible ink and writing a regular message over it is one form of steganography.

HOT PURSUIT (PAGE 247)

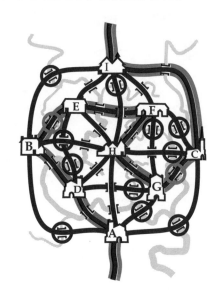

SPY SCRAMBLE (PAGE 248)

1.Buenos Aires, last flight; 2.Singapore, sunrise; 3.Sydney, eleven AM; 4. Chicago, midnight; 5. Johannesburg fifteen hundred hours

SPY FLY (PAGE 249)

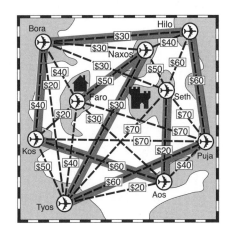

FIND THE WITNESS (PAGE 250)

Rodriguez lives in house D.

TREASURE HUNT (PAGE 251)

The order is: Charleston, South Carolina; Topeka, Kansas; Oklahoma City, Oklahoma; Baltimore, Maryland; Milwaukee, Wisconsin; San Diego, California; Boise, Idaho; Atlanta, Georgia.

BUILDING BLUEPRINTS (PAGE 252)

C.

ALL SECRET PLOTS LEAVE CLUES (PAGE 253)

Answers may vary. PLOTS, slots, slits, flits, flies, flues, CLUES

CRYPTO-LOGIC (PAGE 253)

DECEPTIVE

RACE TO A SOLUTION (PAGE 254)

After an early career as a jockey, Dick Francis became a mystery novelist. The mysteries in his popular bestselling novels often had a connection to the British racing world.

A LADY OF MYSTERY (PAGE 254)

P.D. James, born Phyllis Dorothy James, was a British crime writer. Her protagonist was police commander Adam Dalgliesh, who also wrote poetry. She was given the title of Baroness later in life.

HOT PURSUIT (PAGE 255)

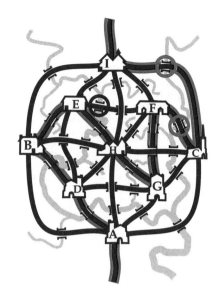

MOTEL HIDEOUT (PAGE 256)

The thief is in room 14.

HELP THE DETECTIVE
(PART II) (PAGE 258)

1. The second floor; 2. The rubies; 3. underneath the carpet in the den on the third floor;
4. The opals

CRACK THE CODE (PAGE 259)

▲ = 1   ◆ = 4   ✹ = 6   ▢ = 7

● = 8   ✳ = 9   ○ = 10

REMEMBERING THE SCENE
(PART II) (PAGE 262)

1. C; 2. False; 3. False; 4. False; 5. B; 6. C

WHAT DO YOU SEE?
(PART II) (PAGE 264)

Picture 3 is a match.

FIND THE WITNESS (PAGE 265)

Mr. Stark lives in House D.

PARADE PARKING (PAGE 266)

Times	License Plates	Locations	Brands
6:10 A.M.	BYS-81S	Racine Blvd.	Alfa Romeo
6:15 A.M.	XR6-192	First St.	Cadillac
6:20 A.M.	A14-S1D	Mitre Sq.	Subaru
6:25 A.M.	QE2-01C	Park St.	Isuzu
6:30 A.M.	JIB-P09	Bolero Ct.	Hyundai

SPY FLY (PAGE 268)

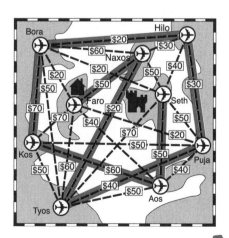

CRYPTO-LOGIC (PAGE 269)

TORTUROUS
F=1
N=16
O=9
R=3
S=7
T=5
U=4

A MAKER OF PUZZLES (PAGE 269)

Henry Dudeney was an English mathematician and puzzle creator who created many mathematical and logic puzzles. He used the pseudonym Sphinx when he first published.

FINGERPRINT MATCH (PAGE 270)

H is the matching fingerprint.

HOT PURSUIT (PAGE 271)

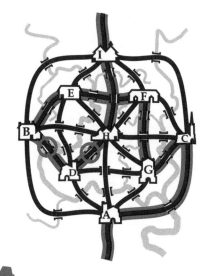

SOLVING CASES (PAGE 272)

Answers may vary. SOLVE, salve, calve, carve, curve, curvy, curly, curls, cures, cares, CASES

SETTING A PRECEDENT (PAGE 273)

Edgar Allan Poe is considered the father of the modern detective story. His protagonist C. Auguste Dupin was an amateur solver of crimes. He established many conventions of later detective fiction.

A MYSTERY FROM HISTORY (PAGE 273)

The Voynich manuscript is a famous manuscript that has challenged cryptographers. The manuscript supposedly dates back to the early fifteen century. It contains drawings of plants and other objects accompanied by text, but no one has been able to decipher the text.

INTERCEPTION (PAGE 274)

Take the first letter and the last letter of each word to reveal: WASHINGTON DC

SPY FLY (PAGE 275)

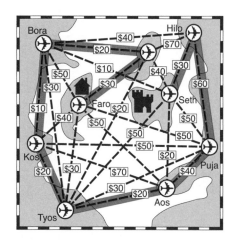

HOT PURSUIT (PAGE 276)

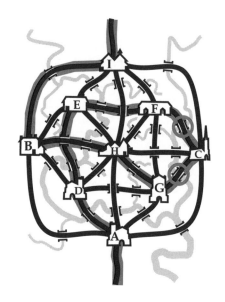

MOTEL HIDEOUT (PAGE 277)

The thief is in room 45.

CRACK THE CODE (PAGE 278)

✳ = 2   ❄ = 3   ☀ = 5   ■ = 6

○ = 8   ❖ = 9   ◗ = 10

FIND THE WITNESS (PAGE 279)

White lives in house C.

INVESTIGATIVE TOOLS (PAGE 280)

E	S	S	T	P	F	H	A	P	A	P	E	R	B	A	G	S
P	Y	L	H	S	G	V	Y	K	M	L	R	M	B	C	S	M
A	V	A	G	T	E	C	B	I	O	E	O	S	C	E	G	R
T	A	I	I	I	G	R	X	R	E	A	T	V	P	S	A	O
G	C	R	L	K	O	L	A	H	K	S	N	U	L	V	B	F
N	B	E	H	T	R	O	O	L	I	R	I	B	A	G	D	H
I	E	T	S	N	S	N	B	G	F	E	A	A	S	J	R	C
R	K	A	I	E	L	R	B	P	Z	P	R	T	J	I	A	R
U	L	M	L	R	I	K	U	P	I	E	Y	R	I	K	Z	A
S	A	G	F	P	T	E	L	S	Z	E	A	I	C	B	A	E
A	H	N	C	T	O	C	E	B	J	W	R	C	B	I	H	S
E	C	I	A	N	O	H	R	N	G	T	P	A	A	N	O	O
M	G	T	M	E	B	G	L	O	V	E	S	D	G	D	I	T
F	A	S	E	T	G	T	A	T	J	I	Q	E	G	L	B	T
S	G	A	R	A	V	L	R	E	G	P	R	T	I	E	V	N
S	X	C	A	L	R	L	Q	B	A	X	Z	A	E	P	Z	E
R	T	Y	V	K	H	F	T	O	T	M	B	P	S	A	J	S
A	G	E	B	V	T	I	S	O	U	U	K	E	B	P	W	N
G	I	C	M	V	D	H	E	K	G	K	H	U	J	E	E	O
R	E	D	R	O	C	E	R	O	I	D	U	A	P	R	A	C

RARE WINES (PAGE 282)

Vintages	Wines	Types	Countries
1954	Weimerund	syrah	Italy
1958	Ania Branco	pinot noir	Spain
1962	Friambliss	pinot gris	Portugal
1966	Ece Suss	chardonnay	Greece
1970	Vendemmia	merlot	France

SPY SCRAMBLE (PAGE 284)

1. Paris, Louvre, noon; 2. New York City, Statue of Liberty, seven PM; 3. Hong Kong, Victoria Peak, ten AM; 4. Barcelona, Parc Guell, morning; 5. Seattle, Space Needle, two PM

BUILDING BLUEPRINTS (PAGE 285)

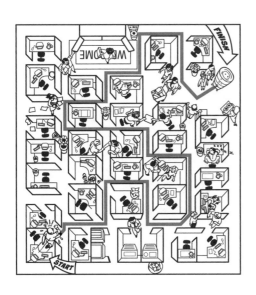

SPY FLY (PAGE 286)

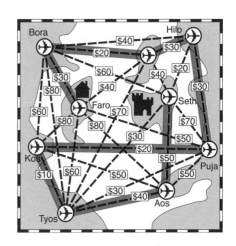

CRYPTO-LOGIC (PAGE 287)

COMPLEX. Z is 25 making C value 5. So T is 10, and 10 - U = L. E + 5 = U - 2. So E + 7 = U. 2E = 10 - U. So E + 7 = 10 - 2E. So 3E = 7, making E value 1. So L is 2, and N is 6. U is 8, M is 3, and P is 4. Therefore O is 9, and H is minus 2. F is 11, and X is 7.

CRACK THE PASSWORD (PAGE 288)

The missing letter is P.
clapper, desperate, flipper, input

WE STILL DON'T KNOW WHO DONE IT (PAGE 288)

One famous unsolved case involves thefts of artwork from the Isabella Stewart Gartner Museum. In 1990, men posing as police officers stole 13 works of art worth hundreds of millions of dollars. Empty frames at the museum show where the artwork was.

DON'T LEAVE A PRINT (PAGE 289)

Answers may vary. LEAVE, heave, heavy, heady, heads, hears, heirs, hairs, pairs, paint, PRINT

QUOTABLE CRYPTOGRAMS (PAGE 290)

1. There are no secrets that time does not reveal. —Jean Racine; 2. I shall be as secret as the grave. —Miguel de Cervantes; 3. A wonderful fact to reflect upon, that every human creature is constituted to be that profound secret and mystery to every other. —Charles Dickens; 4. No one ever keeps a secret so well as a child. —Victor Hugo. 5. Three may keep a secret, if two of them are dead. —Benjamin Franklin

TREASURE HUNT (PAGE 291)

The order is: Seattle, Washington; Washington, D.C.; Albuquerque, New Mexico; Detroit, Michigan; Cleveland, Ohio; Des Moines, Iowa; Richmond, Virginia; Philadelphia, Pennsylvania.

HOT PURSUIT (PAGE 292)

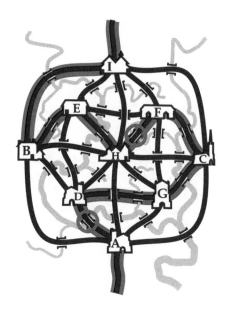

SPY FLY (PAGE 293)

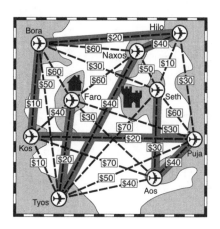

MOTEL HIDEOUT (PAGE 294)

The thief is in room 12.

WHAT DO YOU SEE? (PART II) (PAGE 296)

1. Two, numbered 1 and 4; 2. Wineglass; 3. Fork;
4. True; 5. True

CRACK THE CODE (PAGE 297)

□ = 1   ○ = 3   ● = 4   ❄ = 5
✳ = 6   ❖ = 8   ✳ = 9   ▼ = 10

SMUGGLED ELECTRONICS (PAGE 298)

Departures	Flights	Gates	Items
8:03am	108	11	watches
8:10am	233	18	televisions
8:17am	356	3	tablets
8:24am	510	6	cell phones
8:31am	92	7	laptops

FINGERPRINT MATCH (PAGE 300)

H is the matching fingerprint.

FIND THE WITNESS (PAGE 301)

Perez lives in house D.

GEMSTONE MATH (PAGE 302)

The count is: 1 agate, 2 zircons, 3 rubies,
4 pearls, 5 amethysts, 6 sapphires, and 7 garnets.

CRYPTO-LOGIC (PAGE 302)

NUANCED. U+A=5. So X is 10. So N is 5. The
only values which will make 5 when added, which
are present in the encrypted sequence of letters,
are 2 and 3, which are the values of A and of U.
Therefore D is 1 and C is 9.

INTERCEPTION (PAGE 303)

Take the central letter of each word in the phrase
and you get: ESUOHEFAS, CED, TSRIF,MPENO.
Read each item backwards and you get: safe-
house, Dec. first, One PM.

A SAD STATISTIC (PAGE 304)

The percentage of stolen art that is recovered
is not very high. Only five to ten percent might
be recovered.

A MYSTERIOUS EVENT (PAGE 304)

The year 1911 involved a notable case of art
theft—the Mona Lisa was stolen from the Louvre
by an employee. He was caught two years later
and the painting was returned to its home.

CRYPTO-LOGIC (PAGE 305)

SCRUTINY. If F is 10, then 10 - T - U - I = 5,
making the value of T plus U plus I five or less
(therefore 1, 2 and 3). U is less than I and I is less
than T. So T is 3, I is 2, and U is 1. 3Y is 12, so Y
is 4. Therefore C is 6, and hence S is 8. Therefore
R is 5, and P is 45, and N is 9. So I is 2.

THE CON ARTIST (PAGE 306)

Months	Names	Towns	Careers
March	Abe Avery	Valero	accountant
April	Fred Flores	Opalville	doctor
May	Matt Mintz	Nanaimo	reporter
June	Sean Starr	Beaverton	bank mgr.
July	Pat Perry	Trippany	dentist
August	Lou Lemon	Hoople	lawyer

SPY FLY (PAGE 308)

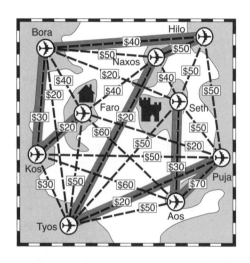

BUILDING BLUEPRINTS (PAGE 309)

MOTEL HIDEOUT (PAGE 310)

The thief is in room 32.

HOT PURSUIT (PAGE 311)

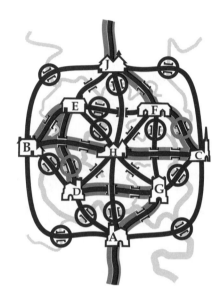

TREASURE HUNT (PAGE 312)

The order is: Ottawa, Canada; Houston, Texas, USA; Salt Lake City, Utah, USA; Toronto, Canada; Mexico City, Mexico; Guadalajara, Mexico; New Orleans, Louisiana, USA; Reno, Nevada, USA.

CRACK THE CLUES (PAGE 313)

Answers may vary. CRACK, track, trick, thick, think, thins, chins, chips, clips, flips, flies, flues, CLUES

LOST LIBRARY BOOKS (PAGE 314)

Years	Borrowers	Authors	Titles
1918	Danica	Keith Koch	*Grey Skies*
1931	Angelica	Heddy Heath	*In or Out*
1944	Edith	Jim Joyner	*Just Friends*
1957	Bailey	Nick Norris	*Fine Days*
1970	Charles	Midge Mintz	*High Tide*

CRACK THE CODE (PAGE 316)

◆ = 2   ● = 3   ▢ = 4   ※ = 5

○ = 6   ✳ = 7   ❖ = 8   ❄ = 10

HELP THE DETECTIVE (PART II) (PAGE 318)

1. B. False; 2. B. False; 3. A. True; 4. A. True; 5. B. False.

IDENTITY PARADE (PAGE 319)

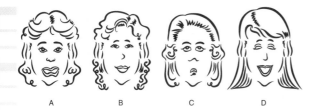

A   B   C   D

ESPIONAGE (PAGE 320)

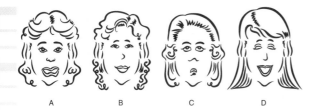

KNOWNS AND UNKNOWNS (PART II) (PAGE 324)

1. Possibly true. If Hrupington did take the laptop to the conference, and it is now missing from the hotel room, it seems likely that the murderer did take the laptop. However, the accounts of the roommate and boyfriend cast some doubt on this. 2. This seems unlikely. While the laptop may have been stolen, other valuables such as jewelry and smartphone were left behind. 3. Possibly true. While we do know that Hrupington withdrew $80 from an ATM on the Wednesday before the murder, it could have been spent prior to the murder. 4. This seems likely, as they did not belong to Hrupington. 5. False. Hrupington attended a panel Friday afternoon.

QUICK CRIME QUIZ (PAGE 325)

1. True. Fingerprints were used as signatures as far back as ancient Babylon; 2. Fingerprints; 3. True. Bertillion's system produced a set of measurements for each person (for instance, the length of their head, their middle finger, and their foot) that were, in theory, unique to that person. 4. Mug shots; 5. 1850

WITNESS STATEMENTS (PART II) (PAGE 328)

Thursday, 8 PM: Hrupington checks into hotel; Thursday, 10 PM: Hrupington visits hotel bar; Friday, 9 AM: Freesia Jones sees Hrupington outside their rooms; Friday, 2 PM: Hrupington at mulch panel; Friday, 4 PM: Hrupington attends rose panel; Friday, 6:30 PM: Hrupington attends dinner at hotel restaurant; Friday, 8 PM: Hrupington leaves restaurant; Friday, 9 PM: Smith hears movement in room next to his (Hrupington's)

Bonus answer: Waxman, the moderator of the mulch panel, said he had first spoken to her at the mulch panel on Friday, but the waitstaff identified him as one of the people to speak to Hrupington at the hotel bar on Thursday night.

WHAT DO YOU SEE? (PART II) (PAGE 330)

1. Open; 2. False; 3. Chest of drawers; 4. Left hand; 5. No.

CRYPTO-LOGIC (PAGE 331)

TANGENTIAL

ADDING INSULT TO INJURY (PAGE 331)

1994 saw the theft of a version of Edvard Munch's painting The Scream from a gallery in Oslo. The thieves left behind a note thanking the museum for poor security. The last laugh was on the museum, though, as police recovered the painting and caught the thieves.

ANNA'S ALIBIS (PAGE 332)

Times	Alibis	Relations	Locations
8:00pm	Penny Pugh	neighbor	Delancey Rd.
8:30pm	Lina Lopez	friend	First St.
9:00pm	Norma Neet	co-worker	Ewing Ave.
9:30pm	Maddy Meyer	bartender	Capitol St.
10:00pm	Oda Osborn	cousin	Border Ln.

CRIME RHYMES (PAGE 334)

1. stolen colon; 2. yuletide homicide; 3. subliminal criminal; 4. indict knight; 5. swaps cops; 6. steal oatmeal; 7. illegal beagle; 8. mime crime

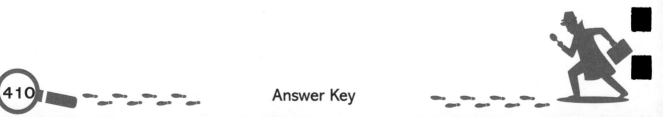

CRACK THE CODE (PAGE 335)

▼ = 1   ● = 2   ✳ = 3   ❋ = 5

❖ = 6   ○ = 7   ❄ = 8   ▢ = 9

FINGERPRINT MATCH (PAGE 336)

The matching pairs are: A and S; B and V; C and P; D and M; E and O; F and G; H and T; I and R; J and X; K and W; L and U; N and Q

MOTEL HIDEOUT (PAGE 337)

The thief is in room 28.

POLICE DISPATCHER (PAGE 338)

Times	Officers	Calls	Locations
8:45am	Neville	bank robbery	Midtown
9:30am	Harry	alarm	Downtown
10:15am	Linda	stolen car	Bus. District
11:00am	Jeffrey	trespassing	South End
11:45am	Dale	cat in tree	Uptown
12:30pm	Brenda	accident	North End

TREASURE HUNT (PAGE 340)

The order is: Krakow, Poland; Prague, Czech Republic; Rabat, Morocco; Antananarivo, Madagascar; Kuala Lumpur, Malaysia; Singapore; Barcelona, Spain; Quito, Ecuador

HOT PURSUIT (PAGE 341)

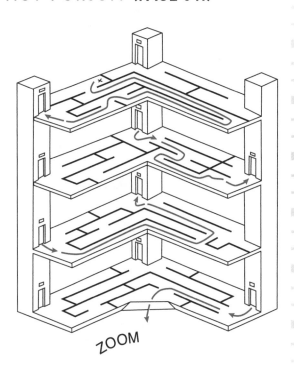

ZOOM

SPY FLY (PAGE 342)

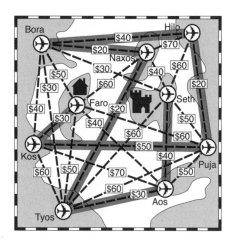

FOUR FUN FACTS (PAGE 343)

In spy terminology, a secret source is called an asset.

Another word for a spy is a birdwatcher.

When an undercover agent's identity is revealed, his or her cover is said to be blown.

When an undercover agent gives real but inconsequential information to the enemy in order to prove himself or herself, that information is called chicken feed.

STOLEN STREET SIGNS (PAGE 344)

Dates	Signs	Streets	Streets
July 4th	One Way	Dwight St.	Ralston Ave.
July 11th	Speed Limit	Casper Blvd.	Tarragon Ln.
July 18th	Dead End	Amble Ln.	Quinella St.
July 25th	Yield	Barnacle Rd.	Selby St.
August 1st	Stop	Falstaff St.	Oracle Rd.
August 8th	No Parking	Everett Ave.	Peabody Ln.

HOT PURSUIT (PAGE 346)

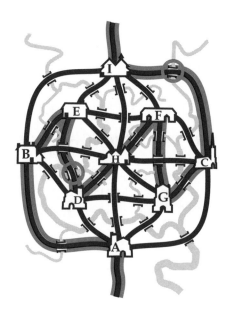

CRYPTO-LOGIC (PAGE 347)

VARNISHED

A PROLIFIC ROBBER (PAGE 347)

John Tillmann, a Canadian art thief, stole more than 10,000 objects of art, including painting, sculptures, and rare books. He was arrested in 2013.

FIND THE WITNESS (PAGE 348)

Brown lives in house E.

SPY FLY (PAGE 349)

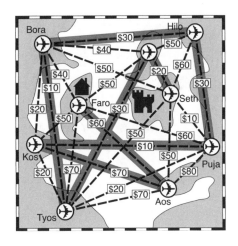

MOTEL HIDEOUT (PAGE 350)

The thief is in room 42.

CRACK THE CODE (PAGE 351)

❄ = 1   ✳ = 2   ● = 3   ❖ = 4

✴ = 5   ▼ = 7   ☐ = 8   ◯ = 9

IN OTHER WORDS (PAGE 352)

Synonyms for mysterious include secret, enigmatic, furtive, shadowy, cryptic, and clandestine.

NOTHING TO DO WITH DOYLE (PAGE 352)

H.H. Holmes wasn't a fictional detective—he was a serial killer, often considered the first in America. Born Herman Webster Mudgett in 1861, he confessed to 27 murders but may have been responsible for more. He was also a bigamist, married to three women at the time of his death.

CRIMINAL BROS (PAGE 353)

Jesse and Frank James joined the Quantrill Raiders gang in their teen years and began their lifestyle of bank and train robbery. Jesse's mother Zerelda wrote a book after his death with the dedication: "In Loving Memory of my Beloved Son, Murdered by a Traitor and Coward Whose Name is not Worthy to Appear Here."

NOTHING TO DO WITH DOYLE (PAGE 352)

H.H. Holmes wasn't a fictional detective—he was a serial killer, often considered the first in America. Born Herman Webster Mudgett in 1861, he confessed to 27 murders but may have been responsible for more. He was also a bigamist, married to three women at the time of his death.

CRIMINAL BROS (PAGE 353)

Jesse and Frank James joined the Quantrill Raiders gang in their teen years and began their lifestyle of bank and train robbery. Jesse's mother Zerelda wrote a book after his death with the dedication: "In Loving Memory of my Beloved Son, Murdered by a Traitor and Coward Whose Name is not Worthy to Appear Here."

THE MASTER FORGER (PAGE 354)

Prices	Paintings	Countries	Artists
$1,000,000	Baby Jane	Germany	Greta Frank
$2,000,000	Cold Hills	Canada	Inga Howell
$4,000,000	Day of Night	Portugal	Margot Lane
$8,000,000	Forever Blue	France	Hal Garrison
$16,000,000	Awestruck	Spain	Freda Estes
$32,000,000	Eighteen	Norway	Lyle Kramer

HOT PURSUIT (PAGE 356)

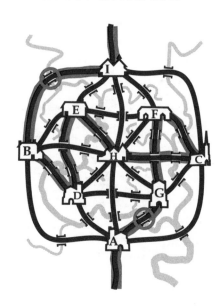

SPY FLY (PAGE 357)

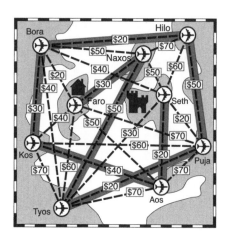

INTERCEPTION (PAGE 358)

Take the first letter of the first word, the last letter of the second word, the first letter of the third word, and the last letter of the fourth word. Continue, alternating between the first letter of one word and the final letter of the next word, until you have the whole message: April third, noon, park, Main Street

TREASURE HUNT (PAGE 359)

The order is: London (England); Paris (France); Pretoria (South Africa); Singapore, Cairo (Egypt); Jakarta (Indonesia); Sydney (Australia); Buenos Aires (Argentina); Rio de Janeiro (Brazil)

BANK ROBBERIES (PAGE 360)

Dates	Banks	Towns	Amounts
June 3	First Trust	Longwood	$1,000
June 5	Moneycorp	Yountville	$1,600
June 7	Wellspring	Tahoe	$4,800
June 9	Bell Largo	Grumley	$2,500
June 11	Apex	Cold Spring	$10,200

SPY SCRAMBLE (PAGE 362)

1. public library, under second table; 2. park gazebo, under largest planter; 3. train station, behind large green sign; 4. swimming pool, third locker from left; 5. outside museum, under red bench

HOT PURSUIT (PAGE 363)

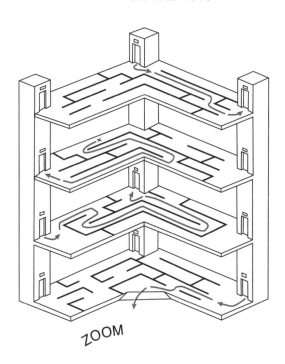

ZOOM

THE CAT BURGLAR (PAGE 364)

Years	Cities	Items	Months
1963	London	sapphires	October
1970	Berlin	gold bars	September
1977	Vancouver	emeralds	July
1984	Paris	cash	June
1991	Antwerp	diamonds	April
1998	Seattle	rubies	May

MOTEL HIDEOUT (PAGE 366)

The thief is in room 59.

Answer Key

WHAT DO YOU SEE? (PART II) (PAGE 368)

1. False; 2. 4; 3; False; 4. True; 5. False

FIND THE WITNESS (PAGE 369)

King lives in house C.

FINGERPRINT MATCH (PAGE 370)

Q and W are the matching fingerprints.

CRACK THE CODE (PAGE 371)

◐ = 1   ❄ = 2   ◆ = 3   ✳ = 5

❖ = 6   ▢ = 7   ✺ = 8   ● = 9

TEST YOUR OBSERVATIONAL SKILLS (PAGE 372)

1. Three men in the mirror; 2. Customer still has hair in mirror image; 3. Person hanging on coatrack; 4. Magazine is upside-down; 5. Sandwich and shoe shine on price list; 6. Everyone is bald; 7. Shampoo costs more than a haircut

CODE-DOKU (PAGE 373)

A	P	N	O	I	M	E	C	L
E	O	M	N	C	L	I	P	A
C	L	I	P	A	E	N	M	O
O	I	A	E	N	C	M	L	P
N	C	P	M	L	I	A	O	E
M	E	L	A	P	O	C	I	N
L	M	E	I	O	A	P	N	C
P	A	O	C	M	N	L	E	I
I	N	C	L	E	P	O	A	M